# Saturn Energy Auditor Field Guide

**Produced by John Krigger and Chris Dorsi**
**Illustrated by John Krigger, Bob Starkey, Steve Hogan, and Mike Kindsfater**
**This edition compiled by Darrel Tenter**

**The *Saturn Energy Auditor Field Guide* describes the procedures used to analyze the performance of existing homes.**

**The companion volumes *Saturn HVAC Systems Field Guide* and *Saturn Hydronic Systems Field Guide* include procedures for inspecting, servicing, and improving the efficiency and safety of residential heating and cooling systems.**

**The companion volume *Saturn Building Shell Field Guide* outlines procedures for improving the effectiveness of insulation, doors, windows, and air-sealing details.**

**In compiling this publication, the authors have benefited from the experience of many individuals who have reviewed our documents, related their experiences, or published information from which we've gained insight. Though we can't name everyone to whom we're indebted, we acknowledge the specific contributions of the following people: Martha Benewicz, Michael Blasnik, Anthony Cox, Bob Davis, Jim Davis, R.W. Davis, Rob de Kieffer, Rick Karg, Rudy Leatherman, Dave Like, Bruce Manclark, David Miller, Rich Moore, Gary Nelson, Russ Rudy, Russ Shaber, Cal Steiner, Ken Tohinaka, John Tooley, Bill Van Der Meer, and Doug Walter. We take full responsibility, however, for the content and use of this publication.**

**Bookstore: www.srmi.biz**
**Online Training: www.SaturnOnline.biz**
**Printed in the U.S.**
**ISBN 978-1-880120-17-0**
**Ver. 070109**

# Foreword

The *Saturn Energy Auditor Field Guide* outlines a set of best practices for home performance organizations. This guide looks at residential structures through the eyes of the auditor who focuses on energy auditing, sales, and quality control.

Chapter 1 describes a methodical audit procedure that helps assure consistent data collection. It includes simple recommendations the auditor can make to help improve the efficiency of their customer's home right away.

Chapter 2 focuses on inspection of the home's insulation and the associated parts of the building shell. It includes tips on assessing hidden areas.

Chapter 3 describes the diagnostic procedures used to evaluate air leakage through the building shell. These procedures help the auditor determine which air-sealing measures will be most beneficial.

Chapter 4 covers the analysis of heating and cooling systems. These procedures are used to specify maintenance, assess the cost effectiveness of system upgrades, and protect the health and safety of the occupants.

Chapter 5 describes the analysis of baseload consumption, including water heating, refrigeration, and lighting. These simple procedures often identify the best energy-saving procedures of all.

Chapter 6 identifies the best ways to improve doors and windows. Though the energy savings from window and replacement are often minimal, these upgrades remain among the most popular home improvements.

Chapter 7 focuses on the well being of both auditors and customers. Health and safety remains paramount to our work in the building trades, and we hope you take to heart the advice contained here.

Chapter 8 includes inspection procedures for mobile homes. Some of these measures can pay off handsomely, especially for the owners of older homes.

The *Saturn Field Guides* have benefited greatly over the years from the generous feedback of our readers. Please help continue this process by sending us your comments and suggestions.

John Krigger
jkrigger@srmi.biz

Chris Dorsi
cdorsi@srmi.biz

# *Table of Contents*

## 1: Energy Audits and Customer Relations


What is an Energy Audit? .............................. 15
  Purposes of an Energy Audit ............................ 15

The Energy Auditing Process ............................ 16
  Screening and Surveys ................................ 17
  Visual Inspection .................................... 18
  Diagnostic Testing ................................... 22
  Numerical Analysis ................................... 23

Understanding Energy Usage ............................. 24
  Baseload Versus Seasonal Use ......................... 24
  Energy Indexes ....................................... 29
  Electricity Peak Load ................................ 31
  Carbon Footprint ..................................... 32

The Work Scope and Contracts ........................... 33
  The Work Scope ....................................... 33
  Contracts ............................................ 34

Work Inspections ....................................... 35
  In-Progress Inspections .............................. 35
  Final Inspections .................................... 35
  Quality Control Versus Quality Assurance ............. 36
  Energy-Auditing Disclosure and Ethics ................ 37

Customer Relations ..................................... 37
  Communication Best Practices ......................... 38
  Customer Interview ................................... 39
  Sales Best Practices ................................. 40

Customer Education ..................................... 40
  Reducing Heating Consumption ......................... 40
  Reducing Hot Water and Laundry Consumption ........... 42
  Reducing Cooling Consumption ......................... 43

## 2: Evaluating Insulation

Infrared Scanning .................................... 48
Evaluating Attic or Roof Insulation ..................... 48
Attic Ventilation.......................................... 49
Attics in Story-and-a-Half Homes......................... 50
Evaluating Closed Roof Cavities.......................... 53
Walk-Up Stairways and Doors.............................. 54
Retractable Attic Stairways................................. 55
Evaluating Wall Insulation ................................. 55
Thermal Boundary Decisions............................... 57
Determining Floor or Foundation Insulation........... 59

## 3: Diagnosing Shell and Duct Air Leakage

Air-Leakage Problems and Solutions ..................... 61
Driving Forces for Air Leakage ........................... 61
Safety Considerations for Air Sealing................... 63
Goals of Air-Leakage Testing.............................. 63
Air Sealing: Three Approaches ........................... 64
Air-Leakage Testing ......................................... 65
Blower-Door Testing ........................................ 66
Preparing for a Blower Door Test......................... 68
Blower Door Test Procedures ............................. 70
Approximate Leakage Area ................................ 72
Evaluating Ventilation Level ............................... 73
Discovering Air-Leakage Trouble Spots.................. 73

Air-Barrier Zone Pressure Diagnosis ..................... 77
When to Use Zone Pressure Diagnostics............... 78
Benefits of Zone Pressure Diagnostics.................. 78
Primary Versus Secondary Air Barriers ................. 79
Simple Zone Pressure Tests ............................ 80
Using a Digital Manometer to Test Air Barriers......... 82
Add-a-Hole Zone-Leakage Measurement.............. 85
Locating the Thermal Boundary........................ 92

## 4: Evaluating Heating and Cooling Systems

Heating System Replacement............................ 95
Combustion Furnace Replacement..................... 96
Combustion Boiler Replacement....................... 97
Gas-Fired Heating Installation......................... 100
Oil-Fired Heating Installation ......................... 100

Gas Space-Heater Replacement ........................ 102
Space-Heater Operation ............................... 103
Un-vented Space Heaters.............................. 103

Testing Gas Furnaces and Boilers....................... 103
Furnace Efficiency Testing ............................ 105

Critical Furnace-Testing Parameters.................... 112
Measuring BTU Input on Natural Gas Appliances ..... 113

Inspecting Gas Combustion Systems ................... 116

Oil-Burner Safety and Efficiency Service ............... 118
Oil-Burner Inspection................................. 118
Oil-Burner Testing.................................... 119
Oil-Burner Adjustment................................ 122
Oil-Burner Maintenance and Visual Checks ........... 123

Wood Stoves .............................................. 123
Wood Stove Clearances................................ 123
Stove Clearances ...................................... 124
Wood Stove Inspection ................................ 125

Draft, Venting, and Combustion Air .................... 126

Essential Combustion Safety Tests ....................... 127
Leak-Testing Gas Piping ............................. 128
Carbon Monoxide (CO) Testing ....................... 128
Worst-Case Testing for Atmospheric Venting Systems 129
Worst-Case Depressurization, Spillage, and CO ....... 130
Improving Inadequate Draft .......................... 133
Zone Isolation Testing for Atmospherically Vented Appliances ............................................... 135

Inspecting Venting Systems............................... 136
Vent Connectors ...................................... 136

Chimneys ................................................ 139
Masonry Chimneys ..................................... 139
Manufactured Chimneys................................. 141
Chimney Terminations ................................. 141
Metal Liners for Masonry Chimneys .................. 142

Special Venting Considerations for Gas................. 144
Venting Fan-Assisted Furnaces and Boilers ........... 144
Combustion Air ....................................... 146

Ducted Air Distribution .................................. 150
Evaluating Forced-Air System Airflow ................ 151
Evaluating Furnace Performance....................... 155
Measuring Airflow..................................... 157
Troubleshooting Airflow Problems..................... 164
Improving Duct Airflow................................ 169

Evaluating Duct Air Leakage ............................ 171
Troubleshooting Duct Leakage ........................ 172
Measuring House Pressure Caused by Duct Leakage.. 176
Duct Air-Tightness Standards ......................... 177
Measuring Duct Air Leakage with a Duct Blower...... 178
Typical Duct Leak Locations .......................... 181

Duct Insulation ........................................... 185

Hot-Water Space-Heating Distribution .................. 186
Boiler Efficiency and Maintenance .................... 186
Distribution System Improvements .................... 187

Steam Heating and Distribution.......................... 190
Steam System Maintenance ........................... 192
Steam System Energy Conservation.................. 192

Programmable Thermostats ............................ 194

Electric Heat............................................ 194
Electric Baseboard Heat.............................. 195
Electric Furnaces ...................................... 196
Electric Radiant Heat ................................. 197
Central Heat-Pump Energy Efficiency ................ 197
Room Heat Pumps ...................................... 199

Evaluating Central Air-Conditioning Systems ........... 200
Central Air-Conditioner Inspection .................... 201
Air-Conditioner Sizing ................................ 203
Duct Leakage and System Airflow...................... 203
Air-Conditioner Charge Checking ..................... 204

## 5: Baseload Measures

Water-Heating Energy Savings.......................... 205
Determining the Water Heater's Insulation Level ..... 205
Water Heater Blankets ................................ 206
Measuring and Adjusting Hot Water Temperature.... 207
Water-Heater Pipe Insulation ......................... 208
Water-Saving Shower Heads........................... 209

Water-Heater Replacement ............................ 210
Gas Storage Water Heaters............................ 210
Water-Heater Replacement Decisions ................. 212
Tankless Gas Water Heaters........................... 213
Solar Hot-Water System Design ....................... 214

Refrigerator Evaluation ............................... 216
Refrigerator Metering Protocol........................ 217

Lighting Improvements................................ 220

## 6: Windows, Doors, and Exterior Insulation

Window Shading . . . . . . . . . . 223
Exterior Window Shading Treatments . . . . . . . . . . 224
Interior Window Shading Treatments . . . . . . . . . . 224
Landscaping for Shade . . . . . . . . . . 225

Exterior Storm Windows . . . . . . . . . . 226

Double Windows . . . . . . . . . . 227

Window and Door Repair . . . . . . . . . . 227
Window Repair and Weatherstrip . . . . . . . . . . 228
Door Repair and Weatherstrip . . . . . . . . . . 228

Window Replacement . . . . . . . . . . 231
Replacement Window Specifications . . . . . . . . . . 232
Window-Replacement Options . . . . . . . . . . 232
Window Safety . . . . . . . . . . 235

Exterior Insulation, Siding, and Windows . . . . . . . . . . 237

## 7: Health and Safety

Pollutant Source Control . . . . . . . . . . 239
Carbon Monoxide (CO) . . . . . . . . . . 240
Gas Range and Oven Safety . . . . . . . . . . 241
Smoke and Carbon Monoxide Alarms . . . . . . . . . . 242
Moisture Problems . . . . . . . . . . 244
Crawl Space Moisture Control . . . . . . . . . . 247
Lead-Safe Weatherization . . . . . . . . . . 249

Electrical Safety . . . . . . . . . . 250

Evaluating Home Ventilation . . . . . . . . . . 251
Control of Pollutants . . . . . . . . . . 252
ASHRAE 62-1989: Minimum Ventilation Requirement (MVR) . . . . . . . . . . 253
ASHRAE 62.2 – 2007 Ventilation Standard . . . . . . . . . . 255

Whole-House Ventilation Systems . . . . . . . . . . 257

## 8: Evaluating Mobile Homes


Mobile Home General Auditing Tasks .................. 264
Health and Safety .................................. 264
Repair Work ........................................ 265
Evaluating Mobile Home Insulation ................... 266
Evaluating Belly Insulation ........................ 267
Evaluating Sidewall Insulation ..................... 269
Specifying Furnace Replacement ...................... 270
Evaluating Duct Air Leakage ......................... 270
Belly Return Air Systems ........................... 272
Belly Pressure Test ................................ 273
Evaluating Shell Air Leakage ........................ 274
Air-Leakage Locations .............................. 274
Specifying Water-Heater Replacement ................. 275
Evaluating Interior Storm Windows ................... 276
Considering Window Replacement ...................... 277
Door Replacement Specifications ..................... 278


## Appendices 279


Required Diagnostic Equipment ....................... 279
R-values for Common Materials ....................... 280
Calculating Attic Insulation ........................ 281
Calculating Wall Insulation ......................... 285
Calculating Mobile Home Insulation .................. 288
Refrigerator Dating Chart ........................... 290
Tables and Illustrations ............................ 291
Index ............................................... 299

# CHAPTER 1: ENERGY AUDITS AND CUSTOMER RELATIONS

This chapter outlines the services delivered during an energy audit. It also discusses ethics, customer relations, and customer education.

## 1.1 WHAT IS AN ENERGY AUDIT?

An energy audit is a package of services that delivers these benefits to customers.

Help customers make decisions about how to conserve energy and save money.

- Help customers increase the comfort, health, safety, and durability of their homes.
- Protect the environment by reducing waste and pollution.

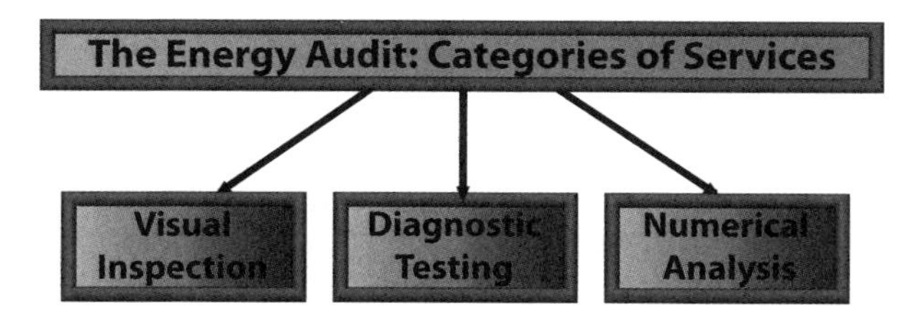


### 1.1.1 Purposes of an Energy Audit

An energy audit includes some or all of the following tasks, depending on the level of the audit.

✔ Encourage behavioral changes that reduce energy waste.

✔ Inspect the building and its mechanical systems to gather the information necessary for decision-making.

✔ Evaluate the current energy consumption and current condition of the building.

- ✔ Diagnose areas of energy waste, health and safety, or durability problems related to energy conservation.
- ✔ Recommend energy conservation retrofits.
- ✔ Project savings expected from energy retrofits.
- ✔ Estimate labor and materials costs for energy retrofits.
- ✔ Note current and potential health and safety problems and how they may be affected by proposed changes.
- ✔ Educating the homeowner about energy usage and conservation options.
- ✔ Provide a written record of the energy audit and the recommendations offered.

### Why We Care about Health, Safety, and Durability

The health and safety of customers must never be compromised by energy auditing or energy conservation measures. Harm caused by our efforts would hurt both our customers and our profession. Energy conservation work can alter the operation of heating and cooling systems, alter the moisture balance within the home, and reduce a home's natural ventilation rate. Energy auditors and technicians must take all possible precautions to avoid harm and instead deliver enhanced safety, indoor air quality, and home durability.

## 1.2 The Energy Auditing Process

Visual inspection, diagnostic testing, and numerical analysis are the three broad types of services that compose energy audits. Screening is also an important energy-audit function, which gathers preliminary information that helps to target further energy auditing. The number of energy-auditing services and their complexity depends on the customer's commitment, the auditor's capabilities, and the requirements of energy programs among other factors. Here, we classify energy audits as Levels 1,

2, and 3, although energy auditing is actually more of a continuum as shown in the chart here.

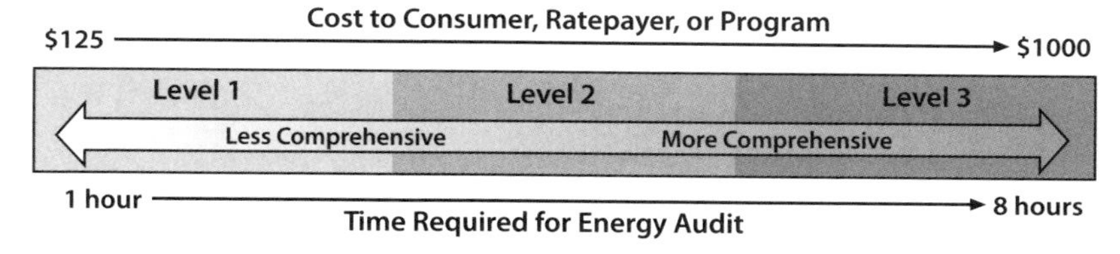


**Energy Audits:** The cost of an energy audit depends on the time it requires and the complexity of the services offered. The customer's commitment to energy conservation and the energy auditor's capabilities determine the level of the energy audit and which services are rendered as part of the audit.

The Level 1 energy audit can be as simple as a paper form or internet survey. Or it may be a limited home visit to collect information and perform simple customer education. Level 2 energy audit usually includes a blower door test and may include computer modeling. Level 3 audits focus on diagnosing specific serious problems and prescribing solutions. The training level of the auditor determines what level of audit he or she is qualified to perform.

### 1.2.1 Screening and Surveys

Many energy conservation programs include screening, which is a preliminary evaluation of customer needs that requires less effort than more comprehensive audits. Screening methods include the internet-based energy audits that are completed by customers and customer phone calls that are processed for further analysis.

The goal of screening is to gather information by a less expensive method than sending a highly trained individual to do a comprehensive energy audit. Screening results in requests for further information, leads for energy contractors, and requests for additional energy-auditing services.

### 1.2.2 Visual Inspection

Visual inspection orients the energy auditor to the physical realities of home and home site. In some cases, the visual inspection may be the primary focus of the energy audit. Among the areas of inspection are the following.

- Building interior and exterior.
- Heating and cooling systems.
- Baseload energy uses.
- Health and safety issues.

#### Inspecting the Building Exterior

The energy auditor should usually inspect the home from the exterior first, to gain an understanding of the building design, state of maintenance, site issues, floor plan, and main utilities.

Inspect the characteristics and condition of the foundation, roof, siding, windows, doors, and overhangs.

Inspect the foundation and note the amount of exposure. Evaluate the site drainage, and look for evidence of moisture accumulation.

Note any additions to the dwelling.

- ✔ View the building through your infrared scanner if appropriate to identify thermal flaws.
- ✔ Evaluate roof and window shading from trees, awnings, sun-screens, and other buildings.
- ✔ Determine cardinal directions and which direction each side of the home faces to evaluate the effect of solar heat gain and the opportunity to use solar energy or to block it.
- ✔ Inspect the chimney(s) and exhaust vents. Note their location and condition.

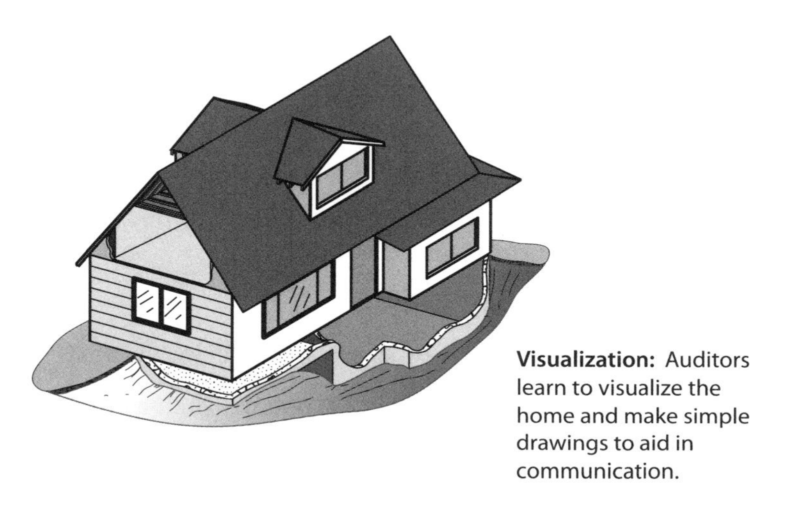

**Visualization:** Auditors learn to visualize the home and make simple drawings to aid in communication.

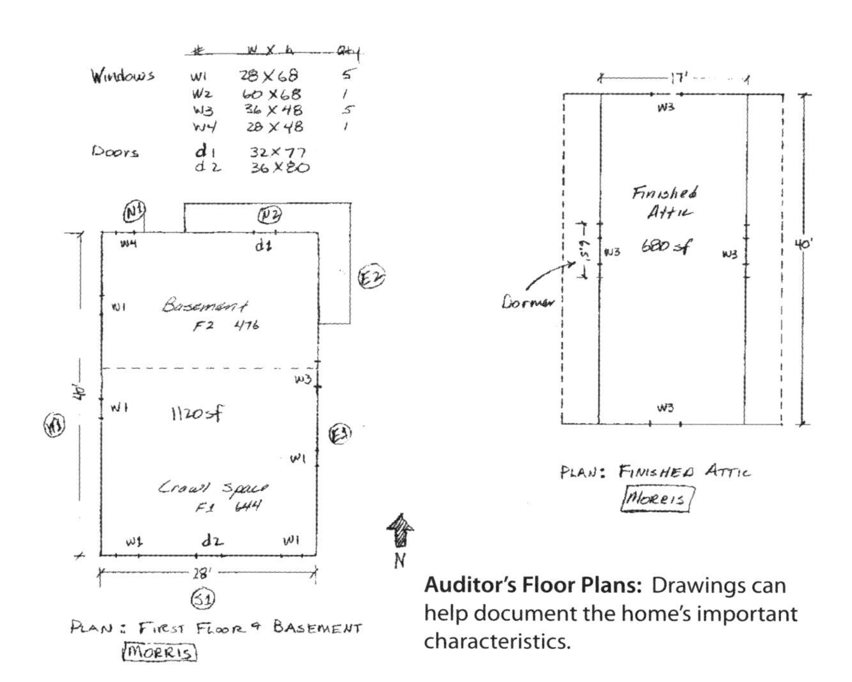


**Auditor's Floor Plans:** Drawings can help document the home's important characteristics.

## Inspecting Dwelling Interior

With the mental map you developed from exterior inspection, now inspect the home's interior.

- ✔ Locate and identify components of the thermal boundary.
- ✔ Evaluate the type, thickness, and condition of insulation in the attic, walls, floors, and foundation.
- ✔ Look for large air leaks.
- ✔ Measure the building's floor space and interior volume.
- ✔ Inspect for evidence of moisture problems such as mold, water stains, or musty smells.
- ✔ Inspect the wiring in the attic or other areas, affected by weatherization measures.
- ✔ Identify other health and safety issues.

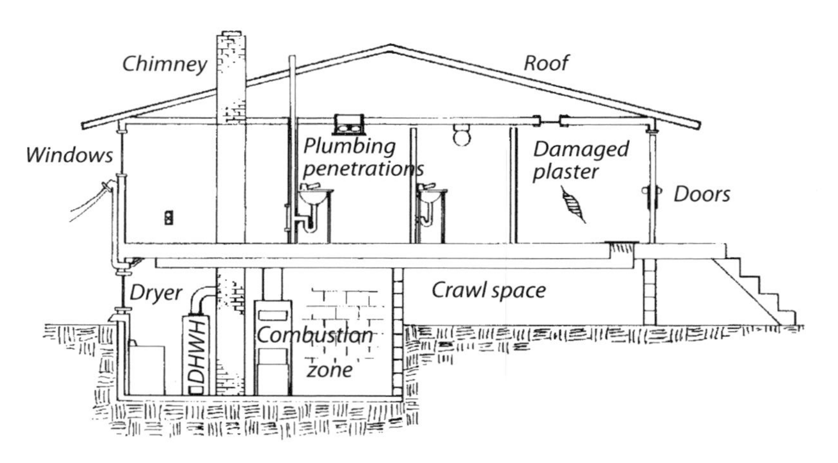


**Interior and Exterior Inspection:** When combined with testing, the inspection of the home's exterior and interior helps the auditor decide on the energy conservation and repair priorities for the home.

## Heating System Inspection

The heating-system inspection documents problems to be solved during home performance contracting or weatherization.

- ✔ Look for signs of spillage, backdrafting, and flame rollout.
- ✔ Measure the clearance to combustibles of chimneys and vent connectors.
- ✔ Check the slope of vent connectors, and compare the size of the venting system with the input rating of the appliances served.
- ✔ Inspect all forced air heat exchangers for deterioration. Inspect the combustion appliances for signs of rust and corrosion.
- ✔ Look for signs of water leaks in boilers and water heaters.

### Cooling Evaluation

Cooling evaluation includes both the cooling equipment and aspects of the building shell that affect cooling in particular.

- ✔ Inspect the roof for shading, insulation, and reflectivity.
- ✔ Inspect the windows for shading and solar transmittance.
- ✔ Examine room air conditioners and condensing units for dirt and airflow restrictions.
- ✔ Evaluate the air conditioning system with professional help as needed.
- ✔ Inspect central air conditioners for leaks in the condensate tray and drain. Inspect vapor line insulation.

### Baseload Inspection

The water heating system, the refrigerator, lights and the clothes dryer are all important energy consumers and should be evaluated during an energy audit.

- ✔ Check for excessive dust on refrigerator's exterior coil.
- ✔ Measure refrigerator electricity consumption.
- ✔ Refrigerator temperature should be 36–40°F, and freezer temperature should be 0–5°F.

- ✔ Inspect the water heater and piping for leakage and safety problems.
- ✔ Water heater temperature should be 120°F
- ✔ Inspect the dryer and dryer vent for lint.
- ✔ Inspect lighting for compact fluorescent replacement bulbs and fixture changes as appropriate.

#### Health and Safety Inspection

Identify energy-related health and safety deficiencies which could be caused by or made worse by weatherization activities. Be very careful and courteous about discussing these problems with customers in order not to alarm them needlessly.

- ✔ Determine the severity of the deficiencies, and whether there is an immediate threat to the health or safety of household members. **Address emergencies immediately.**
- ✔ Test for carbon monoxide and depressurization in homes with combustion appliances.
- ✔ Inspect for moisture problems and other indoor pollution problems.
- ✔ Interview the homeowner about the family's health.
- ✔ Explain all health and safety problems thoroughly, and answer questions patiently and thoroughly.

### 1.2.3 Diagnostic Testing

Measurement instruments provide important information about a building's unknowns, such as air leakage and combustion efficiency. The following diagnostic tests are the most common for energy auditing.

*Blower door testing:* A variety of procedures using a blower door to evaluate the airtightness of a home and parts of its air barrier.

*Duct airtightness testing:* A variety of tests using a duct blower and/or blower door to measure duct leakage and to locate air leaks.

*Combustion safety and efficiency testing:* Combustion analyzers sample combustion by-products to evaluate safety and efficiency.

*Infrared scanning:* Viewing building components through an infrared scanner, shows differences in the temperature of building components inside building cavities.

*Appliance consumption testing:* Electric appliances are monitored with logging watt-hour meters to measure electricity consumption.

*HVAC diagnosis:* A variety of tests including airflow measurement, pressure measurement, temperature measurement, and refrigerant-charge evaluation.

### 1.2.4 Numerical Analysis

Energy auditors use a variety of calculations and tools to model important energy factors. Tools include calculators, computers, and software. The outputs of this analysis include the following.

#### Measurements

Simple measurements and observations are the starting point for calculations and computer modeling and include the following.

- ✔ Measure the home's exterior horizontal dimensions, wall height, floor area, volume, and area of windows and doors.
- ✔ Determine the compass orientation of the home.
- ✔ Extract energy consumption from utility bills.

### Calculations

- ✔ Calculate heating, cooling, water heating, and electric baseload energy use.
- ✔ Calculate an energy index for the home.

### Computer Modeling

There are dozens of spreadsheets and programmed computer software that provide a variety of reports that help with decision-making.

- ✔ Home energy rating
- ✔ Energy bill analysis
- ✔ Energy-consumption modeling
- ✔ Retrofit analysis (BCR/SIR)
- ✔ HVAC equipment sizing
- ✔ Work-order generation

## 1.3 Understanding Energy Usage

A major purpose of any energy audit is to determine where energy waste occurs. With energy-consumption information in hand, the energy auditor makes recommendations according to the potential each energy-conservation measure has to achieve energy savings. A solid understanding of how homes use energy should guide the decision-making process.

### 1.3.1 Baseload Versus Seasonal Use

Energy usage can be divided into two categories: baseload and seasonal energy use. Baseload includes water heating, lighting, refrigerator, and other appliances. Seasonal energy use includes heating and cooling. Understanding which of the two is dominant is important as well as understanding which types of base loads and seasonal loads are most prominent.

Many homes are supplied with both electricity and at least one source of combustion fuel. Electricity can provide all seasonal and baseload energy, however most often there is a combination of electricity and natural gas, oil, or propane. The auditor must have a clear understanding of which loads like the heating system, clothes dryer, water heater, and kitchen range are serviced by electricity or fossil fuel.

If baseload costs are high, potential savings for performing baseload measures are high. If heating costs are high, savings for heating related measures are high. Avoid getting too focused on a single energy-waste category. Electric baseload varies from around 3500 to 9000 kilowatt-hours per year, not counting water heating. Water heating varies from 2500 to 7000 kWh or 150 to 450 therms depending on family size, customer habits, and water-heater efficiency.

A home's total energy consumption determines its potential energy savings. The greatest savings are possible in homes with the highest initial consumption.

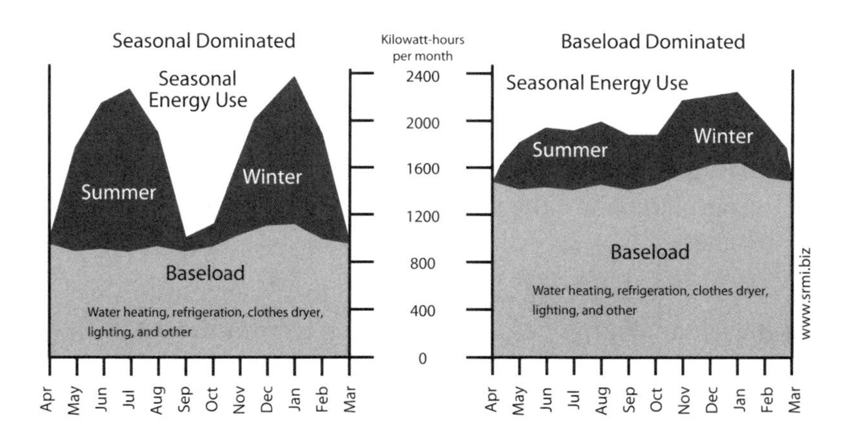


**Seasonal vs. Baseload Domination of Energy Use:** Homes with inefficient shells or in severe climates have large seasonal energy use and smaller baseload. More efficient homes and homes in mild climates are dominated by baseload energy uses.

## Separating Baseload and Seasonal Energy Uses

To separate baseload from seasonal energy consumption for a home with monthly gas and electric billing, perform the following steps.

1. Get the energy billing for one full year. If the customer doesn't have a years worth of energy bills, he or she can usually request an annual summary from their utility company.
2. Add the 3 lowest monthly electrical amounts together.
3. Add the 3 lowest monthly natural gas amounts together.
4. Divide these totals by 3.
5. Multiply each of these three-month low-bill averages by 12. These averages are the approximate annual baseload energy usage.
6. Total all 12 total monthly billings.
7. Separate heating from cooling by looking at the months where the energy is used — summer for cooling, winter for heating.
8. Subtract the annual baseload electricity usage and baseload gas usage from the total electricity and total gas usage. These are the space cooling and space heating usages.
9. If you live in a cold climate, add 5 to 15 percent to the baseload energy before subtracting it from the total energy usage because more hot water and lighting are used during the winter months.
10. For utility bills containing less than 25 days, calculate a daily consumption and add 5 days to correct for the short time period.

In cases where heating and cooling usage appear in all but a month or two, use one or two months rather than the three months suggested here.

**Table 1-1: Top Six Energy Uses for U.S. Households**

| Energy User | Annual kWh | Annual Therms (Natural Gas) |
|---|---|---|
| **Heating** | 3000–15,000 | 250–1500 |
| **Cooling** | 600–7000 | n/a |
| **Water Heating** | 2000–7000 | 150–450 |
| **Refrigerator** | 500–2500 | n/a |
| **Lighting** | 500–2000 | n/a |
| **Clothes Dryer** | 500–1500 | 20–60 |

Estimates by the authors from a variety of sources.

Table 1-2: Separating Baseload from Seasonal Energy Use

| Factor and Calculation | Result |
|---|---|
| **Annual total gas usage from utility bills** | **1087 therms** |
| Monthly average gas usage for water heating<br>Average of 3 low months gas usage<br>$(21 + 21 + 22) \div 3 = 21.3$ therms per month | 21.3 therms per month |
| **Annual gas usage for water heating**<br>Monthly average usage multiplied by 12<br>$12 \times 21.3 = 256$ therms per year | **256 therms** per year |
| **Annual heating gas usage**<br>Annual total minus annual water-heating usage<br>$1087 - 256 = 831$ therms per year | **831 therms** per year |
| **Annual total electric use from utility bills** | **6944 kWh** |
| Monthly average usage for electric baseload<br>Average of 3 low months electricity usage<br>$(375 + 372 + 345) \div 3 = 364$ kWh per month | 364 kWh per month |
| **Annual electric usage for baseload**<br>Monthly average baseload usage multiplied by 12. $12 \times 364 = 4368$ kWh per year | **4368 kWh** per year |
| **Annual heating and cooling electrical usage**<br>Annual total minus annual baseload usage<br>$6944 - 4368 = 2576$ kWh per year | **2576 kWh** per year |

## 1.3.2 Energy Indexes

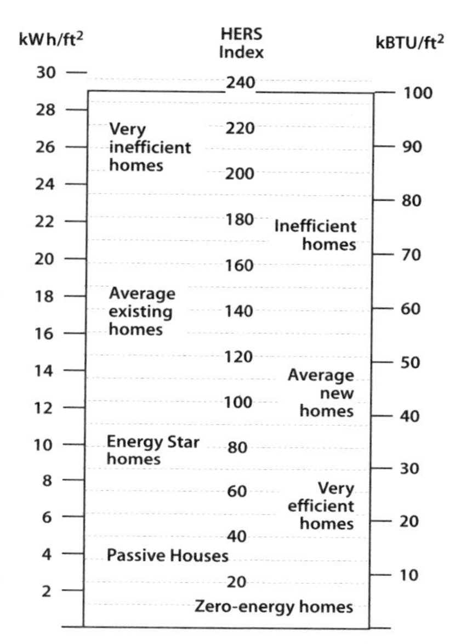


**Total Energy Use and the HERS Index:** Take the total energy use and convert it to kWh or kBTU. Divide this total by house square footage. For single-family homes 1500–2700 square foot of floor space.

Energy indexes are useful for comparing homes and characterizing their energy efficiency. Energy indexes measure the opportunity cost-effective weatherization or home performance work.

Most indexes are based on the square footage of conditioned floor space. The simplest indexes divide a home's energy use in either kilowatt-hours or British thermal units (BTUs) by the square footage of floor space. The examples shown here on the chart work for homes in the average range of floor areas (1500–2700 square feet of floor space). Homes with more floor area should use less energy per square foot and homes with less square footage should use more to be within the levels of efficiency shown here.

Apartments consume more energy per square foot because they have less square footage per person and energy usage is directly related to the number of people as well as a dwelling's square footage. Large homes consume less energy per square foot, not because they are more efficient, but because they have more square footage per person.

The most commonly-used energy index is the HERS index. Home Energy Rating Systems (HERS) is a standardized rating procedure administered by the Residential Energy Services Network (RESNET). By definition, a new home built to current energy codes has a HERS index of 100. The average existing home in the U.S. has an index of about 130. An ENERGY STAR new home scores less than 86. A home which uses no net energy from the grid scores a 0. Lower scores predict lower energy consumption.

The HERS rating is determined by computer modeling of the home. The chart shown here is the authors' estimate of how the HERS index compares to the average total energy consumption of a rated home in thousands of BTUs per square foot or kilowatt-hours per square foot of floor space annually.

The more complex Home Heating Index divides heating energy use in BTUs by both square feet and heating degree days, which is a measure of the climate's severity.

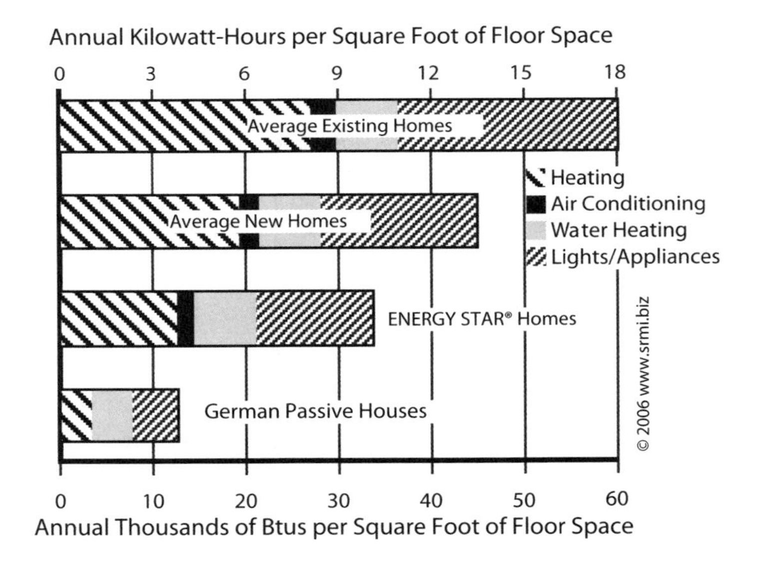

## 1.3.3 Electricity Peak Load

The daily electric peak load during severe weather, especially during summer heat waves, is North America's most severe energy problem. Every additional electric load, like an air conditioner, brings our electric grid one step closer to needing another coal-fired power plant. Current and future energy programs need to mitigate this problem by educating consumers, improving air conditioner performance, and charging more for electricity used during the peak. Utility companies pay considerably more for electricity during the peak as shown on the graph. Electricity conservation is the most important energy issue for improving our economy and our environment.

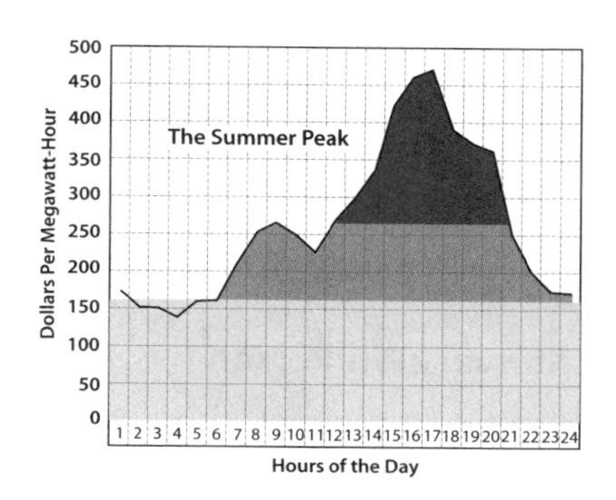


**The Summer Peak:** Electricity used at the summer peak is some of the most expensive and environmentally destructive energy being used today.

It is an energy auditor's duty to educate customers about their electricity consumption. Citizens should know how many kilowatt-hours of electricity their household uses and should set goals for reducing this amount. Citizens must also understand the importance of reducing electricity usage during peak periods.

Table 1-3: Range of Electric Baseload Consumption

| Indicator | Low | Medium | High |
|---|---|---|---|
| **kWh per Year** | <4500 | 4500–8500 | >8500 |
| **kWh per Month** | <375 | 375–700 | >700 |
| **kWh per Day** | <12 | 12–23 | >23 |
| **Annual kWh/Person** | <1900 | 1900–3500 | >3500 |

Doesn't include heating, cooling, or water heating.
Assumes 2.4 persons per household, and average annual consumption of 6500 kWh per household.

## 1.3.4 Carbon Footprint

If a customer is interested in his or her carbon footprint, use the table shown here or $CO_2$ emission data from your local utility to help them calculate annual carbon emissions.

Note that natural gas creates the smallest $CO_2$ emissions of the fossil fuels. Electricity in general produces the highest $CO_2$ emissions, but this varies based on how the electricity is generated.

The table, included here, gives an approximate amount of carbon dioxide emitted for each energy source. It shows two measurements:

- How much $CO_2$ is emitted per unit of fuel consumed.
- The amount of $CO_2$ emitted as a result of generating one therm (100,000 BTU) of energy.

Table 1-4: Carbon Emissions of Various Fuels

| Energy Form | $CO_2$/unit | $CO_2$/therm |
|---|---|---|
| Natural gas | 12 lbs./therm | 12 lbs. |
| Propane | 13 lbs./gal. | 14 lbs. |
| Fuel oil | 26 lbs./gal. | 19 lbs. |
| Wood | 5000 lbs./cord | 21 lbs. |
| Electricity from gas | 1.3 lbs./kWh | 39 lbs. |
| Electricity from oil | 2.2 lbs./kWh | 63 lbs. |
| Electricity from coal | 2.4 lbs./kWh | 69 lbs. |
| Electricity: average from all U.S. sources | 1.5 lbs./kWh | 45 lbs. |

From American Council for an Energy-Efficient Economy, and the Energy Information Administration.

## 1.4 The Work Scope and Contracts

The work scope is a list of materials and tasks that are recommended as a result of an energy audit. A contract or contracts, between a customer and contractor(s), results from the work scope.

### 1.4.1 The Work Scope

Consider the following steps in developing the work scope.

- ✔ Identify deficiencies such as health and safety problems and include solutions in the work scope.
- ✔ Determine which energy conservation activities have an acceptable savings-to-investment ratio (SIR) and belong in the work scope, using a computer program or other decision-making aid.

- ✔ Specify the important characteristics of the materials and equipment needed for the energy conservation measures.
- ✔ Determine the sequence for task completion and develop a work schedule.
- ✔ Include sufficient detail to enable installers or contractors to clearly understand their responsibilities.
- ✔ Facilitate the delivery of program incentives and rebates to the customer.
- ✔ Inform employees and contractors of any hazards, pending repairs, subcontracts, and important procedures, related to their part of the work scope.

### 1.4.2 Contracts

The contract is a written agreement between a contractor and customer. Contracts protect both parties from misunderstandings and disputes. Consider the following when helping contractors and customers to develop contracts.

- The energy auditor's work scope should be a reference and guide to developing the contract.
- The contract should have adequate detail to explain the tasks and outcomes without confusing the customer.
- Make sure that the benefits, anticipated by the customer, are promised to the customer through the contract.
- Help customers verify that the contractor has the capabilities necessary to carry out the contract.
- Contractors should offer warranties for materials and labor.
- Verify that the customer has the cash or financing to pay for the work.

## 1.5 WORK INSPECTIONS

Good inspections provide a real incentive for workers to follow specifications and maintain good quality. There are two common opportunities for inspections: in-progress inspections and final inspections.

### 1.5.1 In-Progress Inspections

Many energy conservation procedures are best inspected while the job is in progress. Visiting while the job is in progress shows your commitment to getting the job done correctly.

These measures are good candidates for in-progress inspections because of the difficulty of evaluating them after completion.

- Dense-pack wall insulation.
- Insulating closed roof cavities.
- Furnace installation or tune-up.
- Air-conditioning service.
- Duct testing and sealing.

In-progress inspections are an excellent way to provide training and technical assistance.

### 1.5.2 Final Inspections

Final inspections are required by many programs after all work is complete. Inspections ensure that weatherization or home performance services have been provided in a quality manner and that the home is left in a safe condition.

✔ Confirm that the specified measures are installed. Inspect the work to ensure that workmanship and materials standards are met.

✔ If insulation has been installed, check the bag count and coverage.

- ✔ Use an infrared scanner to inspect insulation and air-sealing quality.
- ✔ Test combustion appliances to confirm that they currently operate in a safe and dependable manner. Perform worst-case draft tests and CO tests as appropriate.
- ✔ Perform final blower door tests whenever air sealing or major insulation projects are undertaken.
- ✔ Make sure that the job site is cleaned up.
- ✔ Specify corrective actions where initial work does not meet standards.
- ✔ Review operation of the customer's programmable thermostat.
- ✔ Confirm that there are no missed opportunities for additional energy conservation measures.
- ✔ Review all completed work with the customer.
- ✔ Confirm that the customer is satisfied with the work.
- ✔ Process incentives and rebates as appropriate.

### 1.5.3 Quality Control Versus Quality Assurance

Quality control is usually an internal process of a company or an energy conservation program. Quality assurance is a more unbiased look at energy conservation work by a uninvolved party that has no financial interest in the project.

Energy auditors may perform either quality-control or quality-assurance inspections. The following are important elements of these inspections.

- ✔ Verify compliance with specifications, job order, and energy audit.
- ✔ Provide feedback on material quality and worker performance, both good and bad.
- ✔ Issue instructions for correcting errors and omissions.

- ✔ Survey customers for level of satisfaction.
- ✔ Perform energy-conservation monitoring and evaluation, if appropriate.

### 1.5.4 Energy-Auditing Disclosure and Ethics

An energy auditor may be a completely unbiased party with no financial interest in the energy audit or the recommended work scope generated by the energy audit. Or the auditor may be a sales person for an energy conservation company with an incentive to sell products and services. Or the auditor may have a secondary financial interest, such as an agreement to recommend particular contractors.

Whatever energy-auditing approach you pursue, you must explain your approach to the customer. Tell the customer what products and services your company sells in addition to energy audits.

If you are paid a commission or finder's fee, be sure the customer understands this. Or if you have an mutual recommendation agreement with another company, just honestly inform the customer of the relationship.

Customers who want to save energy will happily buy integrated energy services. Someone has to sell these services to the public. Who better to advise customers on selecting a package of products and services than an energy auditor?

## 1.6 Customer Relations

Customer satisfaction depends on the energy auditor's reputation, professional courtesy, and ability to communicate.

Auditors may perform the following customer-contact duties as required by their employers and the energy programs under which they work.

- Taking phone calls, returning customers' phone calls promptly, and scheduling appointments.
- Visiting the home, collecting information, evaluating energy-saving opportunities.
- Producing a proposal, contract, or work order for the recommended work.
- Conducting the final inspection, collecting customer payment, getting customer sign-off, and/or surveying customer satisfaction.

### 1.6.1 Communication Best Practices

Making a good first impression is important for customer relations. Friendly, honest, and straightforward communication helps create an atmosphere where problems and solutions can be openly discussed.

Setting priorities for customer communication is important because there's seldom time to discuss every potential home-improvement opportunity. Auditors must communicate clearly and directly. Limit your communication with the customer to the most important energy, health, safety, and durability issues.

✔ Listen carefully to your customer's reports, complaints, and ideas about their home's condition.

✔ Discuss health and safety hazards with the customer, including combustion-gas spillage, lead-paint hazard, attached garage issues, and storage of flammable materials.

✔ Ask questions to clarify your understanding of your customer's concerns.

✔ Write the proposed work scope to maximize the benefits of energy savings, energy incentives and rebates, and the customer's preferences.

✔ Create written documents that are easy to read and understand.

If your organization performs installations, your work as an auditor should include these approaches.

- ✔ Communicate courteously, clearly, and accurately with installers about energy audits and inspections.
- ✔ Enforce quality control by performing thorough and honest inspections.
- ✔ Strive for constant improvement in work performance and knowledge.
- ✔ Know the limits of your authority, and ask for guidance when you need it.

## 1.6.2 Customer Interview

The customer interview is an important part of the initial energy audit of the home.

- ✔ Ask the customer about comfort complaints, including zones that are too cold or hot.
- ✔ Ask about family health, especially respiratory problems afflicting one or more family members.
- ✔ Discuss space heaters, fireplaces, attached garages and other combustion hazards.
- ✔ Discuss drainage issues, wet basements or crawl spaces, leaky plumbing, and mold infestations.
- ✔ Explain the best way to choose weatherization or home performance retrofits.
- ✔ Discuss the home's existing condition and how the home will change with proposed retrofits.

### 1.6.3 Sales Best Practices

Energy auditing and sales of energy services go hand in hand. After all, energy savings results from changes in homes and their mechanical systems. Energy products and services must be sold in order to make these changes. The person who makes these sales may be a sales specialist with knowledge of energy conservation, a technology specialist such as an insulator or an HVAC technician, or an energy auditor with sales skills.

Whoever is selling the energy products and services should observe sales best practices, which include the following.

- ✔ Know your product.
- ✔ Be absolutely honest with customers.
- ✔ Concentrate on delivering the benefits of energy conservation to customers.
- ✔ Be organized in your record keeping.
- ✔ Listen to customers and be responsive to their needs.

## 1.7 Customer Education

Customer education is a potent energy conservation measure. A well-designed education program engages customers in household energy management, and assures the success of installed measures. Successful energy auditors know that customers appreciate receiving free energy-saving information.

### 1.7.1 Reducing Heating Consumption

For many customers, increasing comfort and reducing heating and air conditioning costs are the primary reasons they are interested in a home's performance.

### Building Shell

The following are the most important customer-education priorities relating to the building shell.

- ✔ Explain the options for attic, wall, and floor insulation.
- ✔ Explain the options for testing and sealing air leaks in the building shell.
- ✔ Explain how windows fit into the overall comfort of the home, and how the cost of window upgrades fits into an overall energy-upgrade package.

### Forced-Air Systems

The following are the most important customer-related energy measures for forced-air furnaces.

- ✔ Show the customer how to use a programmable thermostat if they have one or if one will be installed. Explain the energy savings reaped from setting their thermostat back 5 to 15 degrees at night.
- ✔ Locate the furnace filter and demonstrate how to change or clean it.
- ✔ Show the customer how to open floor registers. Help them remove obstructions like rugs and furniture.
- ✔ Show the customer how to clean supply and return grilles periodically.
- ✔ Explain the options for testing and sealing air leaks in the duct systems.

### Hydronic Systems

Explain the following general practices to homeowners who have a hot-water home heating system.

- ✔ Check for air at the highest radiators. Open bleed valves until water appears.

- ✔ Note if there is discharge from the pressure-relief valve. This could mean a waterlogged expansion tank or excessive system pressure.
- ✔ Show the customer how to clean radiators or convectors periodically.

### Reducing Electric Baseload

Electric baseload includes the refrigerator, lighting, the clothes dryer and other loads. Water heating, though sometimes electric, is discussed in the next section.

Measure refrigerator electricity consumption and advise residents if replacement is appropriate.

- ✔ Recommend lighting controls for lights that are frequently left on.
- ✔ Inspect the clothes dryer and its vent for lint. Advise the client to remove lint from the dryer and vent.
- ✔ Inspect lighting to determine whether incandescent lighting remains in the home. Recommend replacing incandescent lighting with fluorescent or LED lamps.
- ✔ Recommend reduction of standby power consumption by using switchable plug strips for entertainment centers, computers, and computer peripherals.
- ✔ Advise the customer to buy only ENERGY STAR appliances.

## 1.7.2 Reducing Hot Water and Laundry Consumption

The auditor should explain or demonstrate the following habits for reducing hot water and laundry energy costs.

- ✔ Wash clothes in cold water unless warm or hot water is needed to get dirty clothes clean. Wash and dry full loads of clothes.

- ✔ Show the customer how to clean the dryer lint filter after each load.
- ✔ Show the customer how to use the electronic or moisture-sensing clothes-dryer cycle. Have them note the dial reading that gets clothes acceptably dry and use that setting consistently.

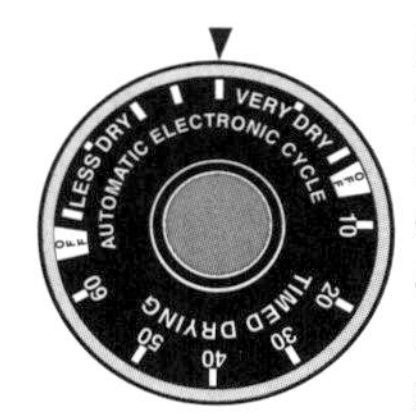


**Modern Dryer Dials:** Somewhere in the middle of the electronic or automatic cycle is the most conservative setting.

- ✔ Show the customer how to remove lint and outdoor debris from the dryer vent termination.
- ✔ If the water heater has been recently replaced, show the customer how to drain a gallon or two of water and sediment regularly to keep the tank bottom clean.
- ✔ Advise the customer to dry clothes on a clothesline during favorable weather.

**Clothes Line:** Drying clothes on a clothesline could save the average family up to $100 per year.

## 1.7.3 Reducing Cooling Consumption

Advise your customers that they can improve their comfort and reduce air conditioning costs by taking these steps.

- ✔ Maximize shading and reflectivity of roofs, walls, and windows.
- ✔ Use circulating fans to improve comfort in rooms that are occupied during the day.

- ✔ Set the air conditioner at the highest thermostat setting where it still provides adequate comfort.
- ✔ Close interior doors to limit the area cooled by room air conditioners. Interior doors and all registers should be open for central air conditioning.
- ✔ Clean air-conditioner coils as needed.
- ✔ Use a programmable thermostat, or change thermostat settings based on occupancy.
- ✔ Avoid using powered attic ventilators because they use a large amount of electricity and tend to increase the home's air leakage.
- ✔ Don't operate the blower continuously because blowers use considerable electricity and continuous operation increases both duct leakage and air leakage through the building shell.
- ✔ Turn off lights, appliances, and circulating fans when not in use to reduce their heat output and electricity consumption.

### Night Cooling with Ventilation

- ✔ Open the house at night and ventilate with cool outdoor air except during very humid weather.
- ✔ Shut the house up and draw the drapes or blinds each morning.

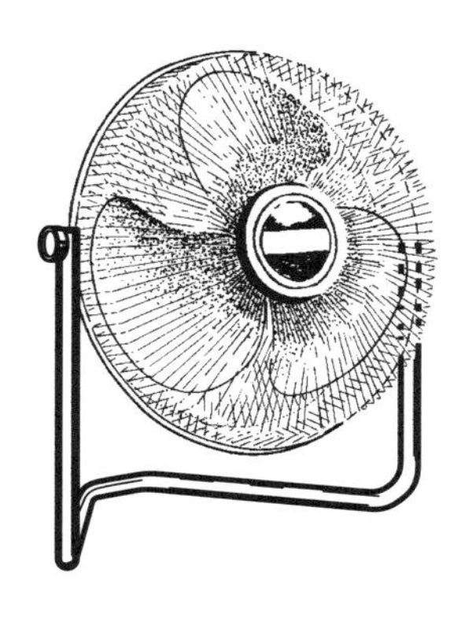

**Circulating Fans:** Floor fans, table fans, and ceiling fans create a wind-chill effect indoors, which can improve comfort and reduce cooling costs. Since no air is moved out of the home, you can use circulating fans at the same time that an air conditioner is running.

**Ventilating Fans:** Window fans and whole-house fans are most effective when used at night to remove heat that has collected in the home during the day. Set them to exhaust air through a window that is high on the south side of the home, then open a window or door that is low on the north side to admit cool air. Do not use ventilating fans while running an air conditioner.

# CHAPTER 2: EVALUATING INSULATION

Determining insulation levels, and estimating labor and materials for retrofit insulation, are among the energy auditor's most important tasks. The auditor should also determine how the crew will access the attic, crawl spaces, and other difficult locations, and, if necessary, obtain customer approval for this access.

This chapter focuses on the thermal resistance provided by insulation. It also addresses the construction details of building components which are commonly retrofitted with insulation.

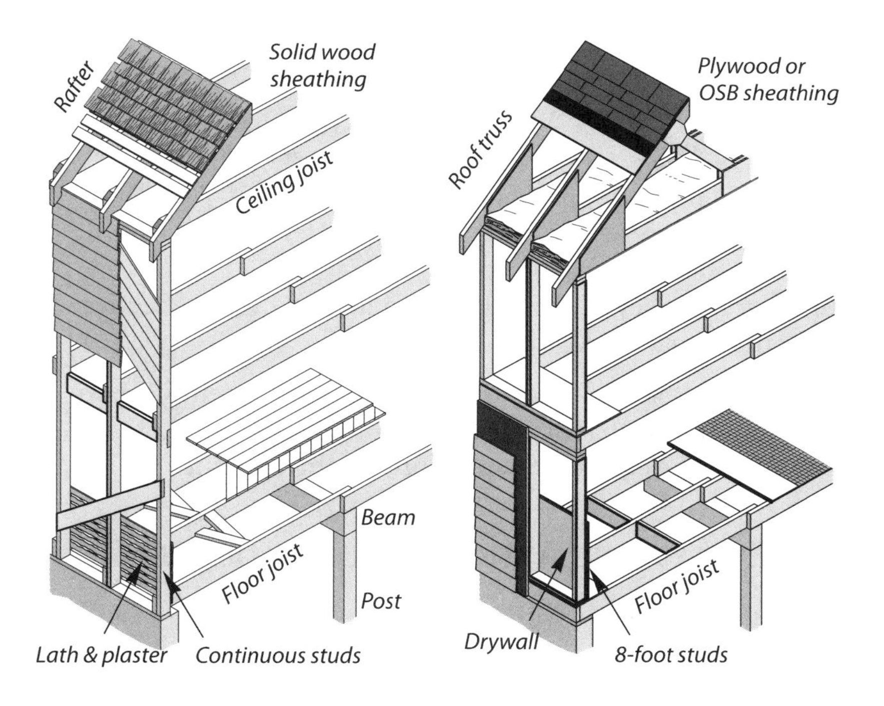


**Balloon Framing:** Balloon framing is characteristic of some older homes. The wall cavities of balloon-framed houses are often open to both the basement and the attic.

**Platform Framing:** Modern homes on the other hand feature pre-built roof trusses, platform framing, and 4′ x 8′-sheets of plywood or OSB sheathing material for walls, floors and ceilings.

## 2.1 Infrared Scanning

Use an infrared scanner, in conjunction with a blower door when possible, to view the wall from the interior or exterior of the home using the following general recommendations.

Try to scan on very hot or very cold days. The quality of definition and contrast of the view depends on the temperature difference between indoors and outdoors. Well-insulated walls have a sharp definition between the studs and insulated cavities. Uninsulated walls have a poorly defined difference between studs and cavity.

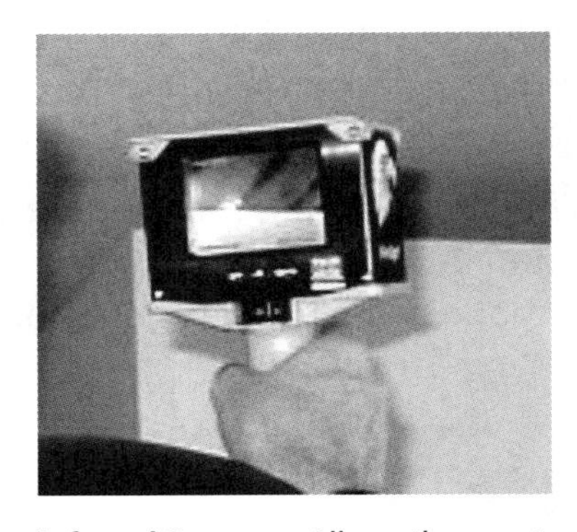

**Infrared Scanner:** Allows the user to see temperature differences which reveal the effectiveness of insulation and air-sealing details in building cavities.

View from indoors when possible because there are fewer solar effects such as warm spots in direct sun. However, viewing from outdoors can be effective at night during cloudy or very cold weather.

Evaluating IR-scanner images from outdoors requires experience with how different weather conditions and solar orientation affects the exterior temperatures of the building.

## 2.2 Evaluating Attic or Roof Insulation

Most attics and roof cavities have access hatches from inside the house. If there is no interior access, remove a roof vent, gable vent, or piece of soffit to look in the attic or roof cavity. If you choose to create a new interior hatch, cut in a closet at least 14 by 20 inches or as conditions permit. Get permission from the customer first.

✔ Try using a digital camera or a borescope held into a hole or cavity to aid your view of the insulation.

- ✔ Try using an IR scanner to find voids and irregularities in existing insulation.

If access to the attic isn't possible, estimate the attic insulation based on any information available, for example customer interview and insulation levels in similar building components. Be sure to note in your paperwork that this is an estimate only.

## 2.2.1 Attic Ventilation

Attic ventilation is intended to remove moisture from the attic during the heating season and/or to remove solar heat from the attic during the cooling season. It is often ineffective, however, and adding attic ventilation during insulation work is seldom necessary.

Many building codes require a minimum ratio of one square foot of net free area to 150 square feet of attic area. With a vapor barrier or with distributed ventilation (high and low), only one square foot per 300 square feet of attic area is required.

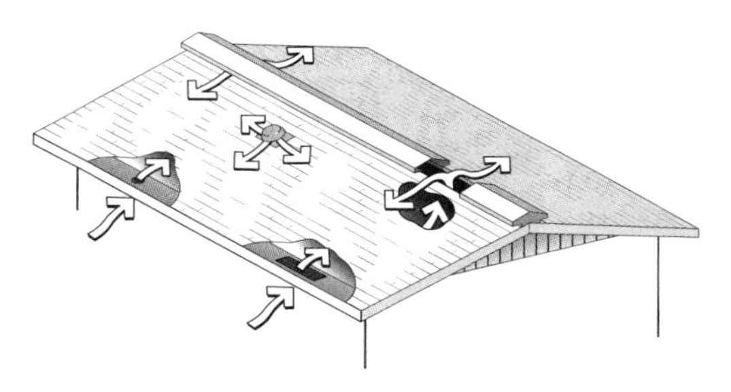

**Low and High Attic Ventilation:** Distributed ventilation — high and low — is more effective than vents that aren't distributed.

Adding attic ventilation won't cure a moisture problem caused by airborne moisture migrating up from the living space. Instead, preventing moisture from entering the attic is the best way to keep attic insulation dry. Ceilings should be thoroughly air-sealed to prevent moist indoor air from leaking through the ceiling.

Excess attic ventilation can drive ceiling air leakage through the stack effect, which can transport moisture from the house to the attic. Nighttime cooling of the roof deck can also cause water vapor that enters on ventilation air to condense on attic surfaces.

Power ventilators have limited value in reducing air-conditioning cost and can consume a lot of electricity themselves. Many of these fans run much longer than they are needed, counteracting any benefit they may provide.

### Unventilated Attics

Attics may be unventilated if there is no vapor barrier on the ceiling and if the roof assembly is insulated with an air-impermeable insulation, like high-density polyurethane.

## 2.2.2 Attics in Story-and-a-Half Homes

Finished attics require special care when installing insulation. They often include several separate sections that require different sealing and insulating methods.

- Exterior walls of finished attic
- Collar-beam attic, above second-story living area
- Sloped roof, where wall and roof finish is installed directly to roof rafters
- Knee walls, between finished attic and unconditioned attic space
- Kneewall attic floor, between knee wall and top plate of exterior wall

Follow these guidelines when specifying insulation for finished attics.

✔ Inspect the structure to confirm that it has the strength to support the weight of additional insulation.

✔ Instruct technicians to seal air leaks adjacent to the conditioned spaces before installing retrofit insulation.

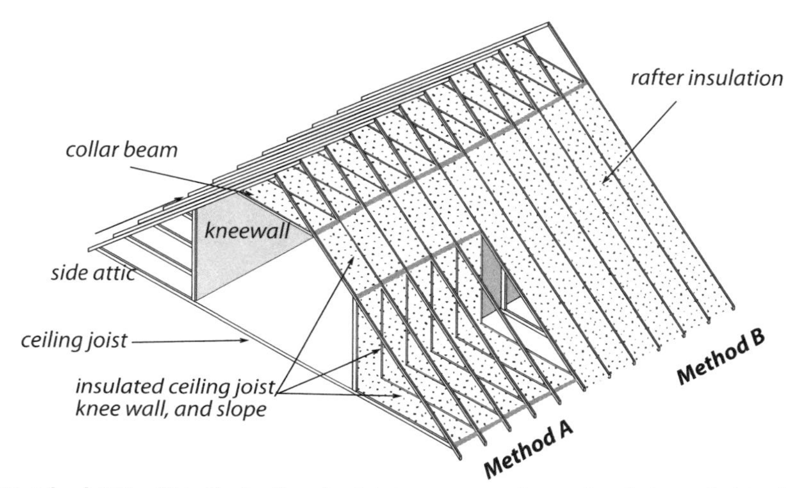


**Finished Attic:** This illustration depicts two approaches to insulating a finished attic. Either A) insulate the kneewall and side attic floor, or B) insulate the rafters. The use of the finished attic must be determined before treating the attic.

- ✔ Specify that an airtight and structurally strong insulated seal be installed in the joist space under the knee wall.
- ✔ Ensure insulation coverage is adequate where the kneewall meets the sloped ceiling joist and where the sloped ceiling meets the collar beam.
- ✔ Specify dense-packed cellulose or dense-packed fiberglass insulation for the attic ceiling.
- ✔ Specify foam, dense-packed cellulose, or fiberglass-batt insulation for knee walls. If the kneewall is filled with cellulose or fiberglass, the wall should be sheeted on the attic side of the wall. For fiberglass batts, a vapor-permeable house wrap can be installed after the batts are in place.

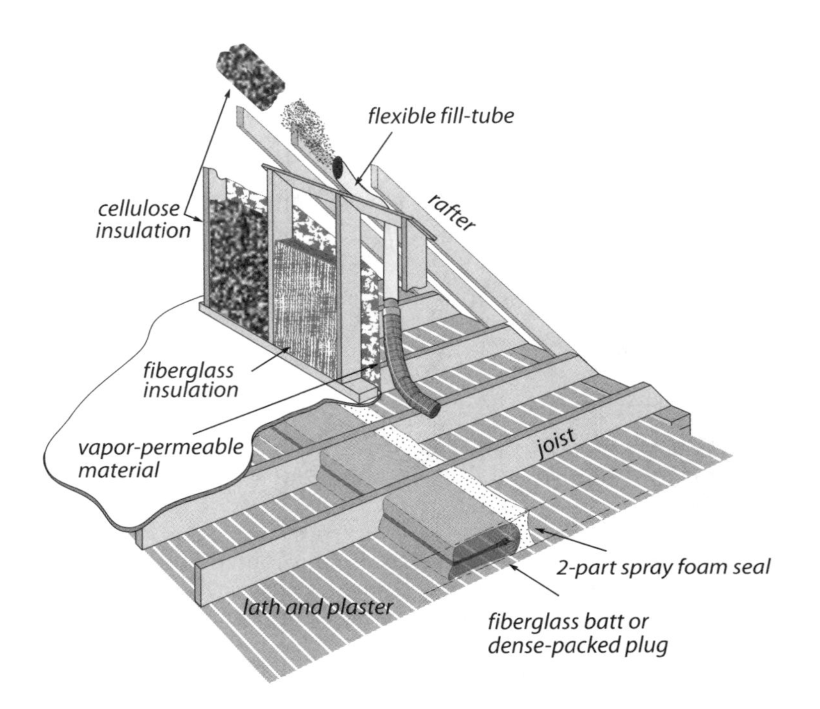


**Finished Attic Best Practices:** Air sealing and insulation combine to dramatically reduce heat transmission and air leakage in homes with finished attics.

- ✔ Specify insulation for attic kneewall access panels to match the R-value of the kneewall insulation or the maximum structurally allowable, whichever is lower. Access panels must be weatherstripped and mechanically fastened.

**Foam-Insulated Kneewall:** Two-part foam provides a continuous insulating air barrier from the joist space below the wall to the rafter space above the wall.

- ✔ Specify dense-packed insulation, installed using a fill tube, in the floor cavity if the joists are covered with flooring.

- ✔ Use extra care to seal and insulate built-in closets, dressers, or cabinets that create a protrusion in the thermal boundary.

## 2.2.3 Evaluating Closed Roof Cavities

Closed roof cavities such as cathedral ceilings, shed roof sections, dormers, and eyebrow attics may be inspected by drilling holes, or by removing a section of siding or interior finish.

- ✔ Inspect the roof to verify that it is in good condition and without visible deterioration.
- ✔ Inspect the cavity through its ends in the attic, through holes in the ceiling, or by drilling a half-inch hole and using a borescope.
- ✔ Consult with the customer about how the insulation could be installed and how that fits with their expectations.

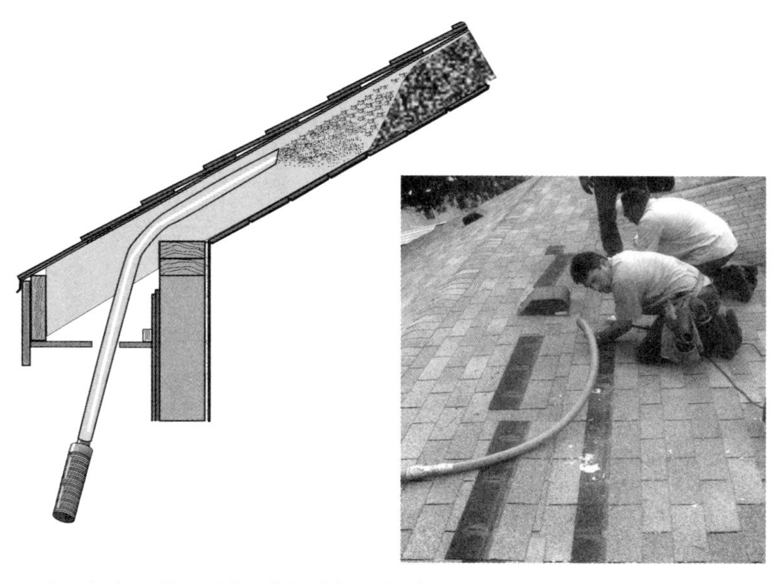

**Insulating Closed Roof Cavities:** Technicians access closed roof cavities from their ends or through drilled holes in the ceiling or roof.

## 2.3 Walk-Up Stairways and Doors

Specify continuous insulation and air barrier around or over the top of attic stairways, including inside cavities within the staircase. Specify a threshold or door sweep, and weatherstrip for the door.

You can also specify that the thermal boundary be at the ceiling level, which requires an insulated and air-sealed horizontal hatch at the top of the stairs.

When planning to insulate stairwells, investigate barriers such as fire blocking that might prevent insulation from filling cavities you want to fill, and consider what passageways may lead to other areas you don't want to fill such as closets or chimney chases. Balloon-framed walls and deep stair cavities complicate the process of insulating stairways.

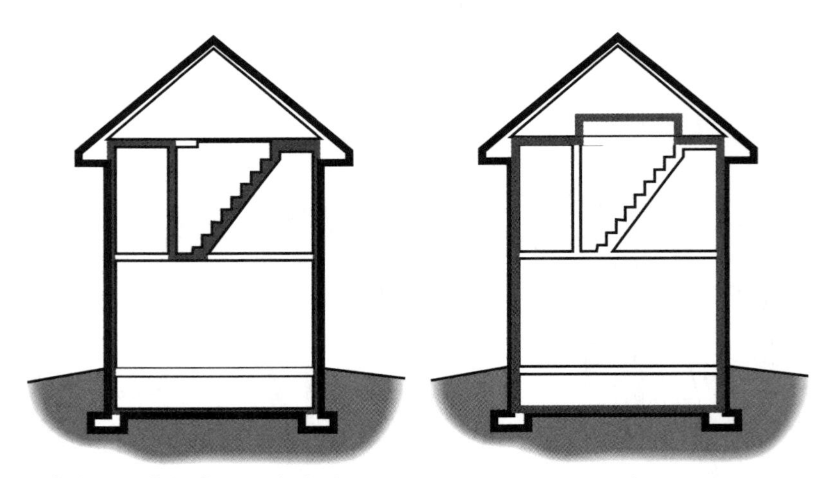

**Insulating and Sealing Attic Stair Walls, Doors, and Stairs:** Insulating and air sealing these is one way of establishing the thermal boundary.

**Insulating and Weatherstripping the Attic Hatch:** Air sealing around the hatch is an alternative way of establishing the thermal boundary.

### 2.3.1 Retractable Attic Stairways

Building an insulated box or buying a manufactured stair-and-hatchway cover are good solutions to insulating and sealing this weak point in the thermal boundary. Insulate the box or hatchway cover to an R-value equal to the attic insulation level or the highest R-value structurally allowable. Use care in establishing a continuous thermal boundary with air sealing and insulation around the hatch opening.

**Stairway Hatch Dam:** Technicians here have built and insulated a dam for the stairway hatch before insulating the attic.

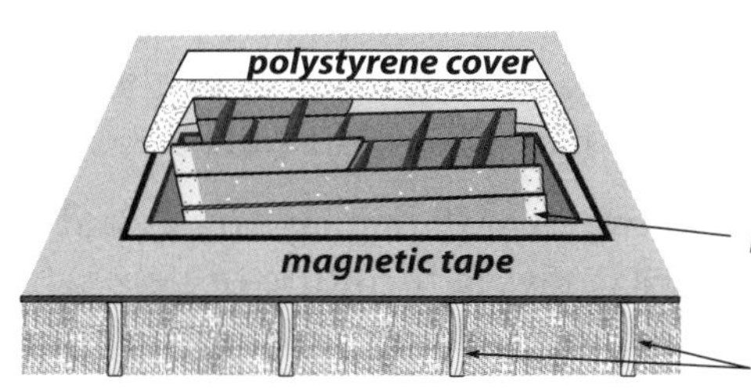


**Manufactured Retractable-Stair Cover:** Magnetic tape forms the seal of this manufactured molded polystyrene insulated cover.

## 2.4 Evaluating Wall Insulation

Be observant when inspecting walls to notice existing damage and discuss the damage with the customer in order to obtain a waiver. Consider whether exterior or interior installation is more practical.

- ✔ Remove cover plates in search of a crack, large enough to peer into the cavity around a outlet box. Insert a non-conductive probe into the crack and try to snag a sample of insulation. This could tell you the type of insulation but not its thickness.
- ✔ Look around the electrical service entrance both indoors and outdoors in search of a crack you can peer into and see insulation.
- ✔ Drill a half-inch hole and look into the wall cavity using a borescope.
- ✔ Drill a 3-inch hole in a closet or behind a cabinet on an outside wall, and determine the thickness of the insulation. Probe these holes for cavity depth with a non-conductive probe.
- ✔ With balloon framing, look into the wall cavities from the basement, attic, or suspended ceiling. Check the gable wall to determine if it is balloon framed.
- ✔ Find a small piece of siding to remove and then drill or cut the sheathing to inspect the cavity. Probe these holes for obstructions and cavity depth. Check various locations for wall insulation: different walls, below windows, walls with different interior or exterior wall coverings. Show the customer what the siding looks like when re-installed.
- ✔ Evaluate the potential for minor wall damage, dust, and temporary inconveniences (moving furniture or items stored outdoors) that may occur during the insulation process and discuss these issues with the customer.

## 2.5 Thermal Boundary Decisions

The conditioned space should have a thermal boundary surrounding it, where insulation and an air barrier are installed adjacent to one another. Energy auditors inspect the continuity of the air barrier and insulation. Auditors then develop a strategy for adding insulation and for sealing air leaks in the chosen air barrier, which may be the building's interior surface, its exterior surface, or some other potential air barrier.

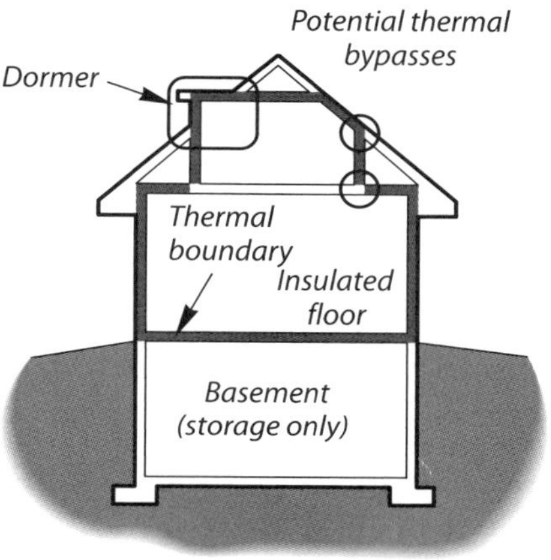

**Story-and-a-Half:** This home, with an attic converted to finished rooms, has thermal weaknesses above and beneath the knee walls. Air from an unheated attic will then enter building cavities at the thermal boundary.

The conditioned space includes the building's heated or cooled areas. Heating and cooling systems are employed to compensate for environmental heat flows, and particularly the following.

- Heat transmission through the shell depends on the insulation's thermal resistance and the shell's surface area.
- Air leakage depends on building pressures and hole sizes – two factors determining the CFM-airflow between the building and outdoors.
- Solar heat gain depends on the color and area of exterior surfaces, and the area and solar transmittance of windows.

Many buildings' total enclosed space is conditioned space, while other buildings contain areas that are not heated or cooled. Unconditioned spaces may include attics, crawl spaces, and attached garages. Some places, such as furnace and boiler rooms, are warmed by waste heat. These are called unintentionally conditioned spaces. *Unintentionally conditioned spaces* and *unconditioned spaces* — also known as *intermediate zones* — act as buffer zones between indoors and outdoors, slowing the building's heat flow.

Defining the conditioned space means identifying the thermal boundary with its air barrier and insulation. The building may not have insulation or an air barrier totally surrounding the conditioned space. In that case, the energy audit should consider the cost-effectiveness of completing the thermal boundary. A thermal boundary may surround only conditioned spaces, or it may include unconditioned spaces also. Factors involved in selecting the thermal boundary's location include the following.

- The shell's existing insulation level and the location of the insulation.
- The air-tightness of existing air barriers and their location with reference to the existing insulation.
- The feasibility of air-sealing insulated assemblies.
- Incorporating rooms or intermediate zones that may be used in the future within the thermal boundary.
- Possibility for future additions, retrofits, and repairs.

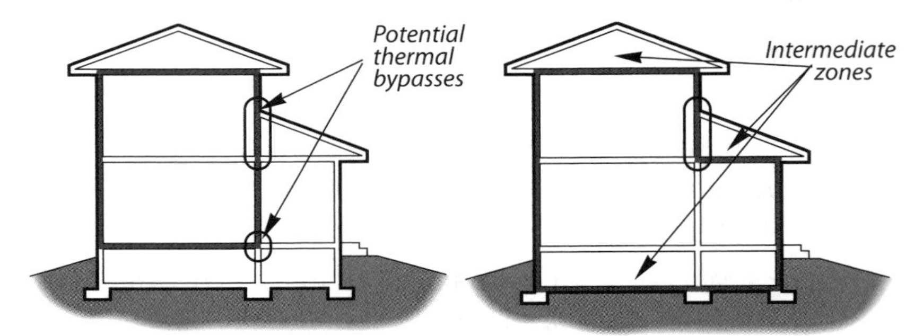


**Thermal Boundary Decisions:** The energy auditor identifies the thermal boundary when they decide where to insulate. Those decision are based on how the home's spaces are used and on practical considerations, like access and cost of materials.

### 2.5.1 Determining Floor or Foundation Insulation

Determine how the crawl space or basement is used and whether the heating system, cooling system, water heater, and/or plumbing lines are present there.

For finished basements, look for where framed walls end and see if you can look behind the wall. If you can, this is a huge bypass, which needs to be sealed but determine the insulation level in the wall before sealing it.

Determine whether the crawl space or basement has adequate protection from moisture intrusion. For example: ground moisture barrier and proper drainage.

Use *Table 2-1 on page 60.* to decide if and whether to insulate the floor or foundation walls based on the presence of plumbing and heating and other factors.

Table 2-1: Locating Foundation Air Barrier and Insulation

| Factors favoring crawlspace wall | Factors favoring crawlspace floor |
|---|---|
| Ground moisture barrier and good perimeter drainage present or planned | Damp crawl space with little or no improvement offered by weatherization |
| Foundation walls test tighter than floor | Floor tests tighter than foundation walls |
| Furnace, ducts, and plumbing located in crawl space | No plumbing or heating located in crawl space |
| Foundation wall is insulated | Floor is insulated |
| **Factors favoring unoccupied basement wall** | **Favors favoring unoccupied basement floor** |
| Ground drainage and no existing moisture problems | Damp basement with no solution during weatherization |
| Interior stairway between house and basement | Floor air-sealing and insulation is a reasonable option, considering access and obstacles |
| Ducts and furnace in basement | No furnace or ducts present |
| Foundation walls test tighter than the floor | Floor tests tighter than foundation walls |
| Basement may be occupied some day | Exterior entrance and stairway only |
| Laundry in basement | Rubble masonry foundation walls |
| Floor air-sealing and insulation would be very difficult | Dirt floor or deteriorating concrete floor |
| Concrete floor | Badly cracked foundation walls |

# Chapter 3: Diagnosing Shell and Duct Air Leakage

This chapter discusses how to diagnose air leakage through the building shell and through ducts. Buildings and their ducts vary widely in air-tightness, making testing and diagnosis an important part of modern energy auditing. Air leakage provides ventilation and combustion air in most homes and this makes diagnosis doubly important to ensure that good indoor air quality and safe combustion are a priority of weatherization and home performance work.

## 3.1 Air-Leakage Problems and Solutions

The testing described here will help you analyze the existing air barriers and decide if air sealing is needed.

Ideally, an air barrier and insulation forms the thermal boundary, which completely surrounds a building. Leaks in the air barrier can cause the following deficiencies. Excessive air leakage is one of the typical home's biggest energy wasters.

- Air leakage can significantly reduce insulation R-value.
- Air leakage moves moisture and other pollutants into and out of the house.
- Air leakage can cause house pressures that can interfere with the venting of combustion appliances.

### 3.1.1 Driving Forces for Air Leakage

Building height and location, weather, and mechanical equipment all effect air leakage in a building.

## Wind

Strong winds may create a positive pressure on one side of a building, and a negative pressure on another side.

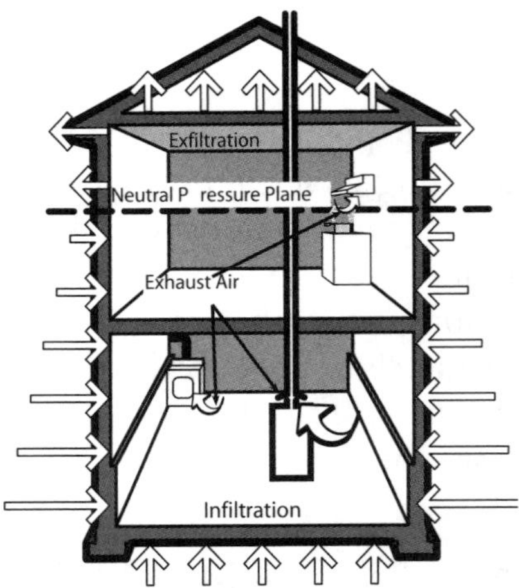


**Air Leakage Concepts:** When performing air sealing, it helps to understand the effects of exhaust appliances, the stack effect, and wind effect.

## Stack Effect

Air moves through a building as if it were a chimney. Depending on the outside temperature, air enters low or high in the building (infiltration) and exits at the top or bottom of the building (exfiltration). This is called the stack effect. The area between the air coming in at the bottom (infiltration) and the air leaving the building at the top (exfiltration) is called the neutral pressure plane.

Not much air leakage comes in or goes out near the neutral pressure plane. As the building is tightened at the bottom, the neutral pressure plane moves up. As the building is tightened at the top the neutral pressure plane moves down. For the best results, specify air-sealing at both the top and bottom of the building.

## Duct Leakage Effects

Ideally, airtight return ducts gather air from the home, feed it to the air handler for heating or cooling, and airtight supply ducts supply the same air back to the home. Duct leaks are responsible for the following deficiencies.

- Duct leakage pressurizes the building, resulting in increased shell air leakage whenever the air handler is operating.

- Duct pressures can bring pollutants into the home and interfere with combustion-appliance venting.
- Unbalanced airflow between supply ducts and return ducts can pressurize and depressurize zones within the home. Recommend that operable supply vents be left open, or be replaced with non-operable grilles.

#### Exhaust Effects of Chimneys and Exhaust Fans

Chimneys and exhaust fans create negative pressure inside a home because they exhaust air from the home.

### 3.1.2 Safety Considerations for Air Sealing

Most homes depend on air leakage to provide outdoor air for ventilation. When air leakage provides ventilation, we evaluate the minimum ventilation requirement (MVR), which is the minimum amount of blower-door-measured air leakage that provides sufficient ventilation by air leakage. *"Evaluating Home Ventilation" on page 251*

Air sealing or duct sealing may affect combustion-appliance venting by changing house pressures or reducing the available supply of combustion air. After all weatherization measures have been performed, technicians must conduct worst-case testing of all combustion appliances. *See "Worst-Case Testing for Atmospheric Venting Systems" on page 129.*

### 3.1.3 Goals of Air-Leakage Testing

The first goal of air-leakage and pressure testing is to decide how much time and effort is required to achieve cost-effective air-leakage and duct-leakage rates, while safeguarding indoor air quality.

The second goal of leak testing is to decide where to locate the thermal boundary with its air barrier and insulation adjacent to one another. An intermediate zone like an attic or crawl space gives you two choices for completing the thermal boundary. The ceiling is usually the thermal boundary, for example, rather than the roof because the insulation is installed there and the air barrier should be at the ceiling too. At the foundation, the air barrier can be located at the first floor deck or at the foundation wall. Air-leakage testing helps establish the best place to locate the air barrier and thermal boundary, especially when neither the floor or foundation wall has insulation (to locate the thermal boundary).

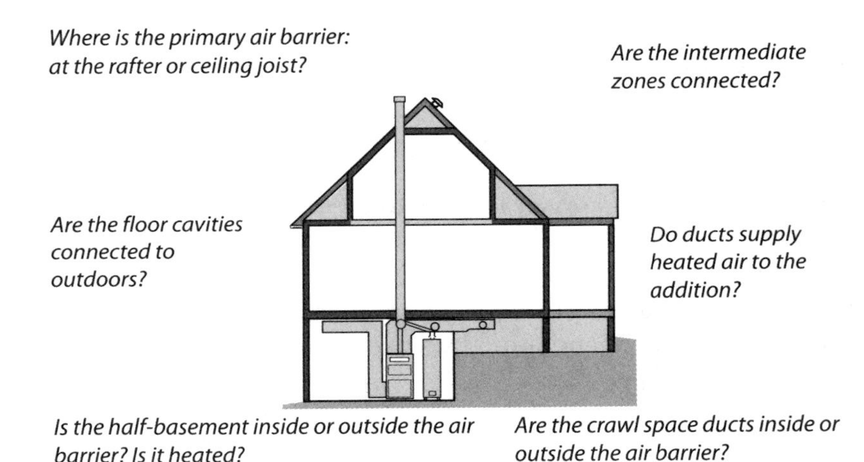


**Questions to Ask and Answer Before Air Sealing:** Your answers help determine the most efficient and cost-effective location for the air barrier.

Duct leakage in the heating system is now established as one of the largest and most treatable energy problems in homes. However, blindly sealing every joint without testing can be a waste of time and money, too. Duct-leakage tests help you determine the severity and locations of duct leaks. *See "Typical Duct Leak Locations" on page 181.*

## 3.1.4 Air Sealing: Three Approaches

Air-leakage testing is a powerful tool for weatherization and home performance, but sometimes it's difficult to decide how much air sealing to do. We believe that there are three basic strategies for reducing air leakage that also provide adequate ventilation.

- Seal the home to its minimum ventilation requirement (MVR) and use spot ventilation to remove pollutants at their source. *"Evaluating Home Ventilation" on page 251*
- Seal the home as tight as you can get it, according to the home-performance or weatherization budget. Provide whole-house ventilation using exhaust or supply ventilation. *See "Whole-House Ventilation Systems" on page 257.*
- Seal the home very airtight, during a major home-performance retrofit and install a heat- or energy-recovery ventilator. *See "Balanced Ventilation" on page 259.*

## 3.2 Air-Leakage Testing

The reason for air-leakage testing is to resolve uncertainty about air leakage. There is no accurate prescriptive method for determining the severity and location of leaks. Depending on the complexity of a home, you may need to perform varying levels of testing to evaluate shell and duct leakage.

✔ Perform shell air-tightness testing using a blower door.

✔ Analyze the test results to determine if air sealing is cost-effective.

✔ Locate and seal the air leaks. *See "Simple Zone Pressure Tests" on page 80.*

✔ Re-test to evaluate the effectiveness of air sealing efforts.

Air sealing ceases when additional air sealing is not cost-effective, when the air-leakage-reduction target is reached, or when the minimum ventilation level is reached. Testing tells technicians when to stop.

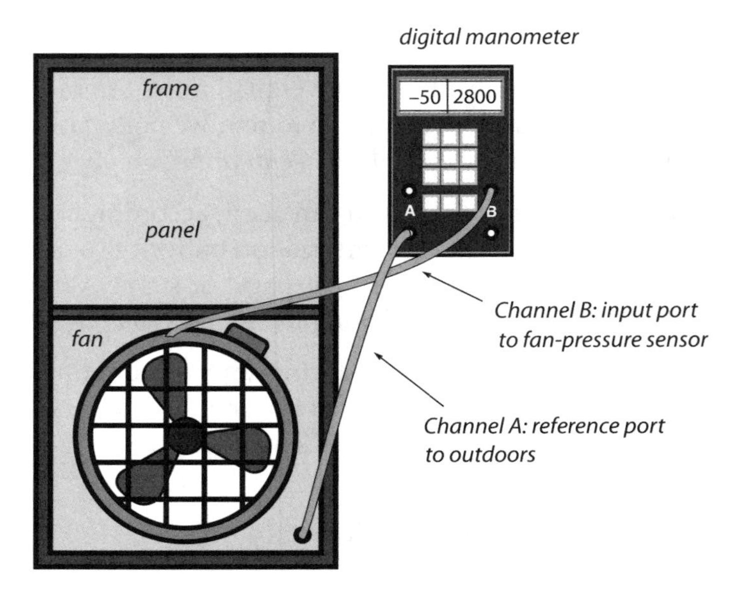


**Blower Door Components:** Include the frame, panel, fan, and digital manometer.

### 3.2.1 Blower-Door Testing

House airtightness testing was made possible by the development of the blower door. The blower door measures a home's leakage rate at a standard house pressure of 50 pascals ($CFM_{50}$). This leakage measurement is very approximate but is quite useful for comparing air-leakage rates before and after air-sealing.

The blower door also allows the technician to test parts of the home's air barrier to locate air leaks. Sometimes air leaks are obvious. More often, the leaks are hidden, and you're seeking clues about their location.

This section outlines the basics of blower door air-leakage measurement along with some techniques for gathering clues about the location of air leaks.

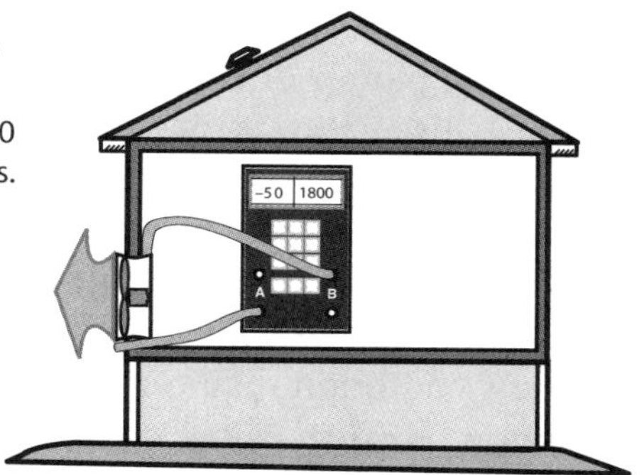


**Blower Door Test:** Air barriers are tested during a blower-door test, with the house at a pressure of –50 pascals with reference to outdoors. This house has 1800 $CFM_{50}$ of air leakage. Further diagnostic tests can help determine where that leakage is located.

## Blower-Door Terminology

Connecting the digital manometer's hoses correctly is essential for accurate testing. There is an accepted method for verbally communicating correct hose connections that helps avoid confusion.

This method uses the phrase *with-reference-to (WRT)*, to distinguish between the input zone and reference zone for a particular measurement. The outdoors is the most commonly used reference zone for blower door testing. The reference zone is considered to be the zero point on the pressure scale.



**Digital Manometer:** Used to diagnose house and duct pressures quickly and accurately.

For example, *house WRT outdoors* = –50 pascals means that the house (input) is 50 pascals negative compared to the outdoors (reference or zero-point). This pressure reading is called house pressure or the house-to-outdoors pressure difference.

### Low-Flow Rings or Range Plates

During the blower door test, the airflow is measured through the fan. This airflow is directly proportional to the surface area of the home's air leaks. For the blower door to measure airflow accurately, the air must be flowing at an adequate speed. Tighter buildings don't have enough air leaks to allow an adequate air-speed to produce the minimum fan pressure of 25 pascals. This low-flow condition requires using one of two low-flow rings also know as range plates, commonly provided with the blower door to reduce the fan's opening and increase air speed, fan pressure, and measurement accuracy.

## 3.2.2 Preparing for a Blower Door Test

Preparing the house for a blower door test involves putting the house in its heating operating condition with all conditioned zones open to the blower door. Try to anticipate safety problems that the blower door test could cause, particularly with combustion appliances.

- ✔ Identify the location of the thermal boundary and determine which house zones are conditioned.
- ✔ Identify large air leaks that could prevent the blower door from achieving adequate house pressure.
- ✔ Survey pollutant sources that may pollute the air during a blower door test — wood-stove or fireplace ashes for example.
- ✔ Put the house in its heating mode with windows and doors closed and air registers open.
- ✔ Turn off combustion appliances temporarily.
- ✔ Open interior doors so that all indoor areas inside the thermal boundary are connected to the blower door. This could include the basement, conditioned kneewall areas, and closets. Don't open access doors between the home and its intermediate zones, which are outside the thermal

boundary, such as attics, crawl spaces, and attached garages.

- ✔ Calculate house volume if you plan to use $ACH_{50}$ (air changes per hour at 50 pascals) or $ACH_n$ (air changes per hour – natural). Calculate volume by multiplying length by width and then by height to arrive at the number of cubic feet of volume.

## Adjusting for Baseline Pressure

To obtain accurate blower door measurements, you must correct your target house pressure reading on the digital manometer to adjust for wind and stack effect. The most common digital manometers have a “Baseline” function that automatically cancels the measurement effect of wind or stack pressures. Follow the manufacturer's instructions about how to adjust the baseline pressure.

Adjust the measured pressure of older or simpler digital manometers by adding or subtracting pressure from the target blower door pressure of 50 pascals. A positive house pressure without blower door operation reduces the target blower-door negative house pressure. A negative house pressure would increase the negative target blower-door house pressure.

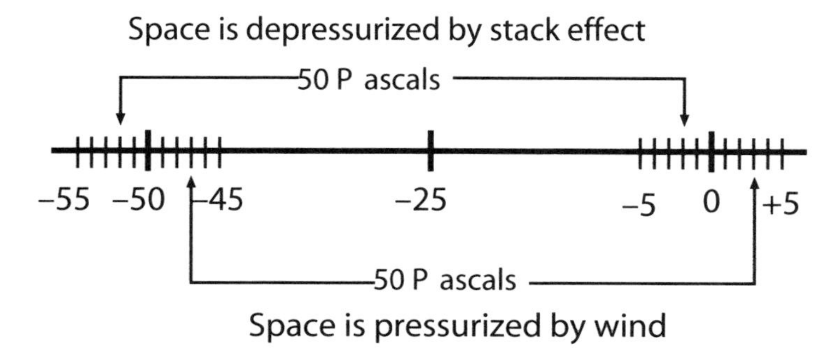


Block the blower door's opening to prevent ambient airflow through the fan before measuring the baseline pressure. Make sure that the house-pressure hose is connected to outdoors and that the fan hose is connected. Measure the baseline house pressure with the blower door off.

If you read a positive house pressure of three pascals with reference to outdoors, add those pascals to –50 pascals and set the house pressure at –47 pascals to get your accurate airflow ($CFM_{50}$). If you read a negative house pressure of 2 pascals subtract those pascals from –50 pascals, and then set the blower door to produce –52 pascals to get your accurate airflow.

### 3.2.3 Blower Door Test Procedures

Follow this general procedure when performing a blower-door test.

- ✔ Set up the house for winter conditions with exterior doors, primary windows and storms closed. The door to basement should be either open or closed according to whether or not the basement is considered to be inside the thermal boundary.
- ✔ Install blower door frame, panel, and fan in an exterior doorway with a clear path to outdoors. On windy days, try not to place the fan opposing the wind direction.
- ✔ Follow manufacturer's instructions for fan orientation and digital-manometer setup for either pressurization or depressurization.
- ✔ Connect Channel A of the digital manometer to measure *house WRT outdoors*. Place the outside hose at least 5 feet to the side of the fan and against the foundation.
- ✔ Connect Channel B to measure *fan WRT zone near fan inlet*. The zone near the fan inlet is indoors for depressurization and outdoors for pressurization. (Hose must run from the reference port on channel B to outdoors for pressurization.)
- ✔ Adjust for the stack or baseline reading, previously referenced in *"Adjusting for Baseline Pressure" on page 69*. If the

manometers used do not zero automatically or manually, the house pressure must be adjusted for this baseline reading (*house WRT outdoors*).

- ✔ Ensure that people, pets, and objects with the potential to become airborne remain at a safe distance from the fan.
- ✔ Turn on the fan and increase its speed slowly until you read –50 pascals of pressure difference between indoors and outdoors.
- ✔ Read the $CFM_{50}$ from channel B of your digital manometer.

## Digital Manometer Set-Up Procedures

Follow these instructions for performing a blower door test, using a digital manometer.

- ✔ Turn on the manometer by pushing the ON/OFF button
- ✔ Use the MODE function to select the displayed results, such as airflow in CFM at 50 pascals for example.
- ✔ Use the DEVICE function to select to select a particular blower door model.
- ✔ Use the BASELINE function to adjust for the baseline pressure.
- ✔ Select the correct configuration for an open fan or one of the flow rings or range plates.
  a. Install the flow ring or range plate in the blower door fan, which produces an adequate airflow rate. The fan pressure should be at least 25 pascals.
  b. Use CONFIG (configuration) function until you match the flow ring or range plate being used.
- ✔ Turn on the blower door fan slowly with the controller. Increase fan speed until the building depressurization on the Channel A screen is between -45 and -55 Pascals. It

does not need to be exactly -50 Pascals unless you are using an older digital manometer.

- ✔ The screen displays the $CFM_{50}$ leakage of the building. If this number is fluctuating a lot, select the TIME AVERAGE function to increase the time-averaging duration. Increasing the time-averaging duration dampens the wind's effect on the reading.

### Blower-Door Test Follow-Up

Be sure to return the house to its original condition after completing the blower door test.

- ✔ Inspect combustion appliance pilot lights to ensure that blower door testing did not extinguish them.
- ✔ Reset thermostats of heaters and water heaters that were turned down for testing.
- ✔ Remove any temporary plugs that were installed to increase house pressure.
- ✔ Document any unusual conditions affecting the blower door test and location where the blower door was installed.

## 3.2.4 Approximate Leakage Area

There are several ways to convert blower-door $CFM_{50}$ measurements into square inches of total leakage area. A simple and rough way to convert $CFM_{50}$ into an approximate leakage area (ALA) is to divide $CFM_{50}$ by 10. The ALA can help you visualize the size of openings you're looking for in a home or section of a home.

$$\mathbf{ALA = CFM_{50} \div 10}$$

## 3.3 Evaluating Ventilation Level

Air leakage and ventilation are linked because most homes depend on air leakage to provide the ventilation needed to dilute pollutants and remove moisture. See *See "Evaluating Home Ventilation" on page 251.*for a complete procedure for evaluating, sizing and selecting ventilation systems.

## 3.4 Discovering Air-Leakage Trouble Spots

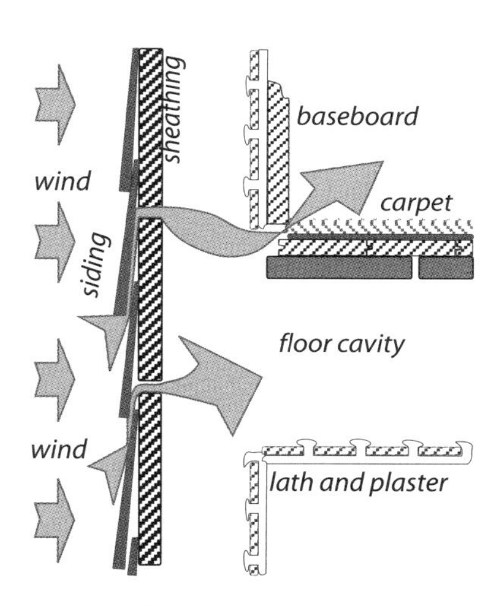


**Floor-Wall Junction:** Wall cavities and floor cavities are connected together in balloon-framed homes. Loose exterior siding connects these cavities to the outdoors.

Most residential air leakage flows through large air leaks. An auditor should learn to recognize and identify air-leakage trouble spots during an audit and to note their location. This information helps crews seal the large air leaks.

Large air leaks reveal themselves during diagnostic testing discussed in *"Using a Digital Manometer to Test Air Barriers" on page 82*. The information you collect from this diagnostic testing indicates whether large leaks are present and their approximate location. If large leaks are present, they are probably related to the following construction details.

Joist cavities under knee walls in finished attic areas

The joist spaces beneath the kneewall connect the ventilated attic with the floor space between two heated areas.

*Kitchen or bathroom interior soffits:* The soffit was framed before the kitchen was drywalled. The area behind the soffit has no sheeting including the ceiling, which connects to the vented attic.

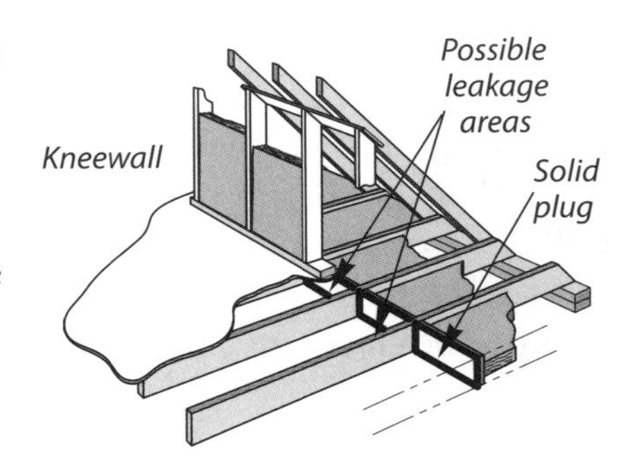


**Finished Attic:** Air leaking into the floor and rafter space of finished attic areas is one of the biggest energy problems of story-and-a-half homes.

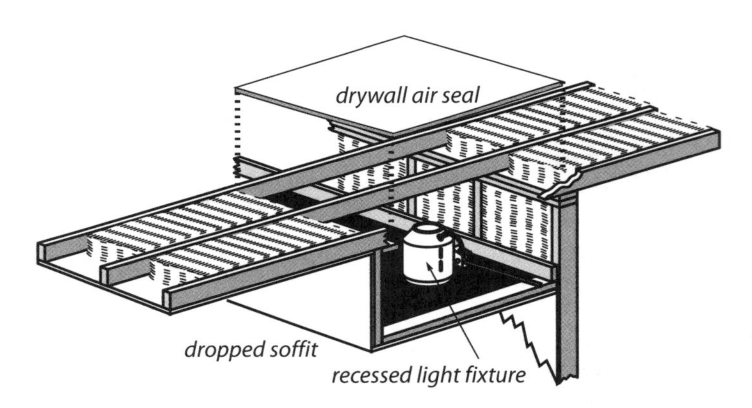


**Recessed Light Fixtures:** These are major leakage sites, but these fixtures must maintain an air space surrounding them to cool their incandescent bulbs. Plug the top of the soffit in this case with drywall.

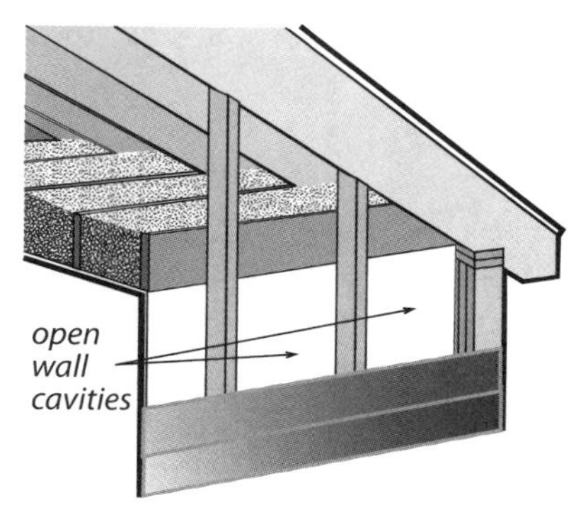


**Balloon-Framed Gable Wall:** Wall cavities are open to the attic. This common detail can be a large air leak and also a place to inspect wall insulation.

*Soil stacks, plumbing vents, and chimneys:* The soil stack and chimney often go from the basement all the way through the roof and leak air substantially where they pass through the thermal boundary.

*Two-level attics in split-level houses:* Where an attic changes its level there is often a un-sheeted wall that allows air from the attic into the wall cavity.

*Tops and bottoms of balloon-framed interior partition wall cavities, missing top plates:* Balloon-framed walls harbor cavities that are open from the foundation to the attic. Balloon-framed gables are common and give the auditor an opportunity to peer into wall cavities from the attic.

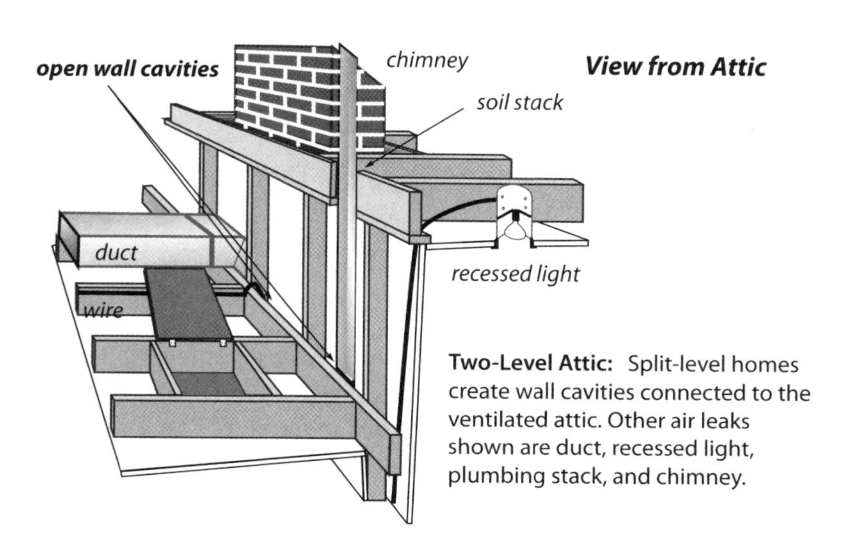


**Two-Level Attic:** Split-level homes create wall cavities connected to the ventilated attic. Other air leaks shown are duct, recessed light, plumbing stack, and chimney.

*Housings of exhaust fans and recessed lights:* Recessed fan housings and especially recessed light fixtures are a major source of air leakage in many homes, built in the past 30 years.

**Bypasses Under Bathtub:** The bathtub drain and adjacent plumbing wall form a huge hole in the home's air barrier.

*Duct boots and registers:* If ducts are located in attic, crawl space, attached garage, or in the floor cavity above garage, caulk or foam the joint between the boot and the ceiling, wall, or floor.

*Duct chases:* If chase opening is large, specify air-sealing with a rigid barrier such as foam board, plywood or drywall. The new air barrier should be sealed to ducts with caulk or foam.

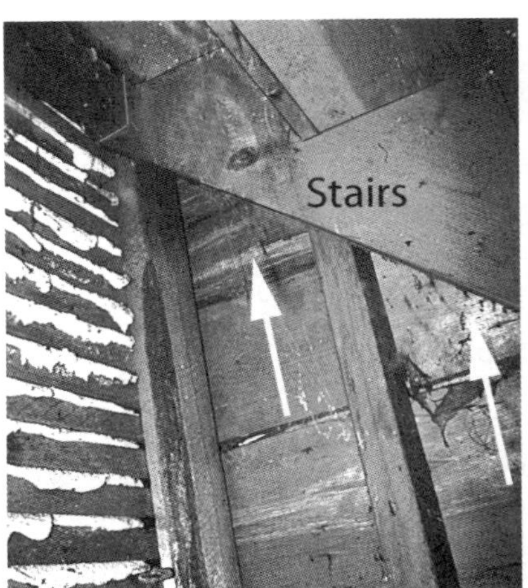


**Exterior Walls & Stairs:** This area is a place to look for insulation. It is often a large air-migration pathway from the heated space to the attic.

*Bathtubs and shower stalls:*

Bathtubs and shower stalls often have large holes beneath them for drains and traps. These holes are seldom sealed during construction and constitute some of the largest air leaks commonly found in homes. These bypasses should be sealed where they pass through the air barrier. The plumbing traps must remain accessible for maintenance.

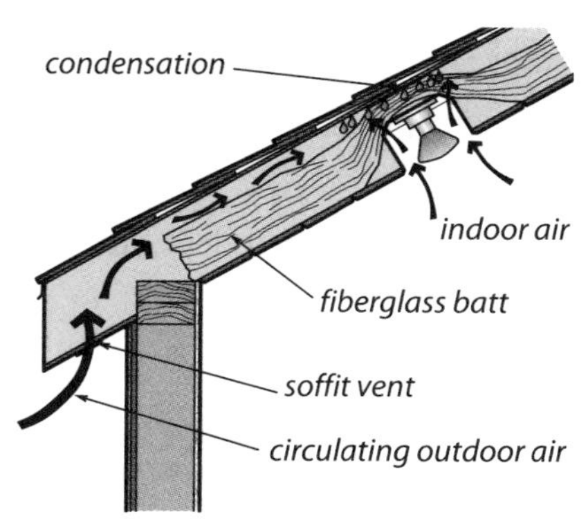


**Cathedral Ceiling with Recessed Light:** This combination results in air leakage, moisture problems and reduced R-value of insulation.

*Pocket door cavities:* When located on the second floor, cap the top of the entire wall cavity in the attic with rigid board, caulked and stapled. Where wall cavities containing the retracted pocket door halves connect with exterior framed walls, stuff narrow strips of unfaced fiberglass batts into the door opening with a broom handle far enough to allow for complete opening of the door.

*Attic hatches and stairwell drops:* Accesses to attic areas, including ceiling hatches and stairways often create substantial air leakage from the attic to the conditioned space.

*Other openings in the air barrier:* Seal with rigid material, caulk, spray foam, or expanding foam depending upon size and nature of opening.

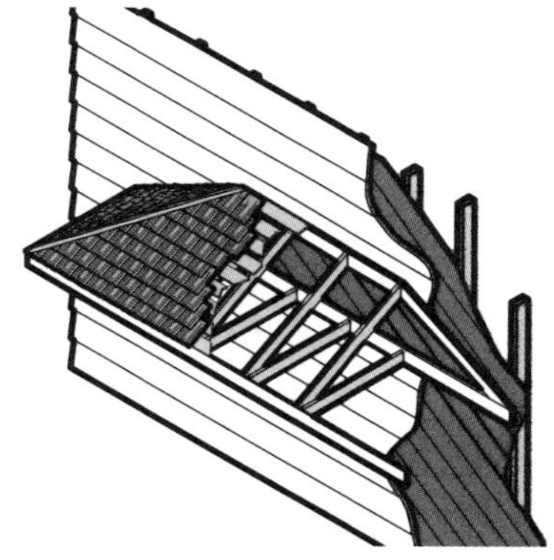

**Porch Air Leakage:** Porch roof cavities often allow substantial air leakage because of numerous joints, and because there may be no siding or sheathing installed in hidden areas.

## 3.5 Air-Barrier Zone Pressure Diagnosis

Air-barrier leak-testing avoids unnecessary visual inspection and air sealing in hard-to-reach areas. Pressure-only tests provide a clue about where the leaks are located during blower door testing. Pressure-flow tests, like the add-a-hole test, measure pressure differences, while creating a hole between two zones in order to estimate air leakage between the zones.

## 3.5.1 When to Use Zone Pressure Diagnostics

Air barrier pressure testing are used when the dwelling has one or more of the following conditions.

- High fuel consumption not obviously linked to lack of insulation or inefficient heating plant.
- A high-$CFM_{50}$ blower door test.
- Multiple zones where determining linkage between zones, or setting air-sealing priorities, is necessary.
- An attached garage.
- Health and safety problems related to a faulty air barrier.

## 3.5.2 Benefits of Zone Pressure Diagnostics

Use zone pressure tests to make decisions about where to direct your air-sealing efforts. The following is a list of possibilities and benefits from zone pressure diagnostics.

✔ Evaluate the airtightness of portions of a building's air barrier — especially floors, ceilings, and walls between the living space and the attached garage.

✔ Decide which of two possible air barriers to air seal — for example, the floor versus foundation walls of a crawl space.

✔ Estimate the air leakage in $CFM_{50}$ through a particular air barrier, for the purpose of estimating the effort and cost necessary to seal the leaks.

✔ Determine whether building cavities like floor cavities, porch roofs, and overhangs are conduits for air leakage.

✔ Determine whether building cavities, intermediate zones, and ducts are connected by air leaks.

Zone pressure tests provide a range of information from simple clues about which parts of a building's air barrier are leakiest, to specific estimates of the airflow and hole size through particular air barriers.

## 3.5.3 Primary Versus Secondary Air Barriers

An effective air barrier is composed of materials that are continuous, sealed at seams, and relatively impermeable to airflow. Where there are two possible air barriers, the most airtight air barrier is the primary air barrier and the least airtight is the secondary air barrier.

The primary air barrier should be adjacent to the insulation to ensure the insulation's effectiveness. Testing is important to verify that insulation and primary air barrier are aligned. Sometimes we're surprised during testing to find that our assumed primary air barrier is actually secondary, and the secondary air barrier is actually primary.

Intermediate zones are unconditioned spaces that are sheltered within the building shell. Intermediate zones can either be included inside the home's primary air barrier or outside it. Intermediate zones include: unheated basements, crawl spaces, attics, enclosed porches, and attached garages.

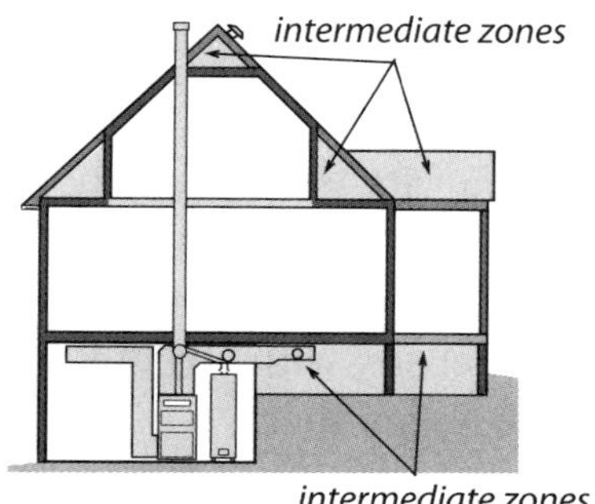


Intermediate zones have two potential air barriers: one between the zone and house and one between the zone and outdoors. For example, an attic has two air barriers: the ceiling and roof. It is useful to know where the best air barrier is located.

## 3.5.4 Simple Zone Pressure Tests

You can find valuable information about the relative leakiness of rooms or sections of the home during a blower-door test. Listed below are five simple methods.

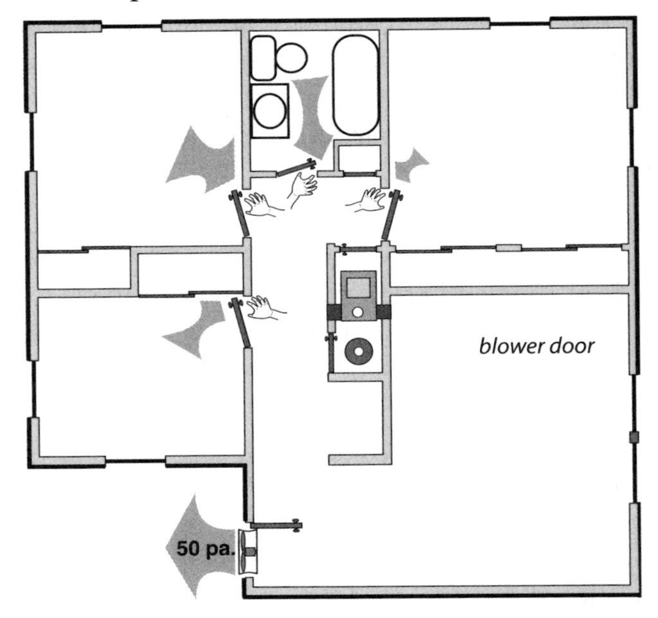


**Interior Door Test:** Feeling airflow with your hand at the crack of an interior door gives a rough indication of the air leakage coming from the outdoors through that room.

1. *Feeling zone air leakage:* Close an interior door partially so that there is a one-inch gap between the door and door jamb. Feel the airflow along the length of that crack, and compare that airflow intensity with airflow from other rooms, using the same technique.
2. *Observing the ceiling/attic floor:* Pressurize the home and observe the top-floor ceiling from the attic with a good flashlight. Air leaks show themselves in movement of loose-fill insulation, blowing dust, moving cobwebs, etc. You can also use a small piece of tissue paper to disclose air movement.

3. *Observing smoke movement:* Pressurize the home and observe the movement of smoke through the house and out of its air leaks.

4. *Room pressure difference:* Check the pressure difference between a closed room and the main body of a home. Larger pressure differences indicate larger potential air leakage within the closed room or else a tight air barrier between the room and main body. A small pressure difference means little leakage to the outdoors through the room or a leaky air barrier between the house and room.

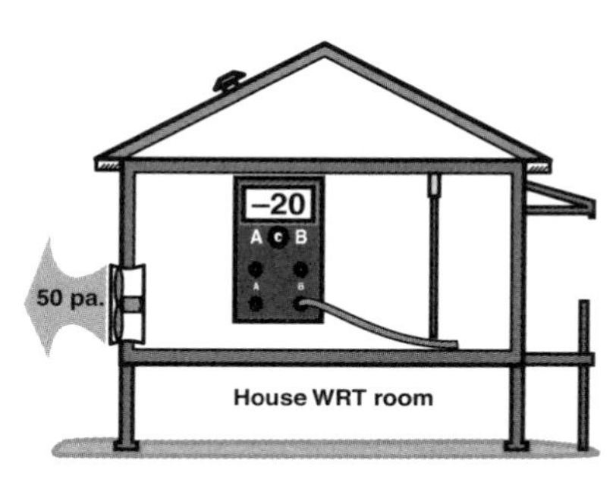


**Bedroom Test:** This bedroom pressure difference may be caused by its leaky exterior walls or tight interior walls, separating it from the main body of the home. This test can determine whether or not a confined combustion zone is connected to other rooms.

5. *Room airflow difference:* Measure the house $CFM_{50}$ with all interior doors open. Close the door to a single room, and note the difference in the $CFM_{50}$ reading. The difference is the approximate leakage through that room.

Tests 1, 2, and 3 present good customer education opportunities. Feeling airflow or observing smoke are simple observations, but have helped identify many air leaks that could otherwise have remained hidden.

When airflow within the home is restricted by closing a door, as in tests 4 and 5, it may take alternative indoor paths that render these tests inaccurate. Only practice and experience can guide your decisions about the applicability and usefulness of these simple tests.

Table 3-1: Building Components and Their Air Permeance

| Good air barriers: <2 $CFM_{50}$ per 100 sq. ft. | Fair air barriers: 2–10 $CFM_{50}$ per 100 sq. ft. | Poor air barriers: 10–1000 $CFM_{50}$ per 100 sq. ft. |
|---|---|---|
| 5/8" oriented strand board | 15# perforated felt | 5/8" tongue-and-groove wood sheeting |
| 1/2" drywall | concrete block | 6" fiberglass batt |
| 4-mil air barrier paper | rubble masonry | 1.5" wet-spray cellulose |
| Asphalt shingles and perforated felt over 1/2" plywood | 7/16" asphalt-coated fiberboard | wood siding over plank sheathing |
| 1/8" tempered hardboard | 1" expanded polystyrene | wood shingles over plank sheathing |
| painted un-cracked lath and plaster | brick veneer | blown fibrous insulation |

Measurements taken at 50 pascals pressure.
Based on information from: "Air Permeance of Building Materials" by Canada Mortgage Housing Corporation, and estimates of comparable assemblies by the author.
Although cellulose reduces air leakage when blown into walls, it is not considered an air-barrier material.

## 3.5.5 Using a Digital Manometer to Test Air Barriers

A digital manometer, used for blower-door testing, also can measure pressures between the house and its intermediate zones during blower-door tests.

The blower door, when used to create a house-to-outdoors pressure of –50 pascals, also creates house-to-zone pressures of between 0 and –50 pascals in the home's intermediate zones. The amount of intermediate-zone depressurization depends on the relative leakiness of the zone's two air barriers.

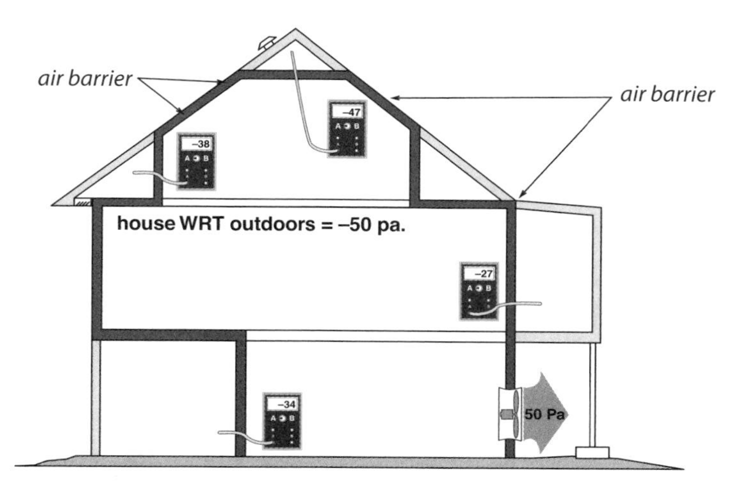


**Pressure-Testing Building Zones:** Measuring the pressure difference across the assumed primary air barrier tells you whether the air barrier and insulation are aligned. If the digital manometer reads close to –50 pascals, they are aligned, assuming the tested intermediate zones are well-connected to outdoors.

For example, in an attic with a fairly airtight ceiling and a well-ventilated roof, the attic is mostly outdoors. We expect the house-to-zone pressure to be –45 to –50 pascals. The leakier the ceiling and the tighter the roof, the smaller the negative house-to-zone pressure will be. This principle holds true for other intermediate zones like crawl spaces, attached garages, and unheated basements.

## Pressure-Only Zone Pressure Diagnostics

Air-sealing technicians should depressurize house to –50 pascals with a blower door, then follow this procedure.

1. Find an existing hole, or drill a hole through the floor, wall, or ceiling between the conditioned space and the intermediate zone.
2. Connect the reference port of the digital manometer to a hose located in the zone.
3. Leave the input port of the digital manometer open to the indoors.

4. Read the negative pressure given by the digital manometer. This is the house-to-zone pressure, which is –50 pascals if the air barrier between house and zone is airtight and the zone itself is open to outdoors.
5. If the reading is significantly less negative than –45 pascals, find the air barrier's largest leaks and seal them.
6. Repeat steps 1 through 5, performing more air-sealing as necessary, until the pressure is as close to –50 pascals as possible.

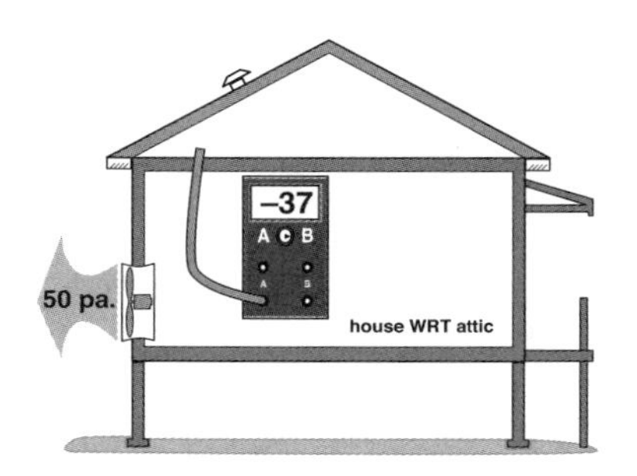


**House-to-Attic Pressure:** This commonly used measurement is convenient because it requires only one hose.

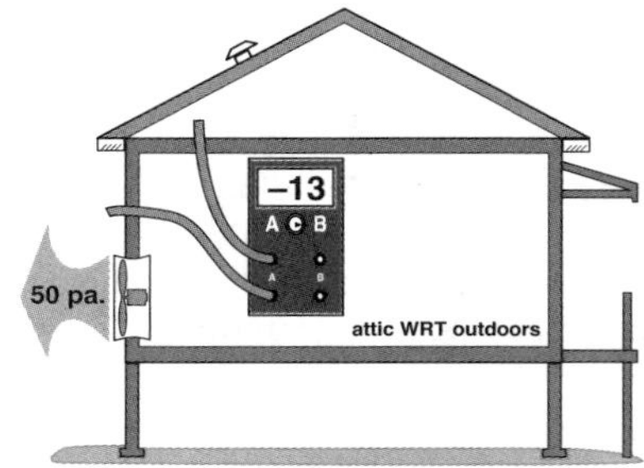


**Attic-to-Outdoors Pressure:** This measurement (–13) confirms the first measurement of – 37 pascals because the two add up to –50 pascals.

## Leak-Testing Building Cavities

Building cavities such as wall cavities, floor cavities between stories, and dropped soffits in kitchens and bathrooms can also be pressure-tested with a digital manometer to determine their connection to the outdoors.

## Testing Zone Connectedness

Sometimes it is useful to determine whether two intermediate zones are connected by an air passage like a large bypass. You can establish whether the two zones are connected by measuring the house-to-zone pressure during a blower door test, and then opening one zone to the outdoors and watching for a pressure change in the other zone. You can also open an interior door leading into one of the zones and check for pressure changes in the other zone.

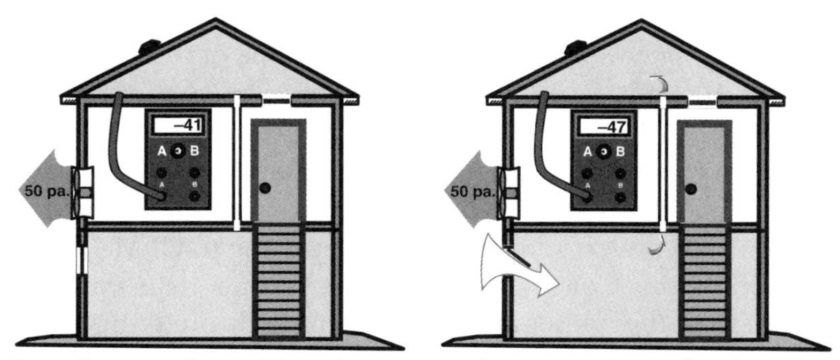


**Zone Connectedness:** The attic measures closer to outdoors after the basement window is opened, indicating that the attic and basement are connected by a large bypass.

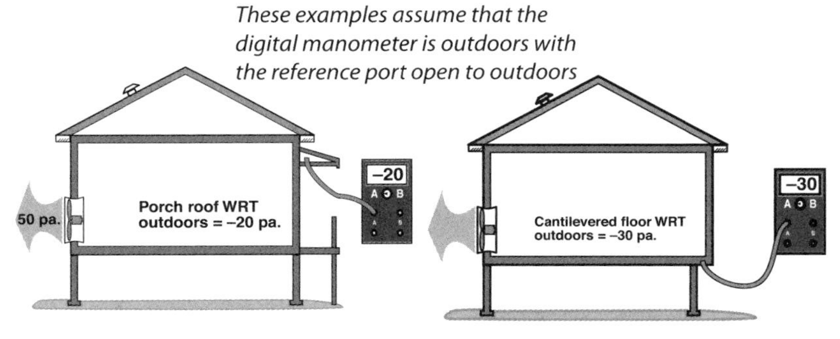


**Porch Roof Test:** If the porch roof were outdoors, the digital manometer would read near 0 pascals. We hope that the porch roof is outdoors because it is outside the insulation. We find here, however, that the porch is partially indoors, indicating that it may harbor significant air leaks through the thermal boundary.

**Cantilevered Floor Test:** We hope to find the cantilevered floor to be indoors. A reading of –50 pascals would indicate that it is completely indoors. A reading less negative than –50 pascals is measured here, indicating that the floor cavity is partially connected to outdoors.

## 3.5.6 Add-a-Hole Zone-Leakage Measurement

If you are still unsure of the location and severity of air leaks after the simpler diagnostic tests, you can use this add-a-hole procedure to estimate the $CFM_{50}$ of air leakage between the house and attic. Use the tables provided here to estimate the air leakage through the intermediate zones.

Based on the original house-to-attic pressure you measure, *Table 3-2 on page 88* allows you to choose one of three pressure drops (5, 10, and 15 pascals) that you create by opening a hole by way of an attic hatch or other opening between the house and attic. Next you estimate the area of the opening required to achieve that pressure drop. *Table 3-2 on page 88* then provides a multiplier to convert square inches of opening to $CFM_{50}$. After determining this $CFM_{50}$ leakage figure, you can determine the percentage of the home's air leakage coming through the attic by following this procedure.

1. Establish hoses into attic (or other zone) for measuring house WRT attic.
2. Depressurize house to –50 pascals.
3. Record the house's $CFM_{50}$.
4. Measure and record the house-to-attic pressure (or other zone pressure). Locate that house-to-zone pressure in the H/Z column of *Table 3-2 on page 88*. For each initial pressure there are values for $CFM_{50}$ per square inch of opening for three specific pressure drops, 5, 10, and 15 pascals.
5. Reduce the pressure you found in Step 4 by 5, 10, or 15 pascals by opening the attic hatch while increasing the blower door's speed to maintain –50 pascals housepressure. When you reach your target house-to-attic pressure, make sure the house pressure is still –50 pascals.
6. Estimate the area of the opening you made in Step 5. Multiply this opening's estimated area in square inches times the factor in *Table 3-2 on page 88* to find the $CFM_{50}$ leaking between house and attic.

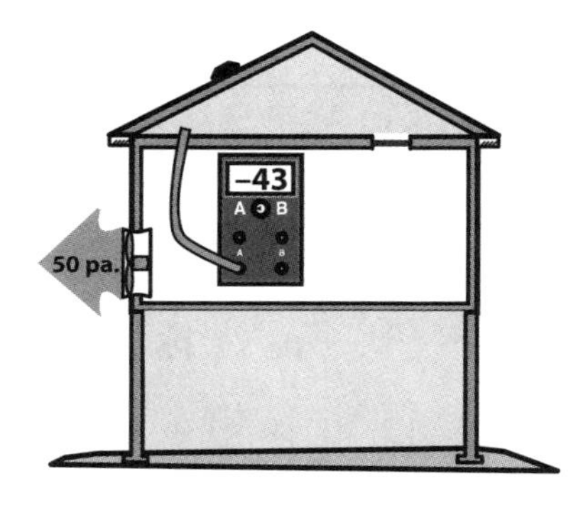


**Add-a-Hole Test 1:** The first house-to-attic pressure is –43 pascals. If we drop the pressure by 10 pascals, every square inch of opening will represent 7 $CFM_{50}$ of leakage between house and attic. See table *Table 3-2 on page 88.*

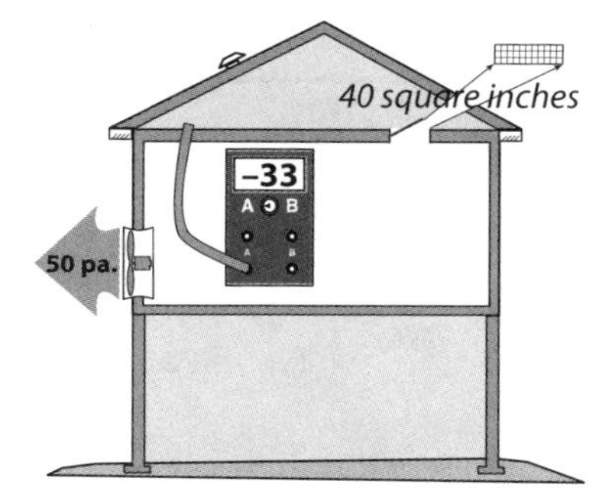


**Add-a-Hole Test 2:** Opening a hole of approximately 40 square inches drops the second house-to-attic pressure by 10 pascals.

**OPENING AREA (SQ. IN.) X FACTOR ($CFM_{50}$ PER SQ. IN.) = $CFM_{50}$**

**40 X 7 = 280 $CFM_{50}$**

Table 3-2: Add-a-Hole Leakage Factors

| Measured Pressure in Pascals | | Pressure Drop | | | Measured Pressure in Pascals | | Pressure Drop | | |
|---|---|---|---|---|---|---|---|---|---|
| H/Z[a] | Z/O[b] | 5 Pa | 10 Pa | 15 Pa | H/Z[a] | Z/O[b] | 5 Pa | 10 Pa | 15 Pa |
| 49 | 1 | 3 | 1.7 | 1.1 | 35 | 15 | 19 | 9 | 6.8 |
| 48 | 2 | 5 | 2.8 | 1.9 | 34 | 16 | 19 | 9 | 6.9 |
| 47 | 3 | 7 | 4 | 2.5 | 33 | 17 | 19 | 9 | 7.0 |
| 46 | 4 | 9 | 5 | 3.1 | 32 | 18 | 19 | 9 | 7.1 |
| 45 | 5 | 11 | 6 | 3.6 | 31 | 19 | 20 | 9 | 7.1 |
| 44 | 6 | 12 | 6 | 4.1 | 30 | 20 | 20 | 9 | 7.1 |
| 43 | 7 | 13 | 7 | 4.5 | 29 | 21 | 20 | 8 | 7.0 |
| 42 | 8 | 14 | 7 | 4.9 | 28 | 22 | 19 | 8 | 7.0 |
| 41 | 9 | 15 | 7 | 5.3 | 27 | 23 | 19 | 8 | 6.8 |
| 40 | 10 | 16 | 8 | 5.6 | 26 | 24 | 18 | 8 | 6.7 |
| 39 | 11 | 17 | 8 | 5.9 | 25 | 25 | 18 | 8 | 6.5 |
| 38 | 12 | 17 | 8 | 6.2 | 20 | 30 | 15 | 6 | -- |
| 37 | 13 | 18 | 8 | 6.5 | 15 | 35 | 10 | 3 | -- |
| 36 | 14 | 18 | 8 | 6.6 | 10 | 40 | 5 | -- | -- |

Courtesy of Michael Blasnik

a. House-to-Zone pressure difference with HwrtO @ 50 pa.
b. Zone-to-Outdoors pressure difference with HwrtO @ 50 pa.

## Open-a-Door Zone-Leakage Measurement

The open-a-door method is a another way of determining how much air leakage in $CFM_{50}$ travels through an intermediate zone like a walk-up attic, basement, or attached garage. This method requires a door between the house and the intermediate zone.

1. Perform a blower door test and measure $CFM_{50}$ with the door between the house and intermediate zone closed.
2. During the test, measure the pressure difference between the house and zone.
3. Open the door between house and zone and measure $CFM_{50}$ again. Also measure the pressure difference between the house and zone. It should now be 0 pascals.
4. Find the exterior leakage factor from *Table 3-3 on page 91*, and multiply the $CFM_{50}$ difference between door-open and door-closed blower door tests by this factor.

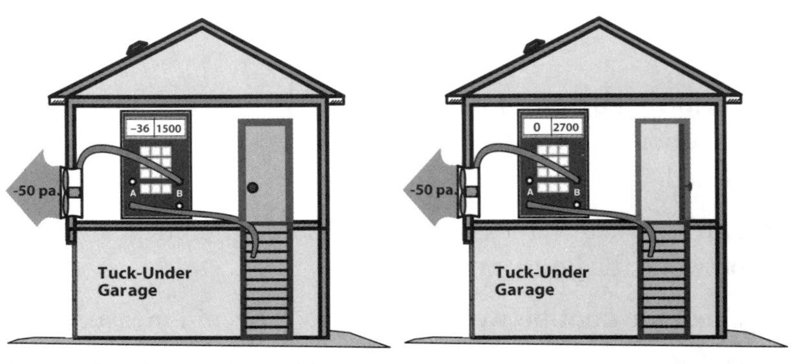


**Open-a-Door Test 1:** Start with a $CFM_{50}$ reading and a pressure difference between house and the basement zone.

**Open-a-Door Test 2:** Now open the door, and read the new $CFM_{50}$, while making sure that there is no pressure difference across the basement door.

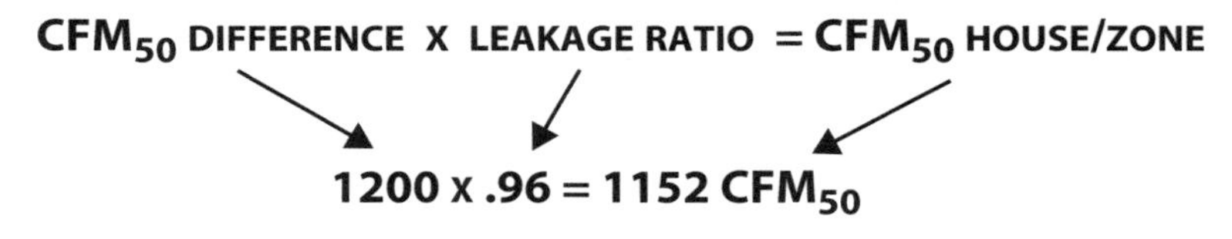


*Calculation for house-to-zone leakage*

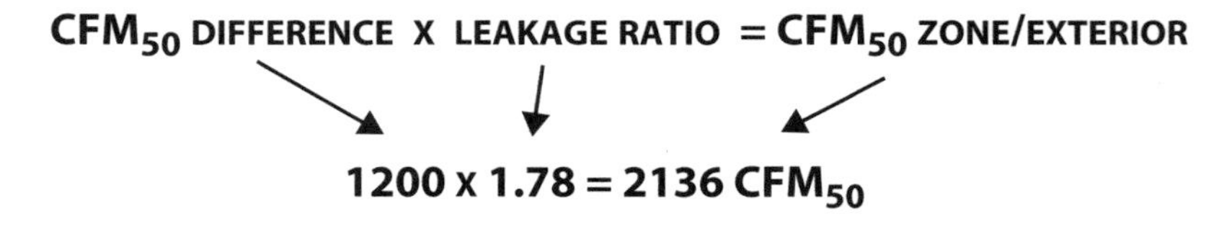


*Calculation for zone-to-outdoors leakage*

### Table 3-3: Open-a-Door Leakage Factors

| House Pressures | | Leakage Ratios | | House Pressures | | Leakage Ratios | |
|---|---|---|---|---|---|---|---|
| H/Z[a] | Z/O[b] | Int Lk | Ext Lk | H/Z | Z/O | Int Lk | Ext Lk |
| 48 | 2 | .14 | 1.14 | 27 | 23 | 2.28 | 2.53 |
| 47 | 3 | .19 | 1.19 | 26 | 24 | 2.5 | 2.64 |
| 46 | 4 | .25 | 1.24 | 25 | 25 | 2.77 | 2.76 |
| 45 | 5 | .31 | 1.29 | 24 | 26 | 3.05 | 2.89 |
| 44 | 6 | .37 | 1.34 | 23 | 27 | 3.41 | 3.04 |
| 43 | 7 | .43 | 1.39 | 22 | 28 | 3.73 | 3.19 |
| 42 | 8 | .49 | 1.44 | 21 | 29 | 4.16 | 3.36 |
| 41 | 9 | .56 | 1.49 | 20 | 30 | 4.61 | 3.54 |
| 40 | 10 | .63 | 1.54 | 19 | 31 | 5.2 | 3.76 |
| 39 | 11 | .70 | 1.6 | 18 | 32 | 5.78 | 3.98 |
| 38 | 12 | .78 | 1.66 | 17 | 33 | 6.58 | 4.24 |
| 37 | 13 | .87 | 1.72 | 16 | 34 | 7.38 | 4.52 |
| 36 | 14 | .96 | 1.78 | 15 | 35 | 8.5 | 4.87 |
| 35 | 15 | 1.06 | 1.85 | 14 | 36 | 9.63 | 5.21 |
| 34 | 16 | 1.17 | 1.91 | 13 | 37 | 11.3 | 5.68 |
| 33 | 17 | 1.3 | 1.98 | 12 | 38 | 12.9 | 6.14 |
| 32 | 18 | 1.42 | 2.06 | 11 | 39 | 15.6 | 6.79 |
| 31 | 19 | 1.54 | 2.12 | 10 | 40 | 18.3 | 7.43 |
| 30 | 20 | 1.71 | 2.23 | 9 | 41 | 22.9 | 8.4 |
| 29 | 21 | 1.99 | 2.31 | 8 | 42 | 27.5 | 9.37 |
| 28 | 22 | 2.07 | 2.42 | Courtesy of Michael Blasnik | | | |

a. House-to-Zone pressure difference with HwrtO @ 50 pa.
b. Zone-to-Outdoors pressure difference with HwrtO @ 50 pa.

## 3.5.7 Locating the Thermal Boundary

Where to air-seal and where to insulate are important retrofit decisions. Zone pressures are one of several factors used to determine where the thermal boundary should be. When there are two choices of where to insulate and air-seal, zone pressures along with other considerations help you decide.

For zone leak-testing, the house-to-zone pressure is often used to determine which of two air barriers is tighter.

Readings of negative 25-to-50 pascals house-to-attic pressure mean that the ceiling is tighter than the roof. If the roof is quite airtight, achieving a 50-pascal house-to-attic pressure difference is difficult. However if the roof is well-ventilated, achieving a near-50-pascal difference is possible.

- ✔ Readings of negative 0-to-25 pascals house-to-attic pressure mean that the roof is tighter than the ceiling. If the roof is well-ventilated, the ceiling has even more leak area than the roof's intentional vent area.
- ✔ Readings around –25 pascals house-to-attic pressure indicate that the roof and ceiling are equally airtight or leaky.
- ✔ Pressure readings more negative than –45 pascals indicate that the primary air barrier is adequately airtight. Less negative pressure readings indicate that air leaks should be located and sealed.

### Floor Versus Crawl Space

The floor shown on page 94 is tighter than the crawl-space foundation walls. If the crawl-space foundation walls are insulated, holes and vents in the foundation wall should be sealed until the pressure difference between the crawl space and outside is as negative you can make it: ideally more negative than – 45 pascals. A leaky foundation wall renders its insulation ineffective.

If the floor above the crawl space were insulated instead of the foundation walls in the previous example, the air barrier and the insulation would be aligned.

If a floor is already insulated, it makes sense to establish the air barrier there at the floor. If the foundation wall is more airtight than the floor, that would be one reason to insulate the foundation wall. *See "Evaluating Home Ventilation" on page 251..*

**Pressure Measurements and Air-Barrier Location:** The air barrier and insulation are aligned at the ceiling as they should be. The crawl-space pressure measurements show that the floor is the air barrier and the insulation is misaligned – installed at the foundation wall. We could decide to close the crawl space vents and air-seal the crawl space. Then the insulation would be aligned with the air barrier.

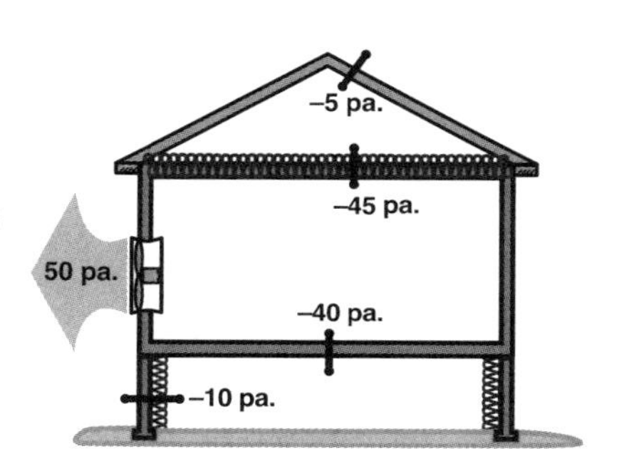


## Attic Boundary

The thermal boundary (air barrier and insulation) is usually located between the conditioned space and attic. However, insulating the roof to enclose an attic air handler and its ducts within a thermal boundary is becoming more common.

## Garage Boundary

The air barrier should always be between the conditioned space and a tuck-under or attached garage, to separate the living spaces from this unconditioned and often polluted zone.

## Duct Location

The location of ducts either within or outside the thermal boundary is an important factor in determining the cost-effectiveness of duct sealing and duct insulation. Inclosing the heating ducts within the thermal boundary is a better option than locating the ducts outside the thermal boundary because inclosing the ducts reduces energy waste from duct leakage and duct heat transmission.

## Decisions About Basement and Crawl Spaces

The air barrier and insulation should be aligned at the thermal boundary. The basement or crawl space walls are often considered to be the thermal boundary. However the floor between the first story and the basement or crawl space may also be the thermal boundary. Moisture issues, furnace location, duct location, and plumbing are factors in making a decision between choosing the floor or the foundation wall as the thermal boundary. The results of air-barrier testing provide information on which location is easier to seal. *See "Locating Foundation Air Barrier and Insulation" on page 60.*

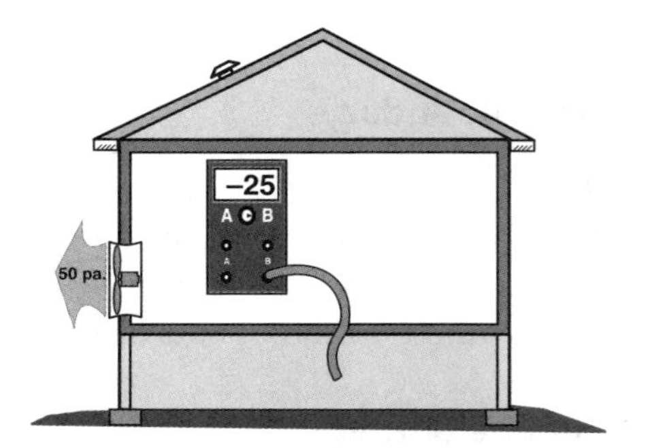


**House-to-Crawl-Space Pressure:** Many homes with crawl spaces have an ambiguous thermal boundary at the foundation. Is the air barrier at the floor or foundation wall? In the case shown here, with 25 pascals difference between the conditioned space and crawl space, the floor and foundation each form an equal part of the air barrier.

# CHAPTER 4: EVALUATING HEATING AND COOLING SYSTEMS

This chapter specifies energy efficiency improvements to heating and cooling systems.

The most important visual-inspection tasks are covered in this chapter. All heating systems should also be tested for combustion safety and steady state efficiency (SSE) as part of a comprehensive energy audit. Heating systems should be adjusted, repaired, or replaced, based on inspection and testing.

Cooling systems should be tested during service work for correct airflow and refrigerant charge. Decisions about air conditioning service or system replacement also depend on testing and visual inspection.

Duct leakage should be evaluated for both heating and cooling systems.

The inspection and testing procedures in this chapter may go beyond the auditor's training and daily practice. The reason they're included is that installation and service problems are common, and it makes sense for the auditor to be able to specify procedures for HVAC technicians. The better your quality control, the better energy savings, comfort, and customer satisfaction you can deliver. Consider the advanced procedures something to learn about as needed.

## 4.1 HEATING SYSTEM REPLACEMENT

Here, we discuss replacing furnaces and boilers. Water heaters are also discussed in this first section. Then we examine the fuel issues for both oil and natural gas.

## 4.1.1 Combustion Furnace Replacement

This section is for the air handlers of combustion furnaces. Successful furnace replacement requires selection of the right furnace and testing to verify that the new furnace is operating correctly.

- ✔ Make sure that the furnace is sized correctly, using an accurate methodology such as Manual J.
- ✔ Select a 90+ AFUE furnace and specify its installation as a sealed-combustion (direct vent) unit.
- ✔ Specify a programmable thermostat, if customers' schedule and behavior allows.
- ✔ Verify that all accessible ducts were sealed as part of installation, from the air handler and plenums to the branch connections.

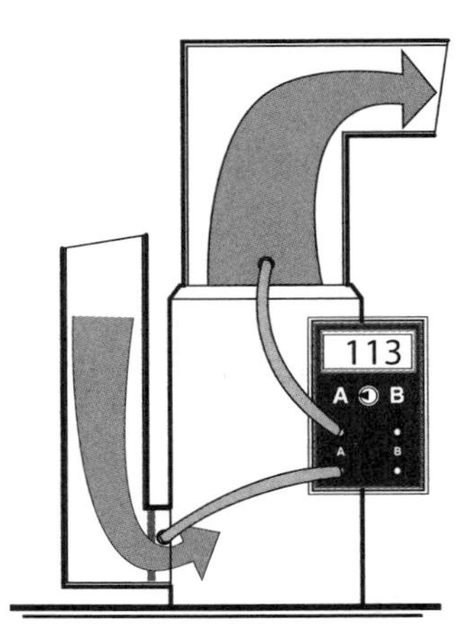


**Static Pressure and Temperature rise:** Testing static pressure and temperature rise across the new furnace should verify that the duct system isn't restricted. The correct airflow, specified by the manufacturer, is necessary for high efficiency.

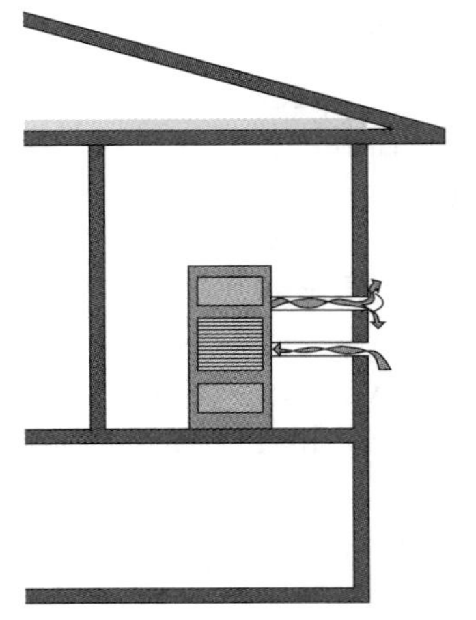

**Sealed Combustion Heaters:** Sealed combustion furnaces and boilers prevent the air pollution and house depressurization caused by some open-combustion heating units.

- ✔ If flue-gas temperature or supply air temperature are unusually high, check static pressure and fuel input. *See "Ducted Air Distribution" on page 150.*
- ✔ Filters should be held firmly in place and provide complete coverage of blower intake or return register. Filters should not permit air to bypass the filter when installed in the return plenum. Filters should be easy to replace.

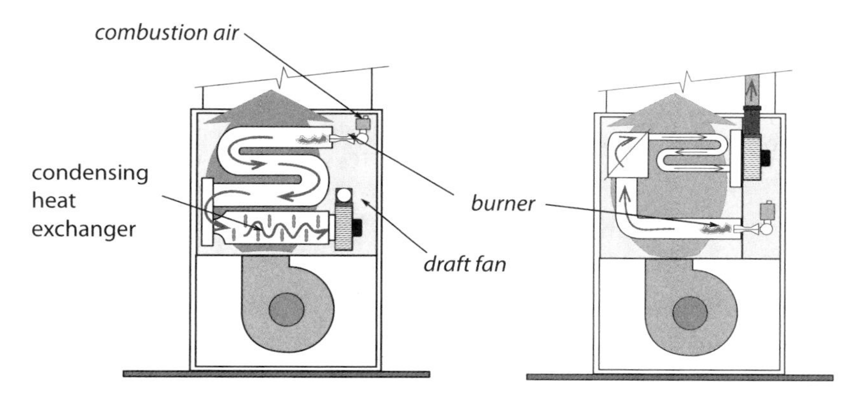


**90+ Gas Furnace:** A 90+ furnace has a condensing heat exchanger and a stronger draft fan for pulling combustion gases through its more restrictive heat-exchange system and establishing a strong positive draft.

**80+ Gas Furnace:** An 80+ furnace has a restrictive heat exchanger, a draft fan, and has no draft diverter or standing pilot.

## 4.1.2 Combustion Boiler Replacement

Boilers are replaced as an energy conservation measure or for health and safety reasons. Boiler seasonal efficiency is more sensitive to proper sizing than is furnace efficiency.

Boiler piping and controls present many options for zoning, boiler staging, and energy-saving controls. Dividing homes into zones, with separate thermostats, can significantly improve energy efficiency over operating a single zone. Modern hydronic controls can provide different water temperatures to different zones with varying heating loads.

**Radiator Temperature Control:** RTCs work well for controlling room temperature, especially in overheated rooms.

Follow these specifications when recommending a replacement boiler.

- ✔ Verify an accurate sizing calculation for the new boiler, taking into account weatherization work that reduced the heating load serviced by the previous boiler. (Boilers are sized according to the installed radiation surface connected to them. The radiators are sized according to room heat loss.)
- ✔ Specify radiator temperature controls for areas with a history of overheating.
- ✔ A functioning pressure-relief valve, expansion tank, air-excluding device, back-flow preventer, and an automatic fill valve must be part of the new hydronic system.
- ✔ Suggest that the pump be installed near the downstream side of the expansion tank to prevent the suction side of the pump from depressurizing the piping, which can pull air into the piping system.
- ✔ The expansion tank should be replaced, unless it is verified to be the proper size for the new system and adjusted for correct pressure during boiler installation. *See page 187.*

- ✔ Verify that return water temperature is above 130° F for gas and above 150° F for oil, to prevent acidic condensation within the boiler, unless the boiler is designed for condensing. Specify piping bypasses, mixing valves, primary-secondary piping, or other strategies, as necessary, to prevent condensation within a non-condensing boiler.
- ✔ Verify that flue-gas oxygen and temperature are within the ranges specified in *Table 4-3 on page 110.*

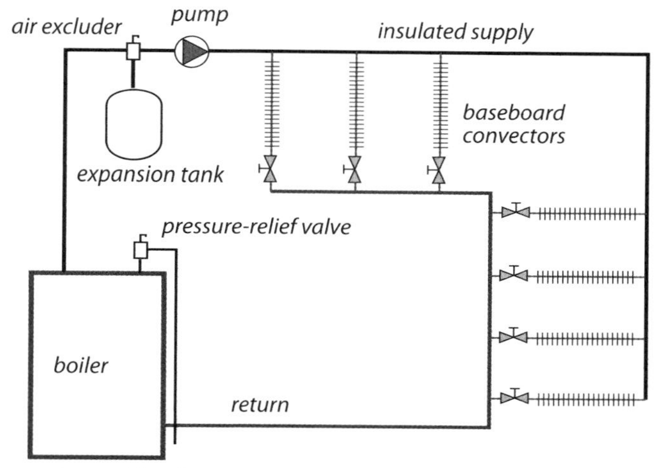


**Simple Reverse-Return Hot-Water System:** The reverse-return method of piping is the simplest way of balancing flow among heat emitters.

- ✔ Maintaining a low-limit boiler-water temperature is wasteful. Boilers should be controlled for a cold start, unless the boiler is used for domestic water heating.
- ✔ Verify that all supply piping is insulated with foam or fiberglass pipe insulation.

- ✔ Extend new piping and radiators to conditioned areas like additions and finished basements, currently heated by space heaters.

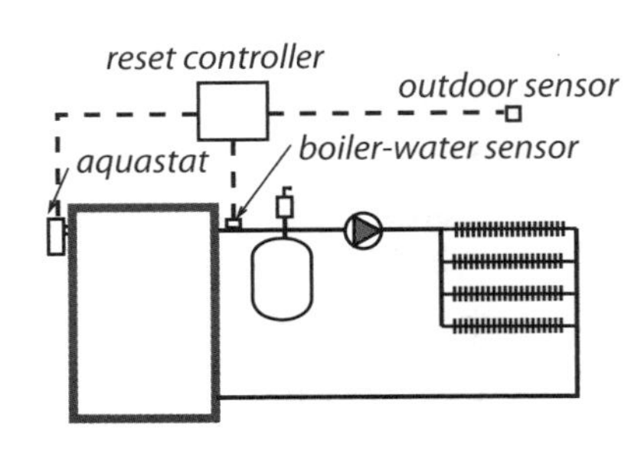


**Reset Controller:** The circulating-water temperature is controlled by the reset controller according to the outdoor temperature.

- ✔ For large boilers, consider installing reset and cut-out controllers that adjust supply water temperature according to outdoor temperature and prevent the boiler from firing when the outdoor temperature is above a certain setpoint where heat is not needed.
- ✔ Verify that the chimney was inspected and up-graded if necessary. This is an important task which is sometimes neglected.

## 4.1.3 Gas-Fired Heating Installation

Specify gas-fired heating-system replacement when appropriate as an energy conservation measure or for health and safety reasons.The general procedures outlined in *"Combustion Furnace Replacement" on page 96*, should be followed when replacing a gas furnace.

## 4.1.4 Oil-Fired Heating Installation

The overall goal of the system replacement is to provide an oil-fired heating system in virtually new condition, even though components like the oil tank, chimney, piping, or ducts may remain. Any maintenance or repair on these remaining components should be considered part of the job. Any design flaws related to the original system should be diagnosed and corrected during the heating-system replacement.

✔ Examine existing chimney and vent connector for suitability as venting for new appliance. The vent connector may need to be re-sized and the chimney may need to be re-lined.

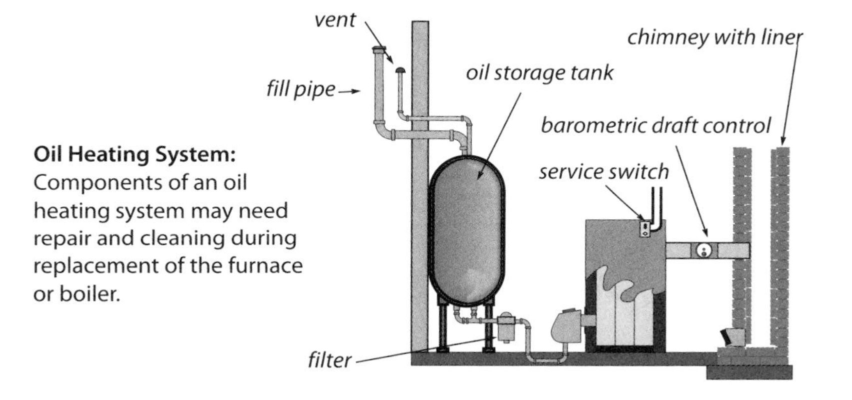


**Oil Heating System:** Components of an oil heating system may need repair and cleaning during replacement of the furnace or boiler.

✔ Check clearances of heating unit and its vent connector to nearby combustibles, by referring to NFPA 31. *See page 126.*

✔ Check for the presence of a control that interrupts power to the burner in the event of a fire.

✔ Test oil pressure to verify compliance with manufacturer's specifications.

✔ Test transformer voltage to verify compliance with manufacturer's specifications.

✔ Test control circuit amperage, and adjust thermostat heat anticipator to match.

✔ Adjust oxygen, flue-gas temperature, and smoke number to match manufacturer's specifications.

✔ Inspect oil tank and remove deposits at bottom of tank as part of new installation.

✔ Install new fuel filter and purge fuel lines as part of new installation.

- ✔ Bring tank and oil lines into compliance with NFPA 31.
- ✔ Check for emergency shut-off, installed in the living space.

## 4.2 Gas Space-Heater Replacement

Space heaters are inherently more efficient than central heaters, because they have no distribution system. As homes become more airtight and better insulated, space heaters become a more practical option for heating the whole home.

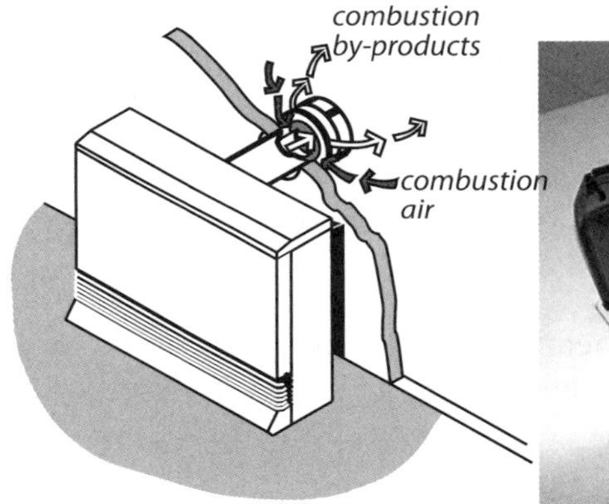


**Sealed Combustion Space Heater:** Sealed combustion space heaters draw combustion air in and exhaust combustion by-products, using a draft fan.

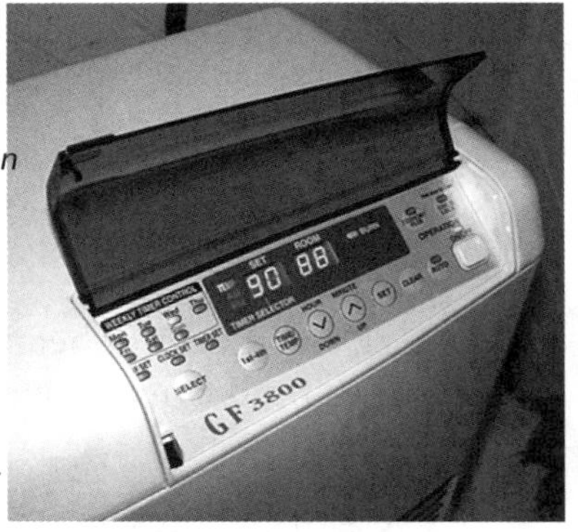


**Space Heater Controls:** Many modern energy-efficient space heaters have programmable thermostats as standard equipment.

Space heaters are replaced as an energy conservation measure or for health and safety reasons. Use the highest efficiency unit available for the application. Inspect units less than 10 years old for health and safety problems.

- ✔ Follow manufacturer's venting instructions carefully. Don't vent sealed-combustion, induced-draft space heaters into naturally drafting chimneys.
- ✔ Verify that flue-gas oxygen and temperature are within the ranges specified in *Table 4-3 on page 110.*

- ✔ If the space heater sits on a carpeted floor, specify a fire-rated floor protector, sized to the width and length of the space heater, as a base.
- ✔ Locate space heater away from traffic, draperies, and furniture.
- ✔ Insist that the space heater be provided with a properly grounded duplex receptacle for its electrical service.

### 4.2.1 Space-Heater Operation

Inform the customer of the following operating instructions.

- ✔ Don't store any objects near the space heater that would restrict airflow around it.
- ✔ Don't use the space heater to dry clothes or for any purpose other than heating the home.
- ✔ Don't allow anyone to lean or sit on the space heater.
- ✔ Don't spray aerosols near the space heater. Many aerosols are flammable or can cause corrosion to the space heater's heat exchanger.

### 4.2.2 Un-vented Space Heaters

Un-vented space heaters are common in some regions of the Southern U.S. These un-vented space heaters deliver all their products of combustion to the indoors. They are not a safe heating option and should be replaced with vented space heaters or electric space heaters.

## 4.3 Testing Gas Furnaces and Boilers

This section includes a lot of detail about testing combustion furnaces and boilers. The auditor may not feel comfortable performing the testing and adjustments detailed in this section. The reason we've included this detail is that the auditor may need to educate heating technicians about how to use these procedures.

The goal of a combustion analysis is to quickly analyze combustion and heat exchange. Within ten minutes of activating a furnace, you can know its most critical operating parameters. This information can save you from uncertainty and a host of unnecessary maintenance procedures or code prescriptions.

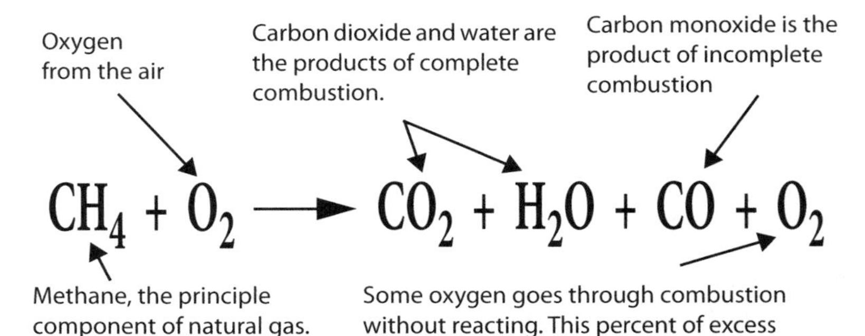


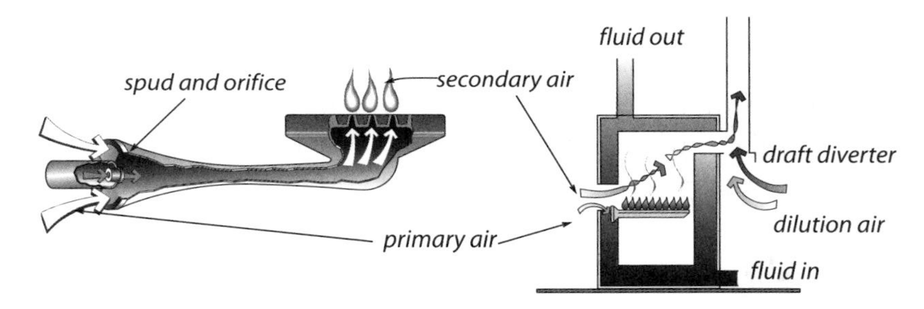


**Atmospheric, Open-Combustion Gas Burners:** Combustion air comes from indoors in open-combustion appliances. These burners use the heat of the flame to pull combustion air into the burner. Dilution air, entering at the draft diverter, prevents over-fire draft from becoming excessive.

Modern flue-gas analyzers measure $O_2$, CO, and flue-gas temperature. The better models also measure draft. Flue-gas analyzers also calculate combustion efficiency or steady-state efficiency (SSE). Using a modern electronic flue-gas analyzer, an experienced technician can test a furnace and obtain its critical operating parameters quickly.

A common furnace-efficiency problem is low fuel input and high $O_2$, resulting in poor heat transfer. This condition can only be detected by combustion testing. Optimizing the steady-state efficiency (SSE) and fuel-air mixture can save 2–8% of the furnace's fuel consumption.

Flue-gas temperature is another important indicator of furnace performance. A low fuel-gas temperature is usually an indicator of efficient performance. However, if the flue-gas temperature is too low in older furnaces or 80+ furnaces, acidic condensation forms in the vent. This acidic condensate can rust metal vents and damage masonry chimneys.

**70+ Furnace:** Sample flue gases within the draft diverter inside each exhaust port.

**80+ Furnace:** Measure draft and sample flue gases in the vent connector above the furnace.

## 4.3.1 Furnace Efficiency Testing

Perform the following procedures to verify a furnace's correct operation.

✔ Perform a combustion test using a electronic flue-gas analyzer. Recommended flue gas temperature depends on the type of furnace and is listed in the table titled, *"Combustion Standards for Gas Furnaces" on page 110.*

- ✔ Measure temperature rise (supply minus return temperatures). Temperature rise should be within the manufacturer's specifications. Estimate the airflow from the furnace's blower specifications and compare the furnace's rated output to output estimated by the table titled: *"Gas-Furnace Output from Temperature Rise and Airflow (1000s Btuh)" on page 108*
- ✔ If $O_2$ is high, or the estimated output from the table is low, increase gas pressure to 6% $O_2$ if possible as long as you don't create CO.
- ✔ Increase gas pressure if needed to increase temperature rise and flue-gas temperature. Before increasing gas pressure, the technician should believe that he can increase airflow to compensate. Otherwise no energy savings may result.

If you know the airflow through the furnace from measurements described in *"Evaluating Forced-Air System Airflow" on page 151*, you can use the table, *"Gas-Furnace Output from Temperature Rise and Airflow (1000s Btuh)" on page 108*, to check whether output is approximately what the manufacturer intended. Dividing this output by measured input from *"Measuring BTU Input on Natural Gas Appliances" on page 113* gives you another check on the steady-state efficiency.

## Troubleshooting Temperature Rise

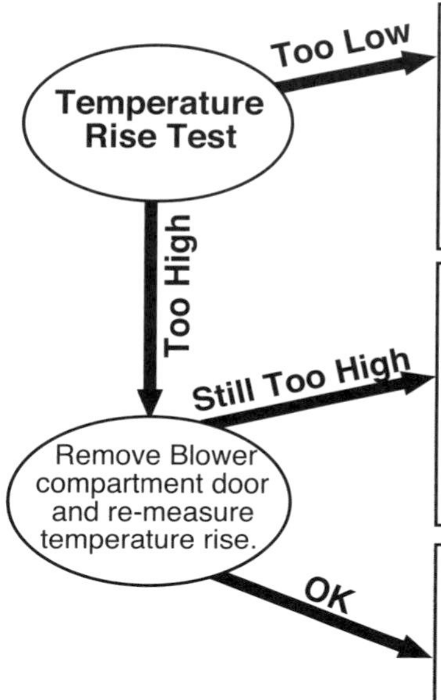


**Temperature rise is too low**

1. Look for signs of corrosion in the vent and heat exchanger.
2. Test gas input and increase if too low.
3. Check for return air leakage from outdoors.
4. Reduce fan speed.

**Supply airflow is inadequate**

1. Clean blower. Increase blower speed.
2. Find and remove restrictions in the supply ducts and registers.
3. Add additional supply branches to hard-to-heat areas.
4. Increase size of supply ducts and registers to hard-to-heat areas.

**Return airflow is inadequate**

1. Look for restrictions in the return ducts and registers.
2. Clean or replace filter.
3. Clean blower. Increase blower speed.
4. Test gas input and reduce if too high.
5. Clean or remove AC coil.
6. Install new return air duct or jumper duct.
7. Install turning vanes in 90°main return.

Table 4-1: Gas-Furnace Output from Temperature Rise and Airflow (1000s Btuh)

| CFM | Temperature Rise (Supply F° – Return F°) | | | | | |
|---|---|---|---|---|---|---|
| | 30 | 40 | 50 | 60 | 70 | 80 |
| **600** | 19.4 | 25.9 | 32.4 | 38.9 | 45.4 | 51.8 |
| **700** | 22.7 | 30.2 | 37.8 | 45.4 | 52.9 | 60.5 |
| **800** | 25.9 | 34.6 | 43.2 | 51.8 | 60.4 | 69.1 |
| **900** | 29.2 | 38.9 | 48.6 | 58.3 | 68.0 | 77.8 |
| **1000** | 32.4 | 43.2 | 54.0 | 64.8 | 75.6 | 86.4 |
| **1100** | 35.6 | 47.5 | 59.4 | 71.3 | 83.2 | 95.0 |
| **1200** | 38.9 | 51.8 | 64.8 | 77.8 | 90.7 | 103.7 |
| **1300** | 42.1 | 56.2 | 70.2 | 84.2 | 98.3 | 112.3 |
| **1400** | 45.4 | 60.5 | 75.6 | 90.7 | 105.8 | 121.0 |
| **1500** | 48.6 | 64.8 | 81.0 | 97.2 | 113.4 | 129.6 |

**Table 4-2: Action Levels for Open-Combustion Gas Appliances**

| CO Level | | Draft and Spillage | Required Action |
|---|---|---|---|
| 0 – 25 ppm | and | Passes | Proceed with work. |
| 26 –100 ppm | and | Passes | Recommend that the CO problem be fixed. |
| 26 –100 ppm | and | Fails at worst-case only | Recommend a service call for the appliance and/or repairs to the home to correct the problem. |
| 100 –400 ppm | or | Fails under normal conditions | **Stop Work:** Work may not proceed until the system is serviced and the problem is corrected. |
| >400 ppm | and | Passes | **Stop Work:** Work may not proceed until the system is serviced and the problem is corrected. |
| >400 ppm | and | Fails under any conditions | **Emergency:** Shut off the fuel to the appliance and ask the homeowner to call for service immediately. |

Courtesy: Building Performance Institute Inc.

Table 4-3: Combustion Standards for Gas Furnaces

| Performance Indicator | SSE 70+ | SSE 80+ | SSE 90+ |
|---|---|---|---|
| Carbon monoxide (CO) (ppm) | ≤ 100 ppm | ≤ 100 ppm | ≤ 100 ppm |
| Stack temperature (˚F) | 350˚–475˚ | 325˚–450˚ | ≤ 120˚ |
| Temperature rise (˚F) | 40–70˚* | 40–70˚* | 30–70˚* |
| Oxygen (%O2) | 5–10% | 4–9% | 4–9% |
| Gas pressure Inches (IWC) | 3.2–4.2 IWC* | 3.2–4.2 IWC* | 3.2–4.2 IWC* |
| Steady-state efficiency (SSE) (%) | 72–78% | 78–82% | 92–97% |
| Draft (Pa) | –5 Pa | –5 Pa | +25–60 Pa |

* pmi = per manufacturer's instructions

### Drilling and Patching Vents for Combustion Testing

- For single-wall metal vents, drill a quarter-inch hole and patch it with high-temperature silicone caulking.
- For double-wall metal vent, drill through both layers. Install a $^{5}/_{16}$-inch automotive lag screw through the two-layer hole. Seal the lag screw's cap with high-temperature silicone.
- For plastic vents, drill in a vertical section and drill slightly downwards. This prevents condensate from flowing into the hole. Again, seal the hole with high-temperature silicone.

Table 4-4: Carbon Monoxide Causes and Solutions

| Cause | Analysis & Solution |
|---|---|
| Flame smothered by combustion gases. | Chimney backdrafting from CAZ depressurization or chimney blockage. |
| Burner or pilot flame impinges. | Align burner or pilot burner. Reduce gas pressure if excessive. |
| Inadequate combustion air with too rich fuel-air mixture. | $O_2$ is ≤6%. Gas input is excessive or combustion air is lacking. Reduce gas or add combustion air. |
| Blower interferes with flame. | Inspect heat exchanger. Replace furnace or heat exchanger. |
| Primary air shutter closed. | Open primary air shutter. |
| Dirt and debris on burner. | Clean burners. |
| Excessive combustion air cooling flame. | $O_2$ is ≥11%. Increase gas pressure. |

Table 4-5: Combustion Problems and Possible Solutions

| Problem | Possible causes and solutions |
|---|---|
| Weak draft with CAZ depressurization | Return duct leaks, clothes dryer, exhaust fans, other chimneys. Seal return leaks. Provide make-up air. |
| Weak draft with no CAZ depressurization | Chimney or vent connector is blocked, leaky, incorrectly sized, or has inadequate slope. Or else CAZ is too airtight. |
| Carbon monoxide | Mixture too rich or too lean. Adjust gas pressure. Check chimney and combustion air for code compliance. |
| Stack temperature or temperature rise too high or low | Adjust fan speed or gas pressure. Improve ducts to increase airflow. |
| Oxygen too high or low | Adjust gas pressure, but don't increase CO level. |

## 4.4 Critical Furnace-Testing Parameters

The following group of furnace-testing parameters are the most important ones because they tell you how efficient and safe the furnace currently is and how much you might be able to improve efficiency.

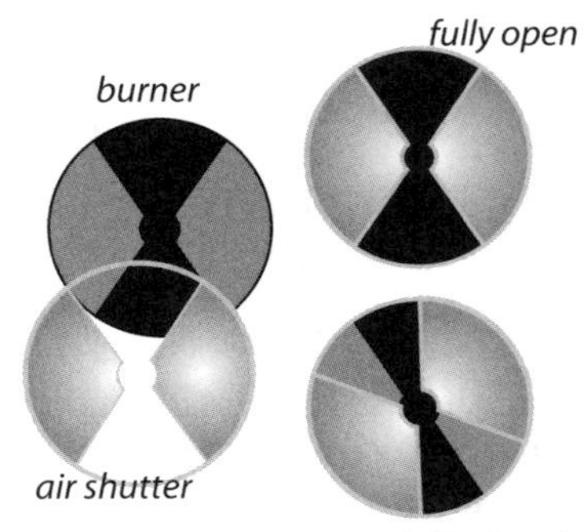


**Primary Air Adjustment:** Primary air shutters are usually fully open for natural gas combustion and partially closed for propane depending on flame characteristics. Too much primary air can cause noise and flame lift-off. Too little causes a lazy flame, searching for air. A good flame is hard and blue with an inner and outer mantle.

*Carbon monoxide (CO) (ppm):* Poisonous gas indicates incomplete combustion. Adjusting combustion to produce less than 100 ppm is almost always possible with gas-pressure adjustments, primary-air adjustments, or burner maintenance.

*Oxygen (percent):* Indicates the percent of excess air and whether fuel-air mixture is correct. Oxygen is directly related to furnace efficiency. Percent $O_2$ may also clarify the cause of CO as either too little or too much combustion air.

*Flue-gas temperature:* The critical heat-exchange measurement, flue-gas temperature is directly related to furnace efficiency. Too high flue-gas temperature wastes energy and too-low flue-gas temperature leads to condensation and inadequate draft.

*Airflow:* The current furnace airflow and the likelihood of being able to increase it are very important to determine. During testing, airflow is artificially increased and the effect on flue-gas temperature and temperature rise is observed. Measuring airflow also allows you to measure furnace output fairly accurately so you can compare it to output as listed on the furnace nameplate.

*Duct leakage to outdoors:* By pressurizing both the house and ducts, you can measure how much ducted air is leaking to outdoors. This value is directly related to the energy savings you can expect from duct sealing.

### 4.4.1 Measuring BTU Input on Natural Gas Appliances

Use the following procedure when it's necessary to measure the input of a natural gas appliance.

1. Turn off all gas combustion appliances such as water heaters, dryers, cook stoves, and space heaters that are connected to the meter you are timing, except for the appliance you wish to test.
2. Fire the unit being tested, and watch the dials of the gas meter.
3. Carefully count how long it takes for one revolution of $^1/_2$, 1, or 2 cubic-foot dial. Find that number of seconds in *Table 4-6* in the columns marked "Seconds per Revolution." Follow that row across to the right to the correct column for the $^1/_2$, 1, or 2 cubic-foot dial. Note that you must multiply the number in the table by 1000. Record the input in thousands of Btus per hour.
4. If the measured input is higher or lower than input on the name plate by more than 10%, adjust gas pressure up or down within a range of 3.2 to 3.9 IWC until the approximately correct input is achieved.
5. If the measured input is still out of range after adjusting gas pressure to these limits, replace the existing orifices with larger or smaller orifices sized to give the correct input.

## Table 4-6: Input in Thousands of Btu/hr for 1000 Btu/cu. ft. Gas

| Seconds per Revolution | Size of Meter Dial | | | Seconds per Revolution | Size of Meter Dial | | | Seconds per Revolution | Size of Meter Dial | | |
|---|---|---|---|---|---|---|---|---|---|---|---|
| | 1/2 cu. ft. | 1 cu. ft. | 2 cu. ft. | | 1/2 cu. ft. | 1 cu. ft. | 2 cu. ft. | | 1/2 cu. ft. | 1 cu. ft. | 2 cu. ft. |
| 15 | 120 | 240 | 480 | 40 | 45 | 90 | 180 | 70 | 26 | 51 | 103 |
| 16 | 112 | 225 | 450 | 41 | 44 | 88 | 176 | 72 | 25 | 50 | 100 |
| 17 | 106 | 212 | 424 | 42 | 43 | 86 | 172 | 74 | 24 | 48 | 97 |
| 18 | 100 | 200 | 400 | 43 | 42 | 84 | 167 | 76 | 24 | 47 | 95 |
| 19 | 95 | 189 | 379 | 44 | 41 | 82 | 164 | 78 | 23 | 46 | 92 |
| 20 | 90 | 180 | 360 | 45 | 40 | 80 | 160 | 80 | 22 | 45 | 90 |
| 21 | 86 | 171 | 343 | 46 | 39 | 78 | 157 | 82 | 22 | 44 | 88 |
| 22 | 82 | 164 | 327 | 47 | 38 | 77 | 153 | 84 | 21 | 43 | 86 |
| 23 | 78 | 157 | 313 | 48 | 37 | 75 | 150 | 86 | 21 | 42 | 84 |
| 24 | 75 | 150 | 300 | 49 | 37 | 73 | 147 | 88 | 20 | 41 | 82 |
| 25 | 72 | 144 | 288 | 50 | 36 | 72 | 144 | 90 | 20 | 40 | 80 |
| 26 | 69 | 138 | 277 | 51 | 35 | 71 | 141 | 94 | 19 | 38 | 76 |
| 27 | 67 | 133 | 267 | 52 | 35 | 69 | 138 | 98 | 18 | 37 | 74 |
| 28 | 64 | 129 | 257 | 53 | 34 | 68 | 136 | 100 | 18 | 36 | 72 |
| 29 | 62 | 124 | 248 | 54 | 33 | 67 | 133 | 104 | 17 | 35 | 69 |
| 30 | 60 | 120 | 240 | 55 | 33 | 65 | 131 | 108 | 17 | 33 | 67 |
| 31 | 58 | 116 | 232 | 56 | 32 | 64 | 129 | 112 | 16 | 32 | 64 |
| 32 | 56 | 113 | 225 | 57 | 32 | 63 | 126 | 116 | 15 | 31 | 62 |
| 33 | 55 | 109 | 218 | 58 | 31 | 62 | 124 | 120 | 15 | 30 | 60 |
| 34 | 53 | 106 | 212 | 59 | 30 | 61 | 122 | 130 | 14 | 28 | 55 |
| 35 | 51 | 103 | 206 | 60 | 30 | 60 | 120 | 140 | 13 | 26 | 51 |
| 36 | 50 | 100 | 200 | 62 | 29 | 58 | 116 | 150 | 12 | 24 | 48 |
| 37 | 49 | 97 | 195 | 64 | 29 | 56 | 112 | 160 | 11 | 22 | 45 |
| 38 | 47 | 95 | 189 | 66 | 29 | 54 | 109 | 170 | 11 | 21 | 42 |
| 39 | 46 | 92 | 185 | 68 | 28 | 53 | 106 | 180 | 10 | 20 | 40 |

## Natural Gas Heat Content

Note that *Table 4-6 on page 114* assumes that gas is 1000 BTUs per cubic foot. Where BTU values differ from this figure – especially at high elevations – obtain the correct BTU value from the gas supplier and apply the formula shown below.

**(BTU VALUE FROM SUPPLIER ÷ 1000) X BTU/HR INPUT FROM TABLE = ACTUAL BTU/HR INPUT OF APPLIANCE**

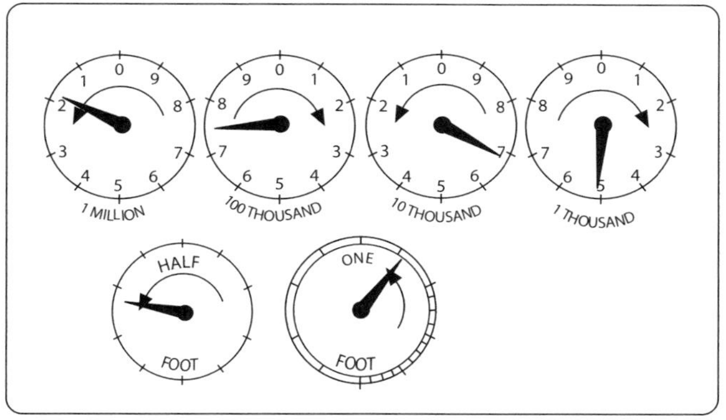


**Clocking the Meter:** Count the number of seconds per revolution of the one-foot dial and refer to*Table 4-6 on page 114* to find the appliance's input.

## 4.5 Inspecting Gas Combustion Systems

Gas burners should be inspected and maintained every 2 to 4 years. These following specifications apply to gas furnaces, boilers, water heaters, and space heaters.

Perform the following inspection procedures and maintenance practices on all gas-fired furnaces, boilers, water heaters, and space heaters, as necessary. The goal of these measures is to reduce carbon monoxide (CO), stabilize flame, and verify the operation of safety controls.

- ✔ Look for soot, melted wire insulation, and rust in the burner and manifold area outside the fire box. These signs indicate flame roll-out, combustion gas spillage, and CO production.
- ✔ Inspect the burners for dust, debris, misalignment, flame-impingement, and other flame-interference problems. Clean, vacuum, and adjust as needed.
- ✔ Inspect the heat exchanger for leaks.
- ✔ Furnaces and boilers should have dedicated circuits with fused disconnects, which must have a safety shutoff within arm's reach off the heating appliance. Verify that all 120-volt wiring connections are enclosed in covered electrical boxes.
- ✔ Determine that pilot is burning (if equipped) and that main burner ignition is satisfactory.
- ✔ Test pilot-safety control for complete gas valve shutoff when pilot is extinguished.
- ✔ Check the conventional thermostat's heat-anticipator setting. The thermostat's heat-anticipator setting should match the measured current in the 24-volt control circuit.
- ✔ For programmable thermostats, refer to manufacturer's instructions about how to control cycle length. These instructions may be printed inside the thermostat.

- ✔ Check venting system for proper diameter and pitch. *See page 136.*
- ✔ Check venting system for obstructions, blockages, or leaks.
- ✔ Test to ensure that the high-limit control extinguishes the burner before furnace temperature rises to 200° F.

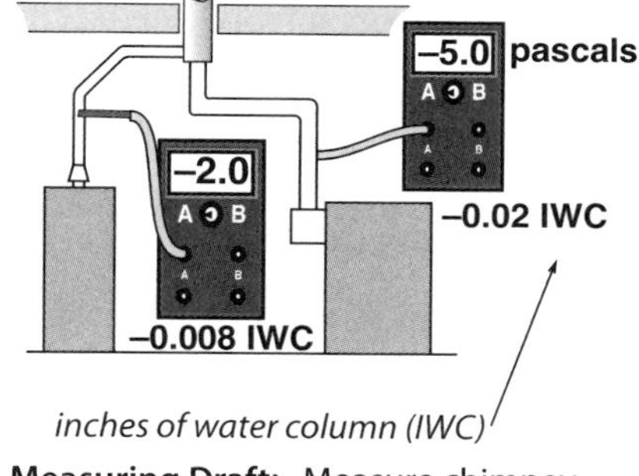


**Measuring Draft:** Measure chimney draft *downstream* of the draft diverter.

- ✔ Measure gas input, and observe flame characteristics if soot, CO, or other combustion problems are present.
- ✔ If you measure CO, open a window while observing CO level on the meter to see if CO is reduced by increasing the available combustion air through the open window. *See page 146.*

Proceed with burner cleaning and adjustment in these cases.

- ✔ CO is greater than 100 ppm.
- ✔ Visual indicators of soot or flame roll-out exist.
- ✔ Burners are visibly dirty.
- ✔ Measured draft is inadequate. *See page 126.*
- ✔ The appliance has not been serviced for two years or more.

Gas-burner and gas-venting maintenance should include the following measures.

- ✔ Remove causes of CO and soot, such as over-firing, closed primary air intake, flame impingement, and lack of combustion air.
- ✔ Remove dirt, rust, and other debris that may be interfering with the burners. Clean the heat exchanger, if there are signs of soot around the burner compartment.

- ✔ Take action to improve draft, if inadequate because of improper venting, obstructed chimney, leaky chimney, or depressurization. *See page 133.*
- ✔ Seal leaks in vent connectors and chimneys.
- ✔ Adjust gas input if combustion testing indicates overfiring or underfiring.

## 4.6 Oil-Burner Safety and Efficiency Service

Oil burners require annual maintenance to maintain acceptable operational safety and combustion efficiency. Testing for combustion efficiency (steady-state efficiency), oxygen, draft, carbon monoxide, and smoke should be used to evaluate the oil burner and to guide adjustment and maintenance. These procedures apply to oil-fired furnaces, boilers, and water heaters.

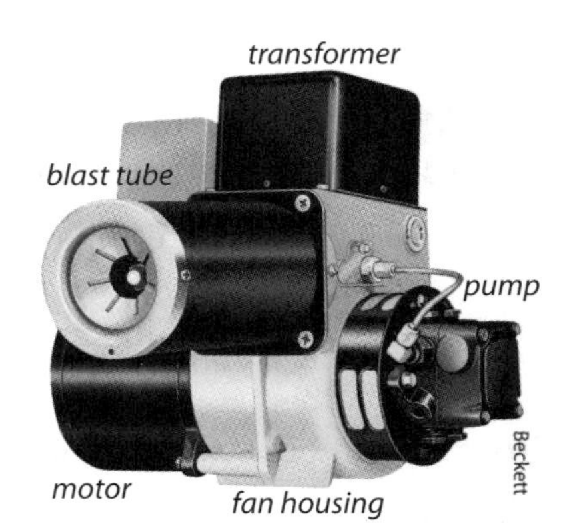


### 4.6.1 Oil-Burner Inspection

Use visual inspection and combustion testing to evaluate oil burner operation. An oil burner passing visual inspection and conforming to the specifications on *page 120* may need no maintenance. If the test results are slightly out of specifications, adjustments are necessary by a qualified technician. Unsatisfactory test results may indicate the need to replace the burner or the entire heating unit.

The energy auditor can perform the following inspections and specify profession service on a work order.

- ✔ Each oil furnace or boiler should have a dedicated electrical circuit. Assure that all 120-volt wiring connections are enclosed in covered electrical boxes.
- ✔ Verify that all oil-fired heaters are equipped with a barometric draft control, unless they have high-static burners or are mobile home furnaces.

**Barometric Draft Control:** This control supplies a stable over-fire draft and controlled flow of combustion gases through the heat exchanger.

- ✔ Assure that barometric draft controls are mounted plumb and level and that the damper swings freely.
- ✔ Inspect burner and appliance for signs of soot, overheating, fire hazards, corrosion, or wiring problems.
- ✔ Inspect fuel lines and storage tanks for leaks.
- ✔ Inspect heat exchanger and combustion chamber for cracks, corrosion, or soot buildup.
- ✔ Check to see if flame ignition is instantaneous or delayed. Flame ignition should be instantaneous, except for prepurge units with delayed oil valves where the blower runs for a while before ignition.

## 4.6.2 Oil-Burner Testing

Combustion testing is the key to a technician's understanding the current oil-burner performance level and potential for improvement. Specify that oil-heating technicians perform the following tasks as part of an oil-burner tune-up.

- ✔ Analyze the flue gas for $O_2$, temperature, CO, and steady-state efficiency (SSE). Sample undiluted flue gases between the barometric draft control and the appliance.

- ✔ Sample undiluted flue gases with a smoke tester, following the smoke-tester instructions. Compare the smoke smudge left by the gases on the filter paper with the manufacturer's smoke-spot scale to determine smoke number.
- ✔ Measure flue draft between the appliance and barometric draft control and over-fire draft over the fire inside the firebox.

Table 4-7: Minimum Oil-Burner Combustion Standards

| Oil Combustion Performance Indicator | Non-Flame Retention | Flame Retention |
|---|---|---|
| Oxygen (% $O_2$) | 4–9% | 4–7% |
| Stack temperature (°F) | 350°–600° | 325°–500° |
| Carbon monoxide (CO) parts per million (ppm) | ≤ 100 ppm | ≤ 100 ppm |
| Steady-state efficiency (SSE) (%) | ≥ 75% | ≥ 80% |
| Smoke number (1–9) | ≤ 2 | ≤ 1 |
| Excess air (%) | ≤ 100% | ≤ 25% |
| Oil pressure pounds per square inch (psi) | ≥ 100 psi | ≥ 100-150 psi (pmi)* |
| Over-fire draft (IWC negative) | –5 Pa. or –.02 IWC | –5 Pa. or –.02 IWC |
| Flue draft (IWC negative) | –10 to 25 Pa. or –0.040 to –0.1IWC | –10 to 25 Pa. or –0.04 to –0.1IWC |

* pmi = per manufacturer's specifications

Table 4-8: Typical Safe Draft for Oil-Fired Appliances

| | **Outdoor Temperature (Degrees F)** | | | | |
|---|---|---|---|---|---|
| **Appliance** | **<20** | **21-40** | **41-60** | **61-80** | **>80** |
| Oil-fired furnace, boiler, or water heater with atmospheric chimney | −15 Pa.<br>−0.06 IWC | − 13 Pa.<br>−0.053 IWC | −11 Pa.<br>−0.045 IWC | −9 Pa.<br>−0.038 IWC | −7 Pa.<br>−0.030 IWC |

✔ Measure high-limit shut-off temperature and adjust or replace the high-limit control if the shut-off temperature is more than 200° F for furnaces or 220° F for hot-water boilers.

✔ Measure oil-pump pressure, and adjust to manufacturer's specifications if necessary.

✔ Measure transformer voltage, and adjust to manufacturer's specifications if necessary.

✔ Time the CAD cell control or stack control to verify that the burner shuts off, within 45 seconds or a time specified by the manufacturer, when the cad cell is blocked from seeing the flame.

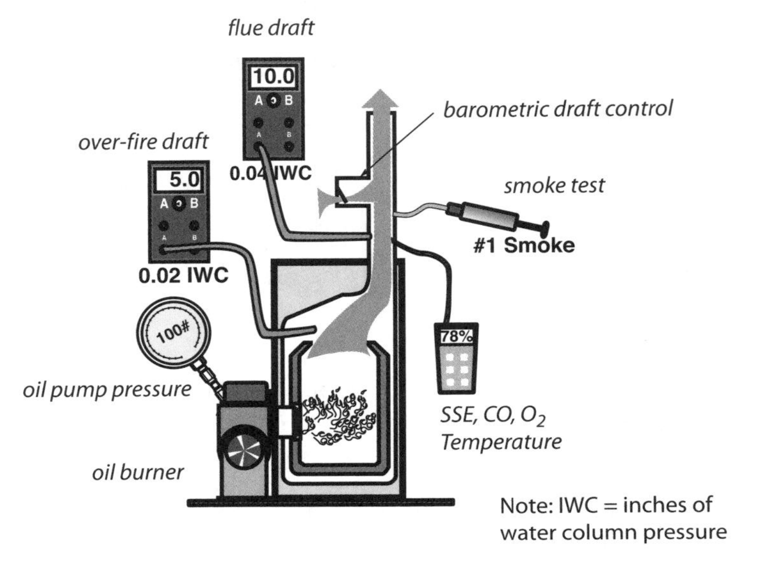


**Measuring Oil-Burner Performance:** To measure oil-burning performance indicators, a manometer, flue-gas analyzer, smoke tester, and pressure gauge are required.

## 4.6.3 Oil-Burner Adjustment

Unlike gas burners, combustion air and draft are adjustable with an oil burner.

Replace burner nozzle after matching the nozzle size to the home's heat-load requirements however don't derate the nozzle more than 20%.

- ✔ Set oil pump to correct pressure.
- ✔ Adjust air shutter to achieve oxygen and smoke values, specified in *Table 4-7 on page 120.*
- ✔ Adjust barometric damper for negative flue draft of 5–10 pascals or 0.02-to-0.04 IWC (before barometric damper).
- ✔ Adjust fan speed or increase ducted airflow to reduce high flue-gas temperature if possible without reducing flue gas temperature below 350°F.

### 4.6.4 Oil-Burner Maintenance and Visual Checks

After evaluating the oil burner's operation, specify some or all of the following maintenance tasks as necessary to optimize safety and efficiency.

Clean the burner's blower wheel.

- ✔ Clean dust, dirt, and grease from the burner assembly.
- ✔ Replace oil filter(s) and nozzle.
- ✔ Clean or replace air filter.
- ✔ Remove soot from combustion chamber.
- ✔ Remove soot from heat exchange surfaces.
- ✔ Adjust gap between electrodes to manufacturer's specifications.
- ✔ Repair the ceramic combustion chamber, or replace it if necessary.
- ✔ Verify correct flame-sensor operation.

After these maintenance procedures, the technician performs the diagnostic tests described previously to evaluate improvement made by the maintenance procedures and to determine if fine-tuning is required.

## 4.7 Wood Stoves

Wood heating is a popular and effective auxiliary heating source for homes. However, wood stoves and fireplaces can cause indoor-air-pollution and fire hazards. It's important to inspect wood stoves to evaluate potential hazards.

### 4.7.1 Wood Stove Clearances

Stoves that are listed by a testing agency like Underwriters Laboratory have installation instructions stating their clearance from combustibles. Unlisted stoves must adhere to clearances specified in NFPA 211.

## 4.7.2 Stove Clearances

Unlisted stoves must be at least 36 inches away from combustibles. However, listed wood stoves may be installed to as little as 6 inches away from combustibles, if they incorporate heat shields and combustion design that directs heat away from the back and sides. Ventilated or insulated wall protectors may also decrease unlisted clearance from one-third to two thirds. Always follow the stove manufacturer's or heat-shield manufacturer's installation instructions.

### Floor Construction and Clearances

Wood stoves must rest of a floor of non-combustible construction. An example of a non-combustible floor is one composed of only masonry material sitting on dirt. This floor must extend no less than 18 inches beyond the stove in all directions. Approved floor protectors or the stove-bottom heat shields of listed stoves can allow the stove to rest on a floor containing combustible materials. The floor would need a minimum of one-quarter inch of grouted tile or an approved floor protector extending 18 inches away from the stove in all directions.

### Vent-Connector and Chimney Clearance

Interior chimneys require a 2-inch clearance from combustibles and exterior chimneys require a 1-inch clearance from combustibles.

Single-wall vent connectors must be at least 18 inches from combustibles. Wall protectors may reduce this clearance up to two-thirds. Type-L double-wall vent pipe requires only a 9-inch clearance from combustibles.

See also *"Chimneys" on page 139* and *"Vent Connectors" on page 136.*

## 4.7.3 Wood Stove Inspection

All components of wood-stove venting systems should be approved for use with wood stoves. Chimney sections penetrating floor, ceiling, or roof should have approved thimbles, support packages, and ventilated shields to protect combustible materials from high temperatures. The energy auditor should perform or specify the following inspection tasks, depending on the customer's instructions and the work scope of the energy program.

- ✔ Inspect stove, vent connector, and chimney for correct clearances from combustible materials as listed in NFPA 211.
- ✔ If the home is tight, the wood stove should be equipped with outdoor combustion air.
- ✔ Galvanized steel pipe must not be used to vent wood stoves.
- ✔ Inspect vent connector and chimney for leaks. Leaks should be sealed with a high-temperature sealant designed for sealing wood-stove vents.
- ✔ Inspect chimney and vent connector for creosote build-up, and suggest chimney cleaning if creosote build-up exists.
- ✔ Inspect the house for soot on seldom-cleaned horizontal surfaces. If soot is present or if the blower door indicates leakage, inspect the wood-stove door gasket. Suggest sealing stove air leaks and improving draft in order to reduce indoor smoke emissions.
- ✔ Inspect stack damper and/or combustion air intake.
- ✔ Check catalytic combustor for repair or replacement if the wood stove has one.
- ✔ Assure that heat exchange surfaces and flue passages within the wood stove are free of accumulations of soot or debris.

✔ Wood stoves installed in mobile or manufactured homes must be approved for use in mobile or manufactured homes.

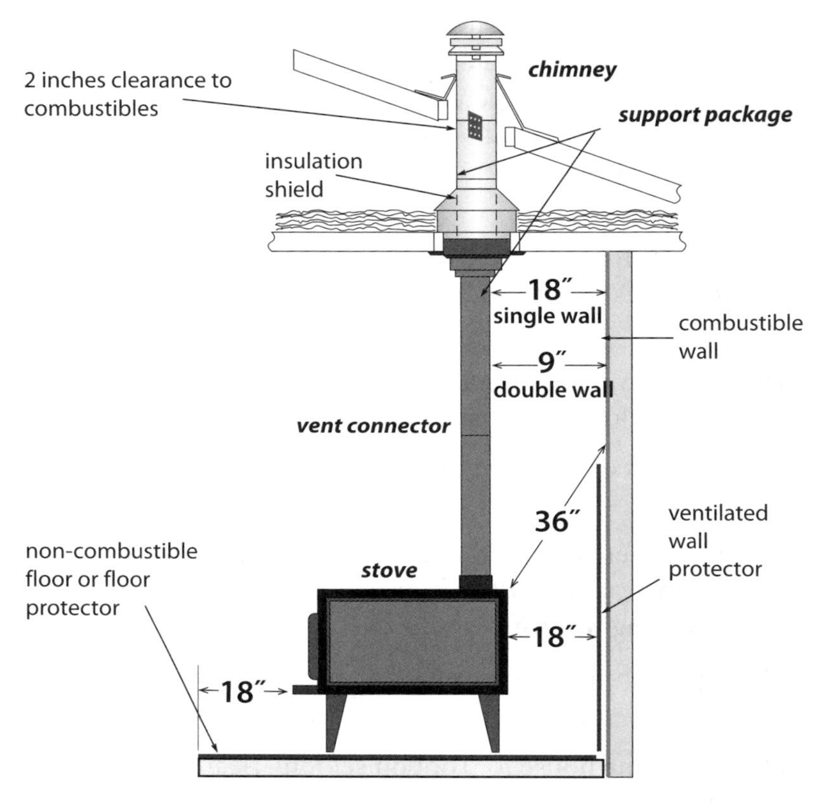


**Wood-Stove Installation:** Wood-stove venting and clearances are vitally important to wood-burning safety. Read manufacturer's instructions for the stove and its venting components, if the wood stove is on your inspection checklist.

## 4.8 Draft, Venting, and Combustion Air

Proper venting is essential to the operation, efficiency, safety and durability of combustion appliances. The National Fire Protection Association (NFPA) publishes authoritative information sources on material-choice, sizing, and clearances for chimneys and vent connectors, as well as for combustion air. The information in this venting section is based on the following NFPA documents.

- ✔ NFPA 54: The *National Fuel Gas Code 2006*
- ✔ NFPA 31: *Standard for the Installation of Oil-Burning Equipment 2006*
- ✔ NFPA 211: *Standard for Chimneys, Fireplaces, Vents, and Solid-Fuel-Burning Appliances* 2006

**Table 4-9: Guide to Venting Standards**

| Topic | Code Reference |
|---|---|
| Vent Specs | NFPA 54, Chapters 12 and 13<br>NFPA 31, Chapter 6<br>NFPA 211 |
| Clearances | NFPA 54, Chapter 12<br>NFPA 31,<br>NFPA 211 |
| Combustion Air | NFPA 54, Chapter 9<br>NFPA 31, Chapter 5<br>NFPA 211, Chapter 12 |

## 4.9 Essential Combustion Safety Tests

The Building Performance Institute (BPI) requires that essential combustion safety tests be performed as part of all energy conservation jobs. BPI requires gas leak-testing and CO testing for all appliances. For naturally drafting appliances, either a worst-case venting test or zone-isolation test is also necessary. BPI considers naturally drafting appliances and venting systems to be obsolete for both efficiency and safety reasons. BPI strongly recommends that these obsolete appliances be replaced with modern direct-vent or power-vent combustion appliances.

## 4.9.1 Leak-Testing Gas Piping

Natural gas and propane piping systems may leak at their joints and valves. Find gas leaks with an electronic combustible-gas detector, often called a gas sniffer. A gas sniffer find all significant gas leaks if used carefully. Remember that natural gas rises from a leak and propane falls, so position the sensor accordingly.

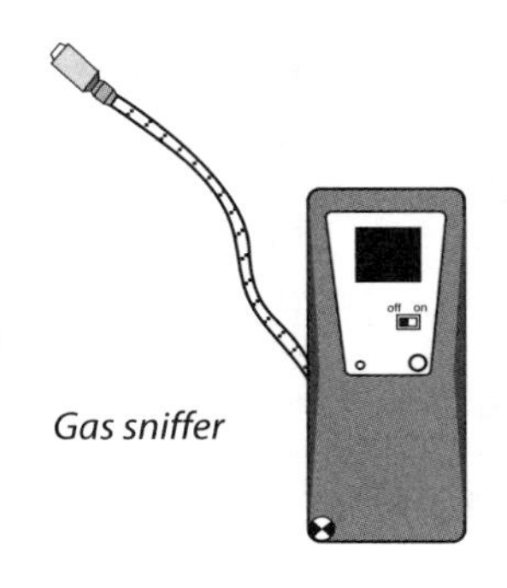

*Gas sniffer*

- ✔ Sniff all valves and joints with the gas sniffer.
- ✔ Accurately locate leaks using a non-corrosive bubbling liquid, designed for finding gas leaks.
- ✔ All gas leaks must be repaired.
- ✔ Replace kinked or corroded flexible gas connectors.
- ✔ Replace flexible gas lines manufactured before 1973. The date is stamped on a date ring attached to the flexible gas line.

## 4.9.2 Carbon Monoxide (CO) Testing

CO testing is essential for evaluating combustion and venting. Measure CO in the vent of every combustion appliance you inspect and service. Measure CO in ambient air in both the home and CAZ during your inspection and testing of combustion appliances.

### Vent Testing for CO

Testing for CO in the appliance vent is a part of combustion that takes place under worst-case conditions. If CO is present in undiluted combustion byproducts more than 100 parts per million (ppm), the appliance fails the CO test.

### Ambient Air Monitoring for CO

BPI standards require technicians to monitor CO during testing to ensure that air in the combustion appliance zone (CAZ) doesn't exceed 35 parts per million. If ambient CO levels in the combustion zone exceed 35 parts per million (ppm), stop testing for the your own safety. Ventilate the CAZ thoroughly before resuming combustion testing. Investigate indoor CO levels of 9 ppm or greater to find their cause.

**Table 4-10: Testing Requirements for Combustion Appliances and Venting Systems**

| Appliance/Venting System | Required Testing |
|---|---|
| All direct-vent or power-vent combustion appliances | Gas leak test<br>CO test at flue-gas exhaust outdoors<br>Confirm venting system connected |
| Combustion appliances (with naturally drafting chimneys) in a mechanical room or attached garage supplied with outdoor combustion air and sealed from the home | Gas leak test<br>CO test<br>Confirm that CAZ is effectively air-sealed from house and has combustion air from outdoors |
| Naturally drafting chimney and appliance located within home | Gas leak test<br>CO test<br>Venting inspection<br>Worst-case draft and depressurization testing |

## 4.9.3 Worst-Case Testing for Atmospheric Venting Systems

Depressurization is the leading cause of backdrafting and flame roll-out in furnaces, boilers, and water heaters that vent into naturally drafting chimneys. The best option is to replace the older appliances and their naturally drafting venting systems with direct-vented or power-vented appliances with airtight venting systems. However, if the atmospheric appliances and venting systems must remain, perform the worst-case testing procedures documented here.

Worst-case vent testing uses the home's exhaust fans, air handler, and chimneys to create worst-case depressurization in the combustion-appliance zone (CAZ). The CAZ is an area containing one or more combustion appliances. During this worst-case testing, you can test for spillage, measure the indoor-outdoor pressure difference, and measure chimney draft.

Worst-case conditions do occur, and venting systems must exhaust combustion by-products even under these extreme conditions. Worst-case vent testing exposes whether or not the venting system exhausts the combustion gases when the combustion-zone pressure is as negative as you can make it. A sensitive digital manometer is the best tool for accurate and reliable readings of both combustion-zone depressurization and chimney draft.

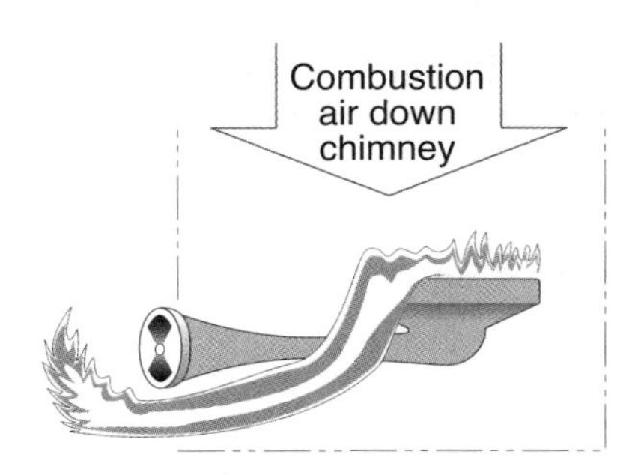


**Flame Roll-Out:** Flame roll-out, a serious fire hazard, can occur when the chimney is blocked, the combustion zone is depressurized, or during very cold weather.

Take all necessary steps to reduce spillage and strengthen draft as necessary based on testing.

## 4.9.4 Worst-Case Depressurization, Spillage, and CO

Start with all exterior doors, windows, and fireplace damper(s) closed and measure the base pressure.

A reading more negative than –5 pascals indicates a significant possibility of backdrafting.

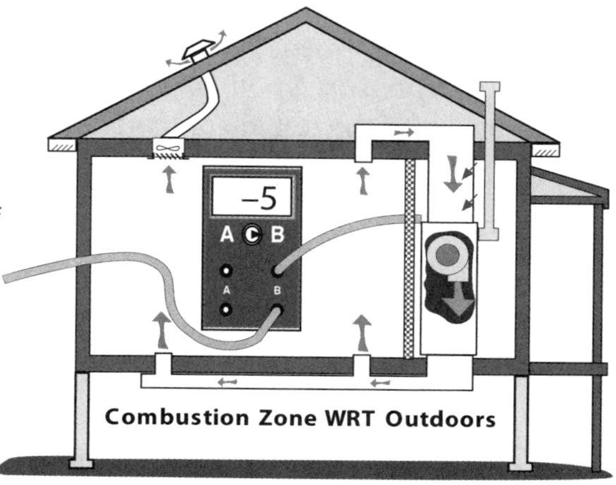


**Worst-Case Depressurization:** Worst-case testing is used to identify problems that weaken draft and restrict combustion air. The testing described here is intended to isolate the negative-pressure source.

Set all combustion appliances to the pilot setting or turn them off at the service disconnect.

Measure and record the base pressure of the combustion appliance zone (CAZ) with reference to outdoors. If the digital manometer has a self-zeroing or "base" function, use this zeroing function now.

Then establish worst-case conditions and measure the maximum worst-case depressurization.

1. Turn on the dryer and all exhaust fans.
2. Close the interior doors, which make the CAZ pressure more negative. Experiment by opening and closing interior doors while the air handler is operating.
3. Turn on the air handler, if present, using the "fan on" switch. Leave on if the pressure in the CAZ becomes more negative. Do not fire the burner of the combustion appliance yet.
4. Measure the net change in pressure from the CAZ to outside, correcting for the base pressure previously.

Record the "worst-case depressurization" and compare to the table entitled, *"Maximum CAZ or Mechanical Room Depressurization for Various Appliances" on page 133* for the tested appliance.

5. Next, fire the combustion appliances and test for spillage and CO.
6. Fire the appliance with the smallest BTU capacity first and then the next largest and so on.
7. Test for spillage at the draft diverter with a smoke generator, a lit match, or a mirror. Note whether combustion by-products spill and how long after ignition that the spillage stops.
8. Test CO in the undiluted flue gases at 5 minutes.

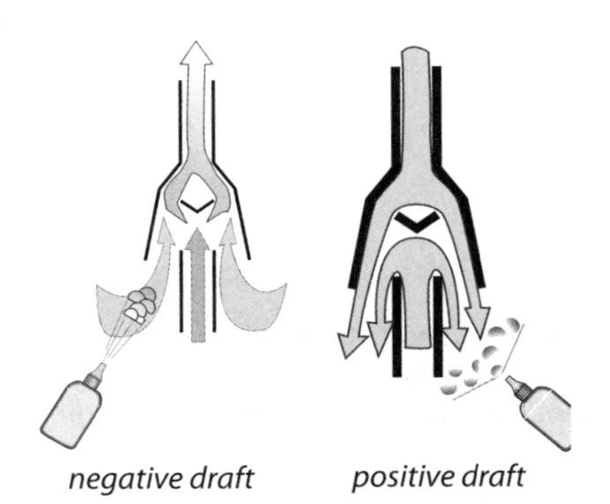


**Negative Versus Positive Draft:** With positive draft air flows down the chimney and out the draft diverter. A smoke bottle helps distinguish between positive and negative draft in atmospheric chimneys.

9. If spillage in one or more appliances continues under worst-case for 1 minute or more, test the appliance again under natural conditions.

**Table 4-11: Maximum CAZ or Mechanical Room Depressurization for Various Appliances**

| Appliance | Maximum Depressurization |
|---|---|
| Direct-vent appliance | 50 pa (0.20 IWC) |
| Pellet stove with draft fan and sealed vent | 15 pa (0.06 IWC) |
| Atmospherically vented oil and gas systems | 5 pa (0.02 IWC) |
| Oil power burner and fan-assisted (induced-draft) gas* | |
| Closed controlled combustion | |
| Decorative wood-burning appliances | |
| Atmospherically vented water heater | 2 pa (0.008 IWC) |

*Individual fan-assisted (induced-draft) appliances with no vent hood attached to intact b-vent and oil appliances with flame retention head power burners are likely to vent safely at greater than 5 pascals depressurization but not enough test data is available to set a higher limit at this time. Since the appliances are possibly connected to an unsealed chimney and most spillage is through joints and the barometric damper these systems are included in the 5pa limit.

## 4.9.5 Improving Inadequate Draft

If measured draft is below minimum draft pressures, investigate the reason for the weak draft. Open a window, exterior door, or interior door to observe whether the addition of combustion air improves draft. If this added air strengthens draft, the problem usually is depressurization. If opening a window doesn't improve draft, inspect the chimney. The chimney could be blocked or excessively leaky.

### Chimney Improvements to Solve Draft Problems

Suggest the following chimney improvements to solve draft problems, uncovered during the previous testing.

- ✔ Remove chimney obstructions.
- ✔ Repair disconnections or leaks at joints and where the vent connector joins a masonry chimney.
- ✔ Measure the size of the vent connector and chimney and compare to vent-sizing information listed in Section 504 of the *International Fuel Gas Code*. A vent connector or chimney liner that is either too large or too small can result in poor draft.
- ✔ If wind is causing erratic draft, consider installing a wind-dampening chimney cap.
- ✔ If the masonry chimney is deteriorated, consider installing a new chimney liner.
- ✔ Increase the pitch of horizontal sections of vent.

### Duct Improvements to Solve Draft Problems

Suggest the following duct improvements to solve draft problems, uncovered during the previous testing.

- ✔ Seal all return-duct leaks near furnace.
- ✔ Isolate the CAZ from return registers by air-sealing.
- ✔ Improve balance between supply and return air by installing new return ducts, transfer grilles, or jumper ducts.
- ✔ Reducing Depressurization from Exhaust Appliances

Consider suggesting the following remedies to depressurization caused by the home's exhaust appliances.

- ✔ Isolate furnace from exhaust fans and clothes dryers by air-sealing between the CAZ and zones containing these exhaust devices.
- ✔ Reduce capacity of large exhaust fans.

✔ Provide make-up air for dryers and exhaust fans and/or provide combustion-air inlet(s) to combustion zone. *See page 146.*

**Table 4-12: Draft Problems and Solutions**

| Problem | Possible Solutions |
|---|---|
| Adequate draft never established | Remove chimney blockage, seal chimney air leaks, or provide additional combustion air as necessary. |
| Blower activation weakens draft | Seal leaks in the furnace and in nearby return ducts. Isolate the furnace from nearby return registers. |
| Exhaust fans weaken draft | Provide make-up or combustion air if opening a door or window to outdoors strengthens draft during testing. |
| Closing interior doors during blower operation weakens draft | Add return ducts, jumper ducts, or grilles between rooms. |

## 4.9.6 Zone Isolation Testing for Atmospherically Vented Appliances

An isolated CAZ improves the safety of atmospherically vented appliances. The CAZ is isolated if it obtains combustion air only from outdoors. An isolated CAZ doesn't require worst-case depressurization and spillage testing. However the zone must be visually inspected for connections with the home's main zone and tested for isolation.

1. Look for connections between the isolated CAZ and the home. Examples include joist spaces, transfer grills, leaky doors, and holes for ducts or pipes.
2. Measure a base pressure from the CAZ to outdoors.
3. Perform 50-pascal blower door depressurization test. The CAZ-to-outdoors pressure should not change more than 5 pascals during the blower door test.

4. If the CAZ-to-outdoors pressure changed more than 5 pascals, perform air sealing to completely isolate the zone and retest as described above. Or alternatively perform a worst case depressurization and spillage test as described in *"Worst-Case Depressurization, Spillage, and CO" on page 130.*

## 4.10 Inspecting Venting Systems

Combustion gases are vented through vertical chimneys or other types of approved horizontal or vertical vent piping. Identifying the type of existing venting material, verifying the correct size of vent piping, and making sure the venting conforms to the applicable codes are important tasks in inspecting and repairing venting systems. Too large a vent often leads to condensation and corrosion. Too small a vent can result in spillage. The wrong vent materials can corrode or deteriorate from heat.

### 4.10.1 Vent Connectors

A vent connector connects the appliance's venting outlet with the chimney. Approved vent connectors for gas- and oil-fired units are made from the following materials.

- Type-B vent, consisting of a galvanized-steel outer pipe and aluminum inner pipe
- Type-L vent connector with a stainless-steel inner pipe and either galvanized or black-steel outer pipe.
- Galvanized-steel pipe (≥ 0.019 inch thick or 20 gauge) for vent connectors 5 inches in diameter or less.
- Galvanized-steel pipe (≥ 0.023 inch thick or 22 gauge) for vent connectors 6-to-10 inches in diameter.

Double-wall vent connectors are the best option, especially for appliances with some non-vertical vent piping. A double-wall vent connector helps maintain flue-gas temperature and prevent condensation. Gas appliances with draft hoods, installed in attics or crawl spaces must use a Type-B vent connector. Type-L vent pipe is commonly used for vent connectors for oil and solid fuels but can also be used for gas.

Observe the following general specifications, concerning vent connectors.

- Vent connectors are almost always the same size as the vent collar on the appliances they vent.
- Single-wall vent-pipe sections should be fastened together with 3 screws or rivets.
- Vent connectors should be sealed tightly where they enter masonry chimneys.
- Vent connectors should be free of rust, corrosion, and holes.
- The chimney combining two vent connectors should have a cross-sectional area equal to the area of the larger vent connector plus half the area of the smaller vent connector. This common vent should be no larger than 7 times the area of the smallest vent. For specific vent sizes, see NFPA codes themselves listed on *page 127*.

**Table 4-13: Areas of Round Vents**

| Vent diameter | 4" | 5" | 6" | 7" | 8" |
|---|---|---|---|---|---|
| Vent area (square inches) | 12.6 | 19.6 | 28.3 | 38.5 | 50.2 |

- The horizontal length of vent connectors shouldn't be more than 75% of the chimney's vertical height or have more than 18 inches horizontal run per inch of vent diameter.

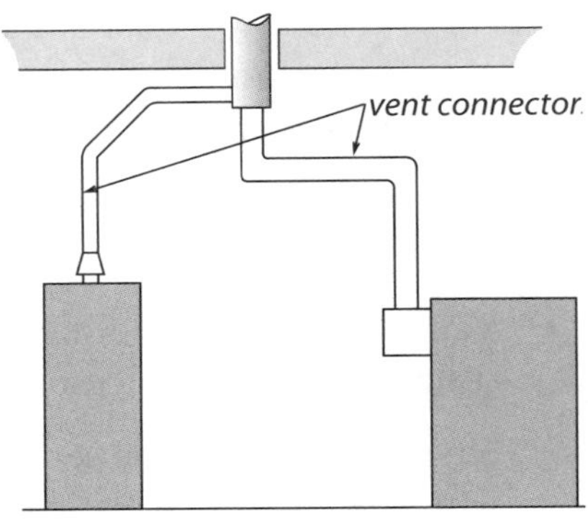


**Two Vent Connectors Joining Chimney:** The water heater's vent connector enters the chimney above the furnace because the water heater has a smaller input.

- Vent connectors must have upward slope to their connection with the chimney. NFPA 54 requires a slope of at least $^{1}/_{4}$ inch of rise per foot of horizontal run to ensure that combustion gases rise through the vent and to prevent condensation from pooling and rusting the vent.

**Table 4-14: Connector Diameter vs. Maximum Horizontal Length**

| Diameter (in) | 3" | 4" | 5" | 6" | 7" | 8" | 9" | 10" | 12" | 14" |
|---|---|---|---|---|---|---|---|---|---|---|
| Length (ft) | 4.5' | 6' | 7.5' | 9' | 10.5' | 12' | 13.5' | 15' | 18' | 21' |

From *International Fuel Gas Code 2000*

- When two vent connectors connect to a single chimney, the vent connector servicing the smaller appliance should enter the chimney above the vent for the larger appliance.
- Clearances for common vent connectors are listed in the following table.

**Table 4-15: Clearances to Combustibles for Vent Connectors**

| Vent Connector Type | Clearance |
|---|---|
| Single-wall galvanized-steel vent pipe | 6" (gas)<br>18" (oil) |
| Type-B double-wall vent pipe (gas) | 1" (gas) |
| Type L double wall vent pipe (stainless steel inner liner, stove pipe or galvanized outer liner) | 9", or 1 vent diameter, or as listed |

## 4.11 CHIMNEYS

There are two common types of vertical chimneys for venting combustion fuels that satisfy NFPA and ICC codes. First there are masonry chimneys lined with fire-clay tile, and second there are manufactured metal chimneys, including all-fuel metal chimneys and Type-B vent chimneys for gas appliances.

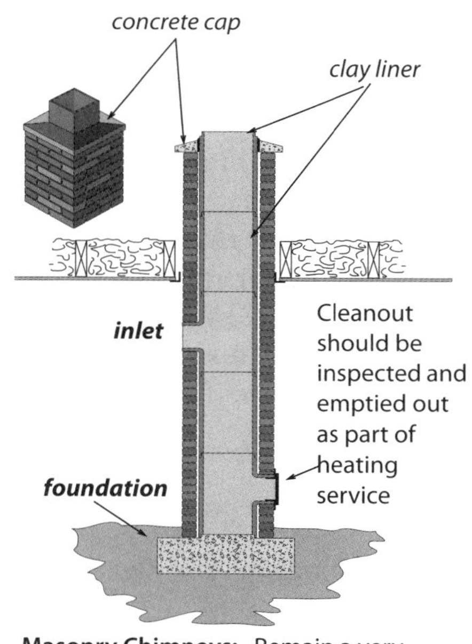


**Masonry Chimneys:** Remain a very common vent for all fuels.

### 4.11.1 Masonry Chimneys

Observe the following general specifications for building, inspecting, and repairing masonry chimneys.

- Masonry chimneys should be supported by their own masonry foundation.
- Existing masonry chimneys should be lined with a fireclay flue liner. There should be a $^1/_2$-inch to 1-inch air gap

between the clay liner and the chimney's masonry to insulate the liner. The liner shouldn't be bonded structurally to the outer masonry because it needs to expand and contract independently of the chimney's masonry structure. The clay liner can be sealed to the chimney cap with a flexible high-temperature sealant.

- Masonry chimneys should have a cleanout 12 inches or more below the lowest inlet. Mortar and brick dust should be cleaned out of the bottom of the chimney through the clean-out door, so that this debris won't eventually interfere with venting.
- The chimney's penetrations through floors and ceilings should be sealed with metal and high-temperature sealant as a firestop and air barrier.
- Deteriorated or unlined masonry chimneys should be rebuilt as specified above or relined as part of a heating-system replacement or a venting-safety upgrade. As an alternative, the vertical chimney may be replaced by a sidewall vent, equipped with a power venter mounted on the exterior wall. In this case, the old chimney should be sealed up and taken out of service.

**Table 4-16: Clearances to Combustibles for Common Chimneys**

| Chimney Type | Clearance |
|---|---|
| Interior chimney masonry w/ fireclay liner | 2" |
| Exterior masonry chimney w/ fireclay liner | 1" |
| All-fuel metal vent: insulated double wall or triple-wall pipe | 2" |
| Type B double-wall vent (gas only) | 1" |
| Manufactured chimneys and vents list their clearance | |

## 4.11.2 Manufactured Chimneys

Manufactured metal chimneys have engineered parts that fit together in a prescribed way. Metal chimneys contain manufactured components from the vent connector to the termination fitting on the roof. Parts include: metal pipe, weight-supporting hardware, insulation shields, roof jacks, and chimney caps. One manufacturer's chimney may not be compatible with another's connecting fittings.

All-fuel chimneys (also called Class A chimneys) are used primarily for solid fuels like wood and coal. All-fuel metal chimneys come in two types: insulated double wall metal pipe and triple-wall metal pipe. Install them strictly observing the manufacturer's specifications.

**All-Fuel Metal Chimney:** These chimney systems include transition fittings, support brackets, roof jacks, and chimney caps. The pipe is double-wall insulated or triple wall.

Type-B vent pipe is permitted as a chimney for gas appliances. Type BW pipe is manufactured for gas space heaters in an oval shape to fit inside. wall cavities.

## 4.11.3 Chimney Terminations

Masonry chimneys and all-fuel metal chimneys should terminate at least three feet above the roof penetration and two feet above any obstacle within ten feet of the chimney outlet.

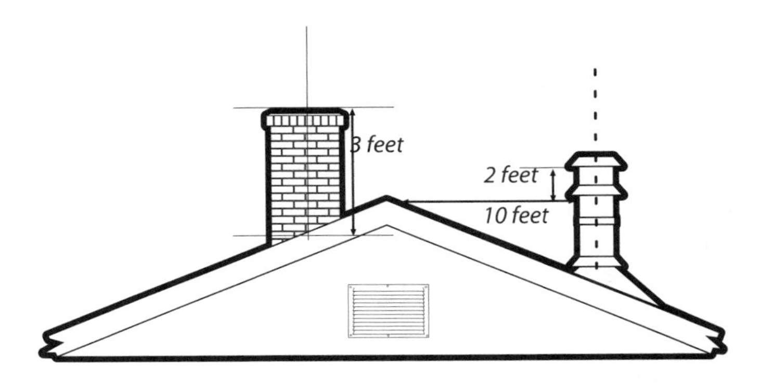


**Chimney Terminations:** Should have vent caps and be given adequate clearance height from nearby building parts. These requirements are for both masonry chimneys and manufactured all-fuel chimneys.

B-vent chimneys can terminate as close as one foot above flat roofs and pitched roofs up to a $^{6}/_{12}$ roof pitch. As the pitch rises, the minimum required termination height, as measured from the high part of the roof slope, rises as shown in the table.

**Table 4-17: Roof Slope and B-Vent Chimney Height (ft)**

| flat-6/12 | 6/12-7/12 | 7/12-8/12 | 8/12-9/12 | 9/12-10/12 | 10/12-11/12 | 11/12-12/12 | 12/12-14/12 | 14/12-16/12 | 16/12-18/12 |
|---|---|---|---|---|---|---|---|---|---|
| 1' | 1' 3" | 1' 6" | 2' | 2' 6" | 3' 3" | 4' | 5' | 6' | 7' |

From *International Fuel Gas Code 2000*

## 4.11.4 Metal Liners for Masonry Chimneys

Unlined masonry chimneys or chimneys with deteriorated liners should be relined as part of heating system replacement. Use either Type-B vent, a flexible or rigid stainless-steel liner, or a flexible aluminum liner.

Flexible liners require careful installation to avoid a low spot at the bottom, where the liner turns a right angle to pass through the wall of the chimney. Follow the manufacturer's instructions, which usually prescribe stretching the liner and fastening it securely at both ends, to prevent it from sagging and thereby creating such a low spot.

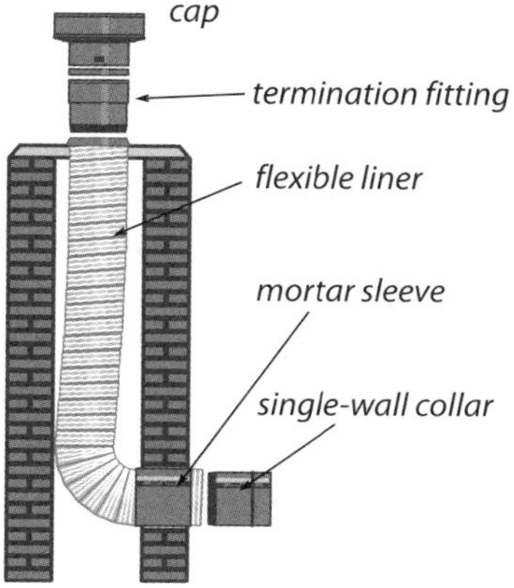

cap
termination fitting
flexible liner
mortar sleeve
single-wall collar

**Flexible Metal Chimney Liners:** The most important installation issues are sizing the liner correctly along with fastening and supporting the ends to prevent sagging.

Flexible liners are easily damaged by falling masonry debris inside a deteriorating chimney. Use B-vent instead of a flexible liner when the chimney is significantly deteriorated.

To minimize condensation, flexible liners should be insulated — especially when installed in exterior chimneys. Consider insulating flexible metal chimney liners with vermiculite or a fiberglass-insulation jackets, if the manufacturer's instructions allow.

Sizing flexible chimney liners correctly is very important. Oversizing is common and can lead to condensation and corrosion. The manufacturers of the liners include vent-sizing tables in their instructions. Liners should bear the label of a testing lab like Underwriters Laboratories (UL).

# 4.12 Special Venting Considerations for Gas

The American Gas Association (AGA) has devised a classification system for venting systems serving natural gas and propane appliances. This classification system assigns Roman numerals to four categories of venting based on whether there is positive or negative pressure in the vent and whether condensation is likely to occur in the vent.

| | Negative-pressure Venting | Positive-pressure |
|---|---|---|
| Non-condensing | I<br>Combustion Efficiency<br>**83% or less**<br>Use standard venting: masonry or Type B vent | III<br>Combustion Efficiency<br>**83% or less**<br>Use only pressurizable vent as specified by manufacturer |
| Condensing | II<br>Combustion Efficiency<br>**over 83%**<br>Use only special condensing-service vent as specified by manufacturer | IV<br>Combustion Efficiency<br>**over 83%**<br>Use only pressurizable condensing-service vent as specified by manufacturer |

American Gas Association Vent Categories

**AGA Venting Categories:** The AGA classifies venting by whether there is positive or negative pressure in the vent and whether condensation is likely.

A majority of gas appliances found in homes and multifamily buildings are Category I, which have negative pressure in vertical chimneys with no condensation expected in the vent connector or chimney. Condensing furnaces are usually Category IV with positive pressure in their vent and condensation occurring in both the appliance and vent. Category III vents are rare but some fan-assisted appliances are vented with airtight non-condensing vents.

## 4.12.1 Venting Fan-Assisted Furnaces and Boilers

Newer gas-fired fan-assisted central heaters control flue-gas flow and excess air better than atmospheric heaters, resulting in their higher efficiency. These are non-condensing Category I furnaces in the 80%-plus Annual Fuel Utilization Efficiency (AFUE) range. Because these units eliminate dilution air and may have slightly cooler flue gases, existing chimneys should be carefully inspected to ensure that the chimneys are prepared for more condensation than they have experienced in the past. The chimney should be relined when any of the following conditions are present.

- When the existing masonry chimney is unlined.
- When the old clay or metal chimney liner is deteriorated.
- When the new heater has a smaller input than the old one. In this case the liner should be sized to the new furnace or boiler and the existing water heater.

For gas-fired 80+ AFUE furnaces, a chimney liner should consist these materials.

- Type-B vent
- A rigid or flexible stainless steel liner
- A poured masonry liner
- An insulated flexible aluminum liner

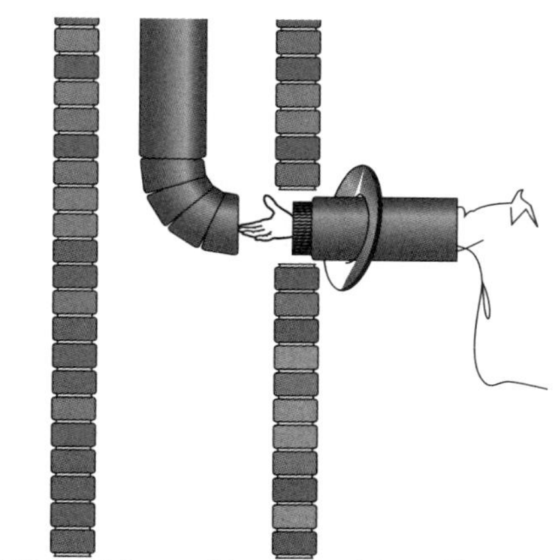

**B-Vent Chimney Liner:** Double-wall Type-B vent is the most commonly available chimney liner and is recommended over flexible liners. Rigid stainless-steel single-wall liners are also a permanent solution to deteriorated chimneys.

Because of the considerable expense that chimney relining can entail, sidewall venting with a power venter or heating-system replacement with a 90+ condensing heater should be considered when an existing chimney is inadequate for new Category I appliances.

**Table 4-18: Characteristics of Gas Furnaces and Boilers**

| Steady-state efficiency | Operating characteristics |
|---|---|
| 70+ | Category I, draft diverter, no draft fan, standing pilot, non-condensing, indoor combustion and dilution air. |
| 80+ | Category I, no draft diverter, draft fan, electronic ignition, indoor combustion air, no dilution air. |
| 90+ | Category IV, no draft diverter, draft fan, low-temperature plastic venting, positive draft, electronic ignition, condensing heat exchanger, outdoor combustion air is strongly recommended. |

## 4.12.2 Combustion Air

A combustion appliance zone (CAZ) is classified as either an un-confined space or confined space. An un-confined space is a CAZ connected to enough building air leakage to provide combustion air. A confined space is a CAZ with sheeted walls and ceiling and a closed door that form an air barrier between the appliance and other indoor spaces. For confined spaces, the IFGC prescribes additional combustion air from outside the CAZ. Combustion air is supplied to the combustion appliance in four ways.

To an un-confined space through leaks in the building.

- To a confined space through an intentional opening or openings between the CAZ and other indoor areas where air leaks replenish combustion air.
- To a confined space through an intentional opening or openings between the CAZ and outdoors or ventilated intermediate zones like attics and crawl spaces.
- Directly from the outdoors to the confined or airtight CAZ through a duct. Appliances with direct combustion-air

ducts are called sealed-combustion or direct-vent appliances.

### Un-Confined-Space Combustion Air

Combustion appliances located in most basements, attics, and crawl spaces get adequate combustion air from leaks in the building shell. Even when a combustion appliance is located within the home's living space, it usually gets adequate combustion air from air leaks, unless the house is airtight or the combustion zone is depressurized. *See page 147.*

### Confined-Space Combustion Air

A confined space is defined by the codes as a room containing one or more combustion appliances that has less than 50 cubic feet of volume for every 1000 BTUs per hour of appliance input.

However, if a small mechanical room is connected to adjacent spaces through large air passages like floor-joist spaces, the CAZ may not need additional combustion air despite sheeted walls and a door separating it from other indoor spaces. The extent of the connection between the CAZ and other spaces can be confirmed by worst-case draft testing or blower-door pressure testing.

On the other hand, if the home is unusually airtight, the CAZ may be unable to provide adequate combustion air, even when the combustion zone is larger than the minimum confined-space room volume, defined above.

Combustion air from adjacent indoor spaces is usually preferred over outdoor combustion air because of the possibility of wind depressurizing the combustion zone. However, if there is a sheltered outdoor space from which to draw combustion air, outdoor combustion air may be a superior choice. Outdoor air is generally cleaner and dryer than indoor air, and a connection to the outdoors makes the confined space less affected by indoor pressure fluctuations.

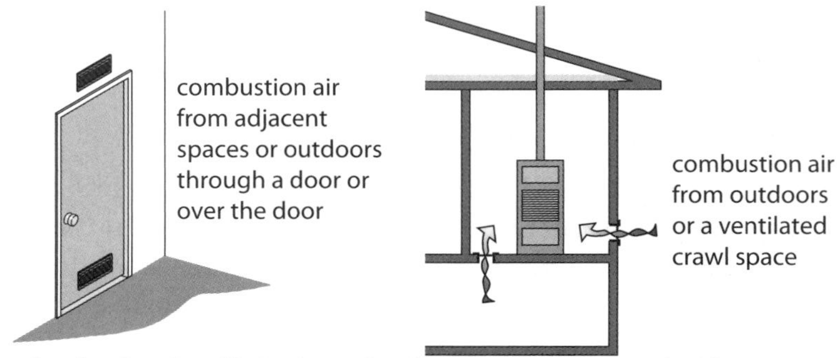


**Passive Combustion-Air Options:** Combustion air can be supplied from adjacent indoor spaces or from outdoors. Beware of passive combustion-air vents into the attic that could depressurize the combustion zone or allow moist indoor air to travel into the attic.

In confined spaces or airtight homes where outdoor combustion air is needed, prefer a single vent opening installed as low in the CAZ as practical. A combustion-air vent into an attic may depressurize the combustion zone or dump warm moist air into the attic. Instead, connect the combustion zone to a ventilated crawl space or directly to outdoors through a single low vent if possible.

Choose an outdoor location that is sheltered, where the wall containing the vent isn't parallel to prevailing winds. Wind blowing parallel to an exterior wall or at a right angle to the vent opening tends to de-pressurize both the opening and the CAZ connected to it. Indoors, locate combustion air vents away from water pipes to prevent freezing in cold climates.

**Table 4-19: Combustion Air Openings: Location and Size**

| Location | Dimensions |
|---|---|
| Two direct openings to adjacent indoor space | Minimum area each: 100 $in^2$<br>1 $in^2$ per 1000 Btuh each<br>Combined room volumes must be ≥ 50 $ft^3$/1000 Btuh |
| Two direct openings or vertical ducts to outdoors | Each vent should have 1 $in^2$ for each 4000 Btuh |
| Two horizontal ducts to outdoors | Each vent should have 1 $in^2$ for each 2000 Btuh |
| Single direct or ducted vent to outdoors | Single vent should have 1 $in^2$ for each 3000 Btuh |

From the *National Fuel Gas Code (NFPA 54)*

Net free area is smaller than actual vent area and takes the blocking effect of louvers into account. Metal grilles and louvers provide 60% to 75% of their area as net free area while wood louvers provide only 20% to 25%. Combustion air vents should be no less than 3 inches in their smallest dimension.

Here is an example of sizing combustion air to another indoor area. The furnace and water heater are located in a confined space. The furnace has an input rating of 100,000 Btu/hour. The water heater has an input rating of 40,000 Btu/hour. Therefore, there should be 280 $in^2$ of net free area of vent between the mechanical room and other rooms in the home.

**([100,000 + 40,000] ÷ 1,000 = 140 X 2 $IN^2$ = 280 $IN^2$)**

Each vent should therefore have a minimum of 140 $in^2$.

## 4.13 Ducted Air Distribution

The annual system efficiency of forced-air heating and air-conditioning systems is affected by the following issues.

- ✔ Duct leakage
- ✔ System airflow
- ✔ Blower operation
- ✔ Balance between supply and return air
- ✔ Duct insulation levels

The forced-air system usually offers more opportunity for energy savings and comfort improvement than improving combustion or refrigeration equipment.

The sequence of testing and evaluation has a logic. First, deal with the airflow problems because you might have to change the duct system substantially. Then test the ducts for leakage and evaluate whether they are located within the thermal boundary or not. Decide whether duct sealing is important and if so, find and seal the leaks. Finally, if supply ducts are outside the thermal boundary, insulate them. The following list summarizes this logical sequence.

1. Evaluate and measure airflow.
2. Troubleshoot specific airflow problems including balancing airflow between rooms and between supply and return air.
3. Make necessary airflow improvements.
4. Evaluate and/or measure duct air leakage.
5. Find duct leaks and seal them.
6. Consider insulating supply ducts.

Measuring duct leakage and airflow are the best ways of evaluating these two critical performance variables. The troubleshooting techniques are helpful in isolating the precise problem, but not in quantifying the problem. The effectiveness of the improvements can again be evaluated by airflow and duct-leakage measurement.

### 4.13.1 Evaluating Forced-Air System Airflow

Airflow evaluation and improvement comes before duct-sealing because you wouldn't want to make substantial modifications to the ducts you just air-sealed with mastic.

The most accurate and reliable methods for measuring system airflow are the duct-blower method and the flow-plate method. Measuring return airflow with a flow hood is sometimes sufficiently accurate if the flow hood is properly calibrated and used according to manufacturer's instructions.

#### Evaluating Duct Design and Recommended Airflow

The air handler's recommended airflow depends on its heating or cooling capacity. For combustion furnaces, there should be 11-to-15 cfm of airflow for each 1000 BTUs per hour (BTUH) of output. To provide this airflow, the supply duct and return duct, connected to the air handler, should have at least 2 square inches of cross-sectional area for each 1000 BTUH of furnace input.

Central air conditioners and heat pumps should deliver 400 cfm ±20% of airflow per ton of cooling capacity. One ton equals 12,000 BTUH. To provide this airflow, the supply duct and return duct, connected to the air handler, should have at least 6 square inches of cross-sectional area for each 1000 BTUH of air-conditioner or heat-pump capacity.

### Table 4-20: Recommended Cross-Sectional Area of Metal Supply and Return Ducts at Air Handler

| Gas Furnaces | | Air Conditioners | |
|---|---|---|---|
| Btuh Input | In$^2$ Area (Supp. & Ret.) | Btuh Capacity | In$^2$ Area (Supp. & Ret.) |
| 40,000 | 80 | 24,000 | 144 |
| 60,000 | 120 | 30,000 | 180 |
| 80,000 | 160 | 36,000 | 216 |
| 100,000 | 200 | 42,000 | 252 |
| 120,000 | 240 | 48,000 | 288 |

Each trunk, supply and return, should have the recommended cross-sectional area shown here. Courtesy Delta-T Inc.

### Table 4-21: Round-Duct Square-Inch Equivalency for Metal Ducts

| Diameter | Square Inches | Diameter | Square Inches |
|---|---|---|---|
| 5 | 20 | 12 | 113 |
| 6 | 28 | 14 | 154 |
| 7 | 38 | 16 | 201 |
| 8 | 50 | 18 | 254 |
| 9 | 64 | 20 | 314 |
| 10 | 79 | 22 | 380 |

For flex duct, use the next largest size to get a similar airflow as through round metal duct. Courtesy Delta-T Inc.

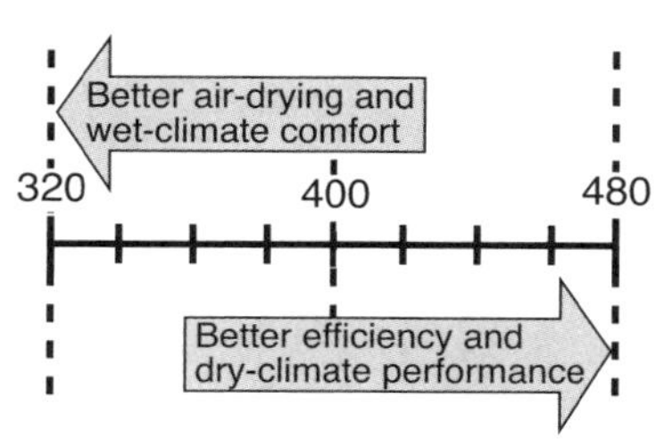


**Airflow and Climate:** More airflow per ton provides better efficiency and performance for dry climates. Less airflow provides better dehumidification for wet climates.

In dry climates, you may increase performance and efficiency by increasing airflow to 480 cfm per ton if noise and comfort allow. In humid climates, the recommended airflow per ton may be less than 400 cfm per ton to facilitate dehumidification by moving air less rapidly across the coil and thereby keeping the coil cooler.

The most accurate way to size new ducts or to evaluate existing ducts is with a duct-sizing computer program.

## Airflow and Blower Speed

A blower can have as many as five speeds. If the air handler's specifications are available, check whether the blower is operating at the correct speeds for heating and cooling. Heating typically uses a lower speed and cooling uses a higher one.

If the blower speed isn't obvious when looking at the air-handler terminal block, clamp an ammeter around the colored wires until you identify the colors corresponding to the heating and cooling modes.

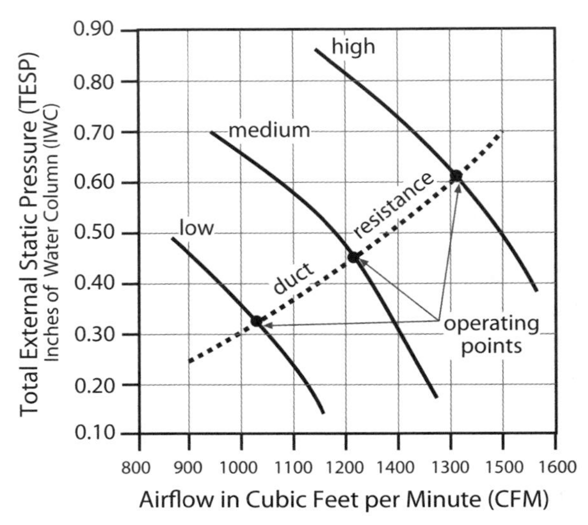


**Fan Curves:** This common type of graph represents the relationship of the blower with the connected ducts. As TESP increases, fan flow decreases as shown by the 3 fan curves. And as airflow increases, TESP increases as shown by the duct-resistance curve. Where the resistance curve meets the fan curves are the operating points, which are your 3 choices of blower speed and airflow for this air handler.

### Solving Obvious Airflow Problems

You probably don't need sophisticated test instruments to discover dirty blowers and coils or disconnected branch ducts. Finding these problems before measuring duct airflow speeds up the process of measurement, troubleshooting, and duct sealing. The following steps precede airflow measurements.

1. Ask the customer about comfort problems and temperature differences in various parts of the home.
2. Based on the customers comments, look for disconnected, restricted ducts, and other obvious problems.
3. Inspect the filter(s), blower, and indoor coil for dirt. Clean them if necessary. If the indoor coil isn't easily visible, a dirty blower is a fair indicator that the coil may also be dirty.

4. Inspect for dirty or damaged supply and return grilles that restrict airflow. Clean and repair them.
5. Look for closed registers or balancing dampers that could be restricting airflow to rooms.
6. Notice moisture problems like mold and mildew. Moisture sources, like a wet crawl space, can overpower air conditioners by introducing more moisture into the air than the air conditioner can remove.

## 4.13.2 Evaluating Furnace Performance

The effectiveness of a furnace depends on its temperature rise, fan-control temperatures, and flue-gas temperature. For efficiency, you want a low temperature rise. However, you must maintain a minimum flue-gas temperature to prevent corrosion in the venting of naturally drafting combustion furnaces. Apply the following furnace-operation standards to maximize the heating system's seasonal efficiency and safety.

- ✔ Perform a combustion analysis as described in *"Testing Gas Furnaces and Boilers" on page 103.*
- ✔ Check temperature rise after 5 minutes of operation. Refer to manufacturer's nameplate for acceptable temperature rise (supply temperature minus return temperature). The temperature rise should be between 40°F and 70°F with the lower end of this scale being preferable for energy efficiency.
- ✔ The fan-off temperature should be between 95° and 105° F, with the lower end of the scale being preferable for maximum efficiency.
- ✔ The fan-on temperature should be 120-140° F. The lower the better.
- ✔ On time-activated fan controls, verify that the fan is switched on within two minutes of burner ignition and is

switched off within 2.5 minutes of the end of the combustion cycle.

✔ The high-limit controller should shut the burner off before the furnace temperature reaches 200°F.

✔ All forced-air heating systems must deliver supply air and collect return air only within the intentionally heated portion of the house. Taking return air from an un-heated area of the house such as an unoccupied basement is not acceptable.

✔ There should be a strong noticeable flow of air from all supply registers.

### Table 4-22: Furnace Operating Parameters

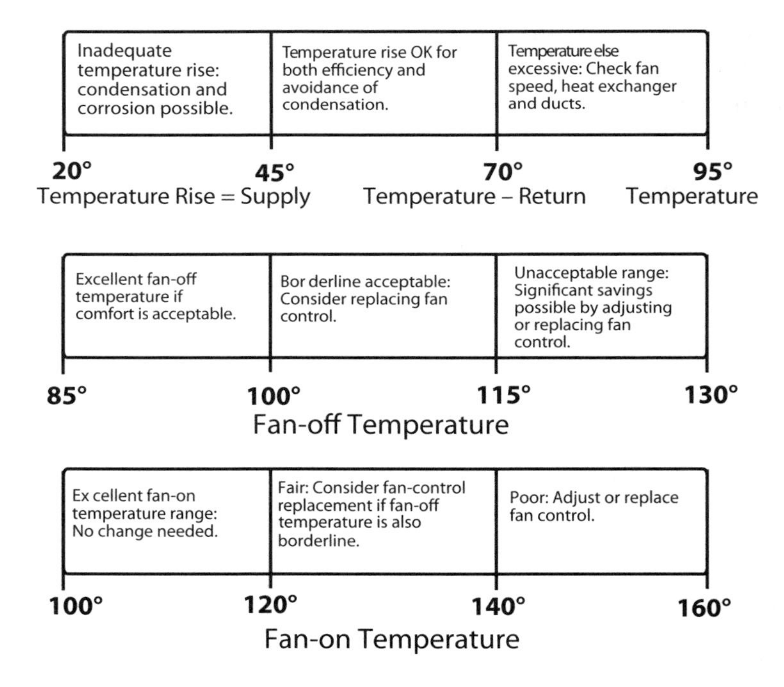

If the forced-air heating system doesn't meet these standards, consider the following improvements.

- ✔ Clean or change dirty filters. Clean air-conditioning coils.
- ✔ Clean the blower, increase fan speed, and improve ducted air circulation. *See page 169.*
- ✔ Adjust fan control to conform to these standards, or replace the fan control if adjustment fails. Some fan controls aren't adjustable.
- ✔ Adjust the high-limit control to conform to the above standards, or replace the high-limit control.

After adjustments, measured temperature rise should be no lower than manufacturer's specifications or the listed minimum values in *Table 4-3 on page 110.*

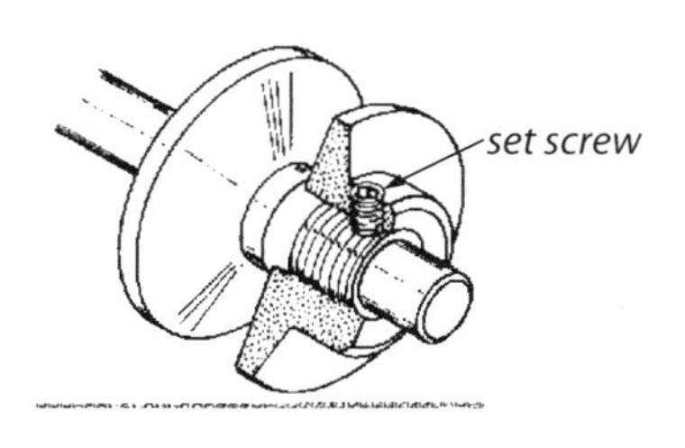


**Adjustable Drive Pulley:** This adjustable pulley moves back and forth allowing the belt to ride higher or lower, adjusting the blower's speed.

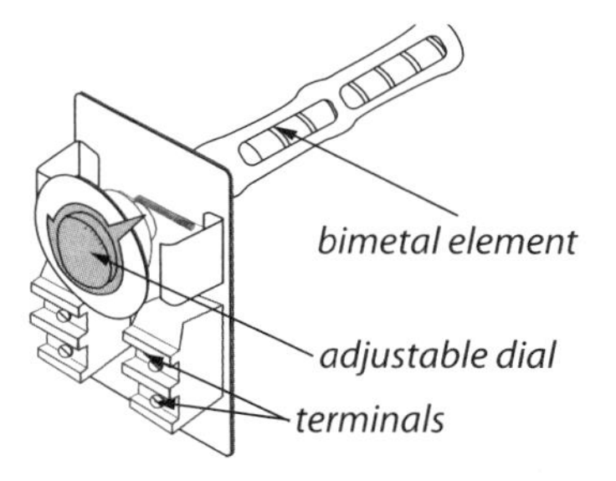


**A Fan/Limit Control:** Turns the furnace blower on and off, according to temperature. Also turns the burner off if the heat exchanger gets too hot (high limit).

## 4.13.3 Measuring Airflow

Measuring airflow provides the number of cubic feet per minute of airflow through the air handler. If this measured airflow is adequate, you know that airflow isn't a problem. On the other hand, if measured airflow is low, you troubleshoot the problem and make improvements.

If you don't have a duct blower, flow plate, or flow hood, skip to *"Troubleshooting Airflow Problems" on page 164.*

## Duct-Blower Airflow Measurement

The duct blower is a fan mounted in an aerodynamic housing and equipped with a precise pressure-sampling tube. The duct blower is the most accurate airflow-measuring device currently available.

During this airflow test, all return air is routed through the duct blower where the airflow can be measured. The return air traveling through the duct blower is moved by the air handler's blower aided by the duct blower.

1. Set up a static pressure manometer to measure the duct pressure in the supply plenum, or a few feet away from the supply plenum, in a main supply. Tape the static pressure probe to hold it in place. The point of the probe should face into the oncoming airflow with the probe's static-pressure openings perpendicular to the airflow direction.

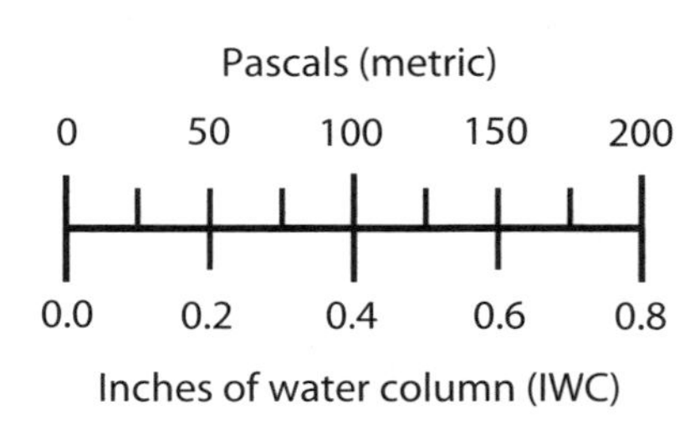


**Pressure in T wo Measurement Systems:** Technicians and engineers use both Pascals (metric) and inches of water column (American) to measure duct pressures.

2. Make sure all supply registers and return grilles are open. Leave filters installed.
3. Turn on the system and measure static pressure from the probe installed in Step 1.
4. Shut off power to the air handler. Connect the duct blower to blow into the air handler at the blower com-

partment or into the single return register, using one of the two options outlined next.

### Blocking the Main Return

The preferred method of connecting the duct blower is to block the return plenum's main return entry to the air handler in one of the following ways.

- ✔ Install the temporary barrier in a filter slot.
- ✔ Support the main return and move it temporarily out of your way, while you seal the opening to the air handler with cardboard and tape.
- ✔ If there is room, install a cardboard barrier from the open door of the blower compartment, taping the edges of the perimeter to air-seal the barrier. Be careful not to scratch your arms and hands.
- ✔ After installing and sealing the barrier, remove the blower-compartment door and connect the duct blower to the blower compartment.

**Duct Blower Mounted to Air Handler:** The best way to measure airflow with a duct blower is to connect the duct blower to the air handler and seal off the main return.

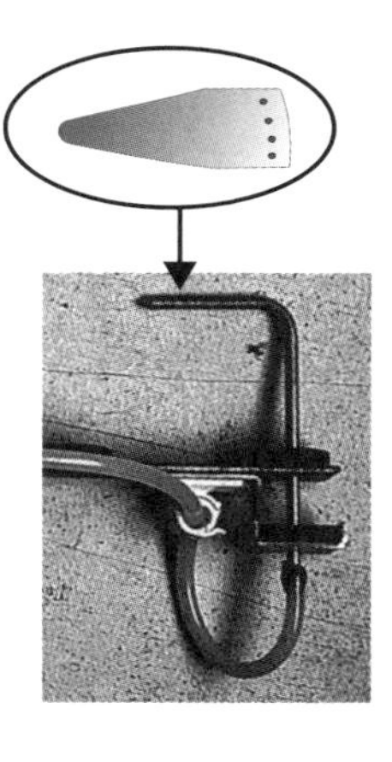

**Static Pressure Probe:** Tiny holes near the tip sense static pressure.

### Connecting the Duct Blower to a Main Return

**Duct Blower Mounted to Main Return:** With a single return, it's convenient to attach the duct blower to the single main return register. However, this option may result in an artificially high airflow reading.

Remove the grille at the single return register. Connect the duct blower through its flexible tube or else directly to the register, using cardboard to block off the excess area of the register. (Note: If there is significant return leakage, airflow measurement is deceptively high.)

All the return air should now flow through the duct blower. If the duct blower is connected to an air handler, located outside the conditioned space, the door or access panel between the conditioned space and the air handler location must be opened. Now you are ready to measure system airflow.

1. Turn on the air-handler fan once again, making sure the air-handler fan is running at the correct speed for cooling.
2. Turn on the duct blower to blow into the air handler, increasing airflow until the manometer measuring supply-plenum static pressure reads the same as your original static-pressure measurement.
3. Measure and record the airflow through the duct blower. Refer to the duct-blower instruction book, if necessary, to insure that you know how to take the reading. The airflow reading you take directly from the digital manometer or look up in the manufacturer's

table for converting pressure to flow is total system airflow in cubic feet per minute (CFM).

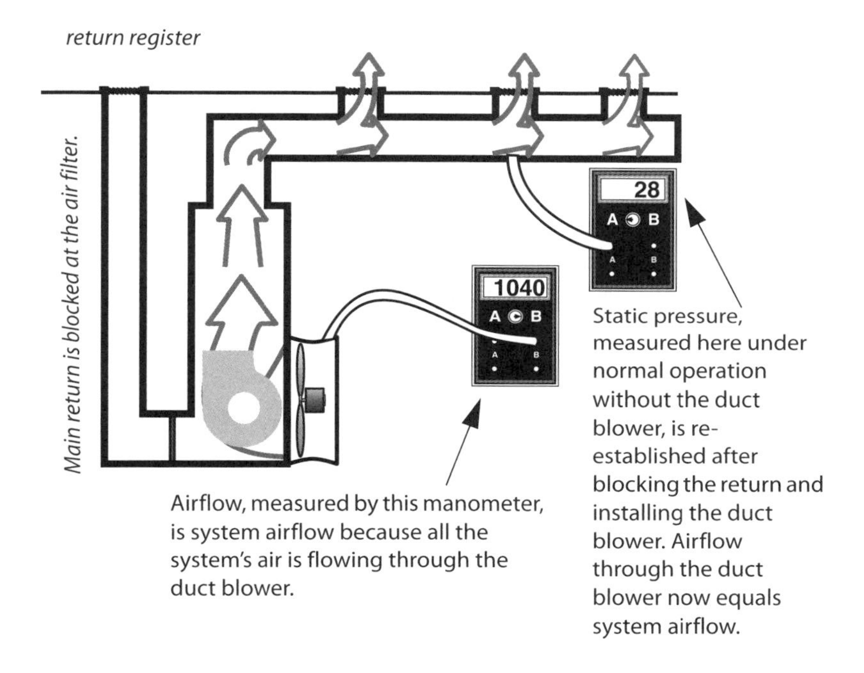


## Flow-Plate Method for Measuring System Airflow

The TrueFlow® air-handler flow meter, manufactured by The Energy Conservatory of Minneapolis, is relatively fast and easy to use. This flow meter is a plate with holes and sampling tubes that measure and average velocity pressures and convert these pressures into an airflow measurement in CFM.

One of two flow plates is inserted into the filter slot or bracket and sealed at its edges within the air handler. Then, the static-pressure drop across the flow plate is measured and airflow is found on printed tables supplied by the manufacturer or automatically by the digital manometer.

When used according to the manufacturer's instructions, which are summarized below, the accuracy of this method is better than the other tests described on these pages, with the exception of the duct-blower test. Refer to the manufacturer's instructions for the precise testing method. A summary follows.

1. Measure and record the normal system operating pressure, with a standard filter in place, using a static pressure probe in the supply plenum or supply duct near the air handler.

2. Replace the existing filter with the flow plate. Seal the flow plate into the slot, according to the manufacturer's recommendations.

3. Measure and record the system's operating pressure with the flow plate in place, at the same location as when the filter was in place.

4. Measure the flow through the TrueFlow Meter using the digital manometer supplied by the manufacturer. Obtain flow from the numerical table or the digital manometer itself.

5. Calculate a correction factor from the measured operating pressures (using a correction table) and multiply by the measured flow to get the original flow rate, moving through the air handler when the first measurement was taken.

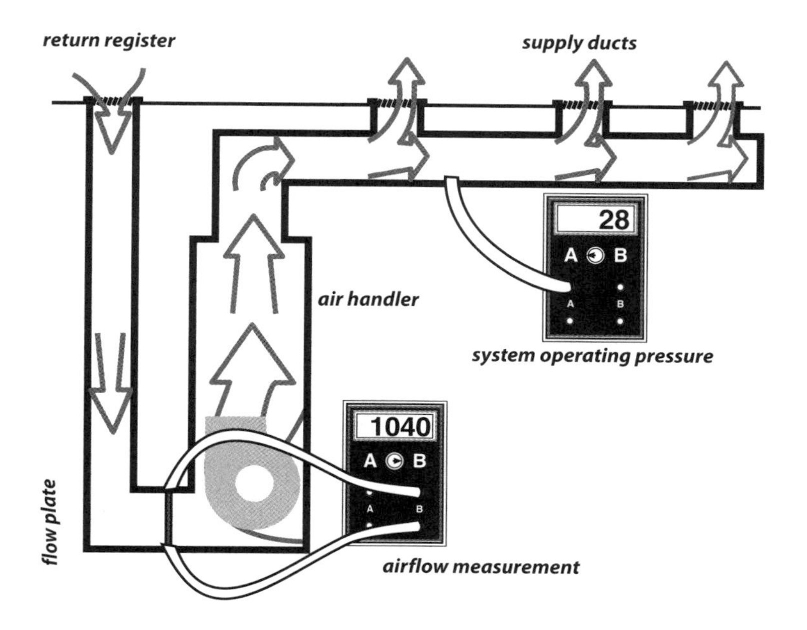


**True Flow® Meter:** The True Flow® flow plate installs in a filter slot and measures system airflow almost as accurately as the duct blower.

## Measuring Airflow with a Flow Hood

This test measures the fairly laminar airflow at return registers. Measuring supply-register airflow isn't as accurate as measuring return airflow because supply air is more turbulent. The flow-hood inlet must be larger than the return grilles, although 10 percent of the register may be blocked with tape to allow the flow hood to cover that reduced opening.

This test works best on systems with one to four return grilles located in areas where a flow hood can cover the grilles and be centered over them. If the return ducts are very leaky, the return airflow may appear low, when measuring return airflow with a flow hood. This low reading may mean that the system is drawing some of its return air from a crawl space, attic, or attached garage, which doesn't go through the flow hood.

1. Turn on the air handler to run at the higher fan speed, normally used for cooling.
2. Center the flow hood over the return register, covering it completely. If the register is larger than the flow hood, seal up to 10 percent of the register with tape before covering it.
3. Read and record the airflows through the return registers. Add the measured airflows of the return registers together to get the total system airflow.

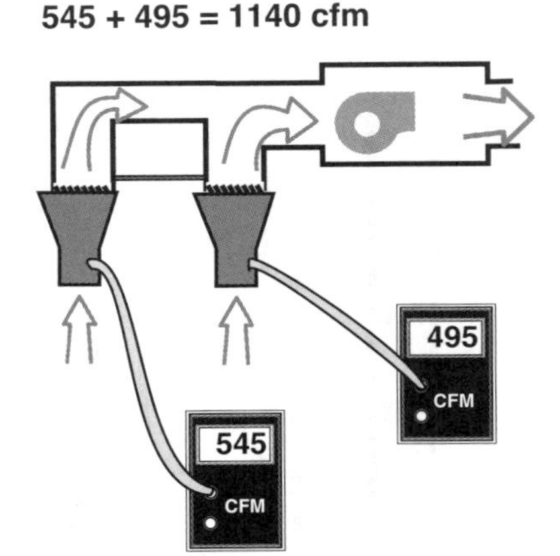

**Measuring Return Air with a Flow Hood:** This method provides an estimate of system airflow. It can significantly underestimate airflow because return duct leakage bypasses the measurement.

This method isn't usually as accurate as measuring with a duct blower or flow plate. The flow plate measures airflow right at the air handler, not at the return. And, the duct-blower airflow test at the air handler simply duplicates the normal airflow, taking the leaky return ducts out of the loop by blocking them off.

## 4.13.4 Troubleshooting Airflow Problems

Measurements of static pressure, while they don't measure airflow, are useful for troubleshooting.

### Measuring Total External Static Pressure

The ducts, registers, and a coil mounted in the ducts (if present) create the duct system's resistance, which is measured by static pressure in inches of water column (IWC) or pascals. The return static is negative and the supply static is positive. Total exterior static pressure (TESP) is the sum of the absolute values of the supply and return static pressures. The positive or negative signs are disregarded when adding supply static and return static to get TESP because this addition represents the distance on a number line as shown in the illustration here.

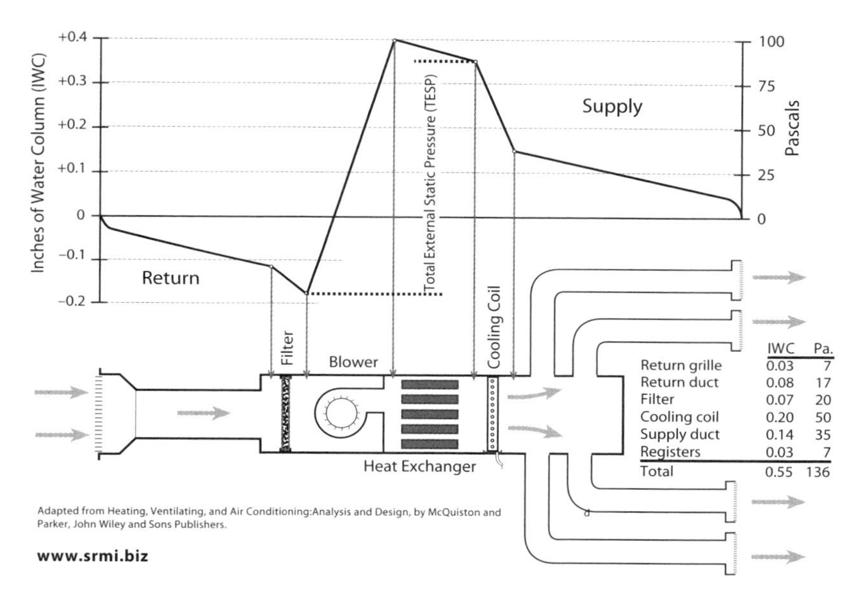


**Visualizing TESP:** The blower creates a suction at its inlet and a positive pressure at its outlet. As the distance between the measurement and blower increase, pressure decreases because of the system's resistance.

The greater the TESP, the lower the airflow. TESP gives a rough indicator of whether airflow is adequate. The supply and return static pressures by themselves can indicate whether the supply or return or both are restricted. For example, if the supply static pressure is 0.3 and the return static pressure is 0.7, you can assume that most of the airflow problems are due to a restricted or undersized return. The TESP test can give a very rough estimate of airflow if the manufacturer's graph or table for static pressure versus airflow is available.

1. Attach two static pressure probes to tubes leading to the ports of the manometer. For analog manometers, attach the high-side port to the probe inserted downstream of the coil or air handler.

2. Take the readings on each side of the air handler to obtain both supply and return static pressures separately. Disregard positive or negative signs given by a digital manometer when performing addition.
3. Consult manufacturer's literature for a table, relating static pressure difference to airflow for the blower or air handler. Find airflow for the static pressure measured above.

Air handlers deliver their airflow at a TESPs ranging from 0.30 IWC (75 Pascals) and 1.0 IWC (250 Pascals) as found in the field. Manufacturers maximum recommended static pressure is usually a maximum 0.50 IWC for standard air handlers. TESPs greater than 0.50 IWC indicate the possibility of poor airflow in standard residential forced-air systems.

The popularity of pleated filters, electrostatic filters, and high-static high-efficiency evaporator coils, prompted manufacturers to introduce premium air handlers that can deliver adequate airflow at TESP of greater than 0.50 IWC. Premium residential air handlers can provide adequate airflow with TESP up to 0.90 IWC through more powerful blowers and variable-speed blowers. TESPs greater than 0.90 IWC (225 pascals) indicate the possibility of poor airflow in these premium residential forced-air systems.

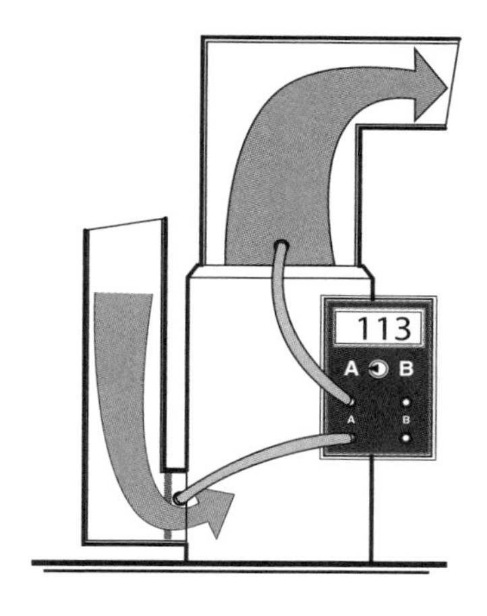


**Total external static pressure (TESP):** The positive and negative pressures created by the resistance of the supply and return ducts produces TESP. The measurement shown here simply adds the two static pressures without regard for their signs. As TESP increases, airflow decreases. Numbers shown below are for example only.

**Table 4-23: Total External Static Pressure Versus System Airflow for a Particular System**

| TESP (IWC) | 0.3 | 0.4 | 0.5 | 0.6 | 0.7 | 0.8 |
|---|---|---|---|---|---|---|
| CFM | 995 | 945 | 895 | 840 | 760 | 670 |

*Example only*

## Unbalanced Supply-Return Airflow Test

Closing interior doors often isolates supply registers from return registers in homes with central returns. This imbalance often pressurizes bedrooms and depressurizes central areas with return registers. These pressures can drive air leakage through the building shell, create moisture problems, and bring pollutants in from the crawl space, garage, or CAZ.

The following test uses only the air handler and a digital manometer to evaluate whether the supply air is able to cycle back through the return registers. Activate the air handler and close interior doors.

First, measure the pressure difference between the home's central living area and the outdoors with a digital manometer. Then, measure the bedrooms' pressure difference with outdoors. As an simpler alternative, you can measure the pressure difference between the central zone and the bedroom.

If difference between those two measurements is more than ±2.0 pascals with the air handler operating, pressure relief is desirable. To estimate the amount of pressure relief needed, slowly open the bedroom door until the pressure difference drops to below 1 pascal. Estimate the surface area of door opening. This is the area of the permanent opening required to provide pressure relief. Pressure relief may include undercutting the door or installing transfer grilles or jumper ducts.

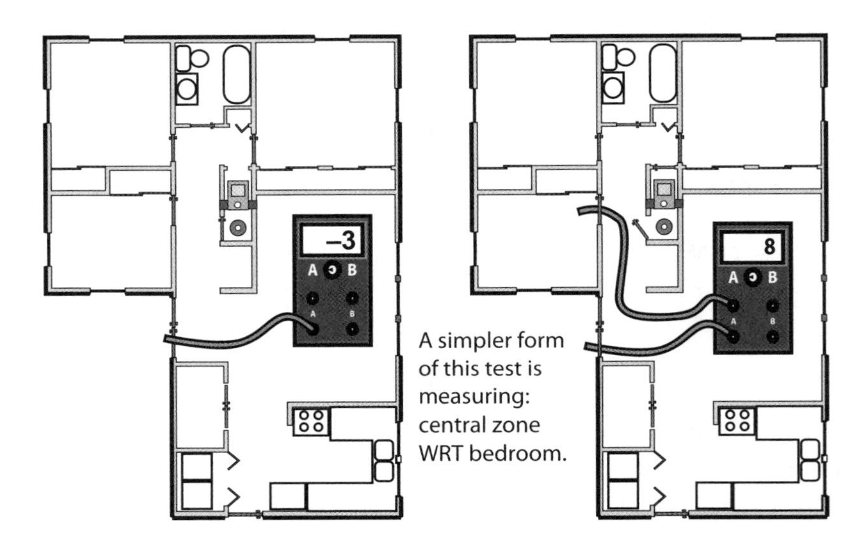


**Depressurized Central Zone:** The air handler depressurizes the central zone, where the return register is located, when the bedroom doors are closed. This significantly increases air infiltration through the building shell.

**Pressurized Bedrooms:** Bedrooms with supply registers but no return register are pressurized when the air handler is on and the doors are closed. Pressures this high can double or triple air leakage through the building shell.

## 4.13.5 Improving Duct Airflow

Inadequate airflow is a common cause of comfort complaints. When the air handler is on there should be a strong flow of air out of each supply register. Low airflow may mean that a branch is blocked or separated, or that return air is not sufficient. When low airflow is a problem, consider the following obvious improvements mentioned previously.

- ✔ Clean or change filter.
- ✔ Clean furnace blower.
- ✔ Clean air-conditioning or heat pump coil. (If the blower is dirty, the coil is probably also dirty.)
- ✔ Increase blower speed.
- ✔ Make sure that balancing dampers to rooms that need more airflow are wide open.
- ✔ Lubricate blower motor, and check tension on drive belt.
- ✔ Repair or replace bent, damaged, or restricted registers.

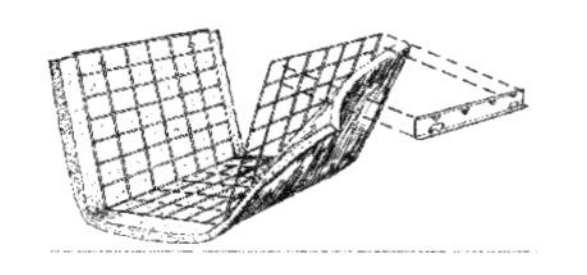

Washable filter installed on a rack inside the blower compartment.

Panel filter installed in filter slot in return plenum

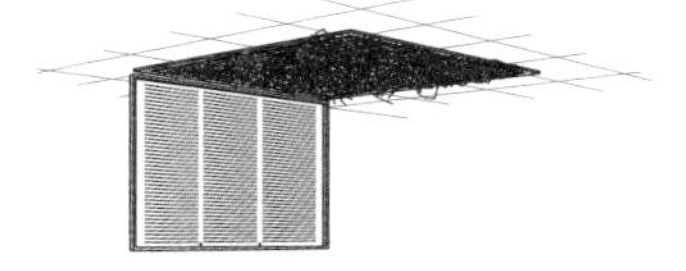

Panel filter installed in return register

**Furnace Filter Location:** Filters are installed on the return-air side of forced air systems. Look for them in one or more of the above locations.

## Duct Improvements to Increase Airflow

Consider the following improvements in response to customer complaints and conditions you observe during a thorough duct inspection. Unbalanced airflow through ducts can pressurize or depressurize rooms, leading to increased air leakage through the building shell. Consider the following duct changes to increase system airflow and reduce the imbalance between supply and return.

- ✔ Clean dirty filters and modify the filter installation to allow easier filter changing, if filter changing is currently difficult.
- ✔ Remove obstructions to registers and ducts such as rugs, furniture, and objects placed inside ducts, such as children's toys and water pans for humidification.
- ✔ Remove kinks from flex duct, and replace collapsed flex duct and fiberglass duct board.
- ✔ If the blower is dirty, an air conditioning coil, if present, is probably also dirty. Clean the blower and coil.
- ✔ Install additional supply ducts and return ducts as needed to provide heated air throughout the building, especially in additions to the building.
- ✔ Install a transfer grille between the bedroom and main body of house to improve airflow.
- ✔ Undercut bedroom doors, especially in homes with single return registers.
- ✔ Retrofit jumper ducts, composed of one register in the bedroom, one register in the central return-air zone, and a duct in between (usually running through an attic or crawl space).
- ✔ Install registers and grilles where missing.

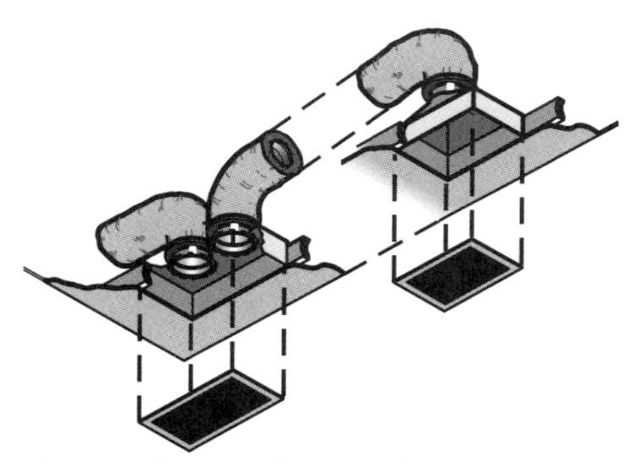

Jumper ducts can bring air from a restricted area of the home back to a main return register.

Installing transfer grilles in doors or through walls allows return air to escape from bedrooms.

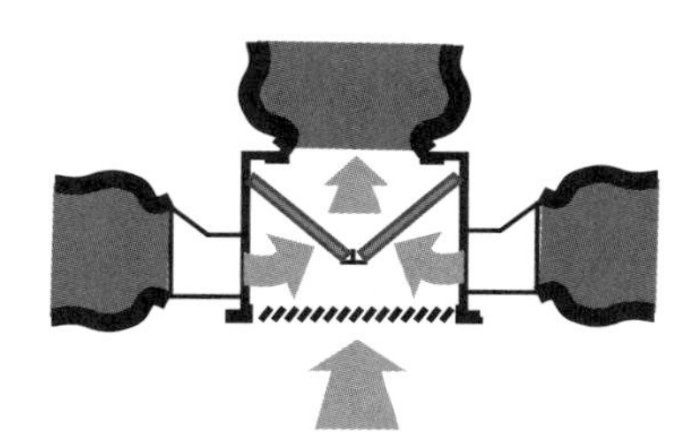

You can expand an existing return register by connecting a return box and then run one or more branch returns into the box in a way that all the air is filtered.

**Restricted Return Air:** Return air is often restricted, requiring a variety of strategies to relieve the resulting house pressures and low system airflow. Installing an additional return duct directly into the air handler is a preferred strategy.

## 4.14 Evaluating Duct Air Leakage

Duct air leakage is a major energy-waster in homes where the ducts are located outside the home's thermal boundary in a crawl space, attic, attached garage, or leaky unoccupied basement. When these intermediate zones remain outside the thermal boundary, duct air-sealing is usually cost-effective.

There are two common approaches to duct sealing: prescriptive and guided. With guided air sealing, there are simple methods and duct air-tightness testing with a duct blower.

The energy impact of duct leakage depends on whether the ducts are located within or outside of the thermal boundary. Not all duct leaks are an energy problem.

## 4.14.1 Troubleshooting Duct Leakage

There are several methods for finding the locations of the leaks and gaging their severity.

### Finding Duct Leaks Using Touch and Sight

One of the simplest ways of finding duct leaks is feeling with your hand for air leaking out of supply ducts, while the ducts are pressurized by the air handler's blower. Duct leaks can also be located using light. These tests can be used to locate air leaks.

- Use the air handler blower to pressurize supply ducts. Closing the dampers on supply registers temporarily or partially blocking the register with pieces of carpet, magazines, or any object that won't be blown off by the register's airflow increases the duct pressure and make duct leaks easier to find. Dampening your hand makes your hand more sensitive to airflow, helping you to find duct air leaks.

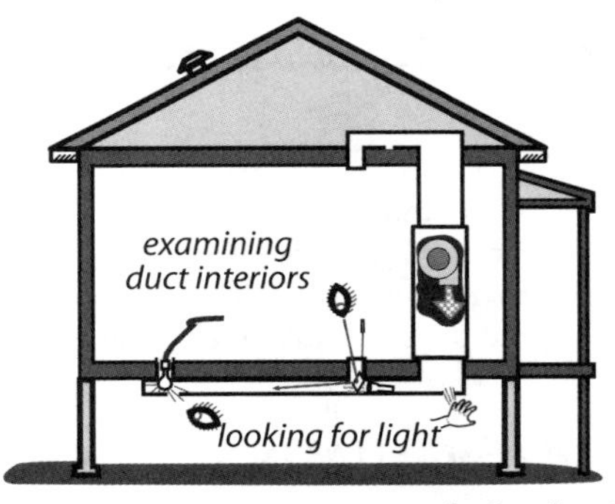


**Finding Duct Air Leaks:** Finding the exact location of duct leaks precedes duct air-sealing.

- Place a trouble light, with a 100-watt bulb, inside the duct through a register. Look for light emanating from the exterior of duct joints and seams.

- Determine which duct joints were difficult to fasten and seal during installation. These joints are likely duct-leakage locations.

Feeling air leaks establishes their exact location. Ducts must be pressurized in order to feel leaks because you can't usually feel air leaking into depressurized return ducts. Pressurizing the home with a blower door forces air through duct leaks, located in intermediate zones, where you can feel the leakage coming out of both supply and return ducts.

A trouble light, flashlight, and mirror help you to visually understand duct interiors so that you can plan an air-sealing procedure.

## Pressure-Pan Testing

Pressure-pan tests can help identify leaky or disconnected ducts. With the house depressurized by the blower door to –25 or –50 pascals with reference to outdoors, pressure-pan readings are taken at each supply and return register. Pressure-pan testing is reliable for mobile homes and small site-built homes where the ducts are outside the air barrier.

**A Pressure Pan:** Blocks a single register and measures the air pressure behind it, during a blower door test. The magnitude of that pressure is an indicator of duct leakage.

Basements are often considered part of the conditioned living space of a home. In this case, pressure-pan testing isn't necessary, although air-sealing the return ducts for safety is still very important. If instead, the basement is accessed from the outside and rarely used, the basement may be considered outside the conditioned living space. In this case, a window or door between the basement and outdoors should be opened, and any door or hatch between conditioned spaces and basement should be closed during pressure-pan testing.

1. Install blower door and set-up house for winter conditions. Open all interior doors.
2. If the basement is conditioned living space, open the door between basement and upstairs living spaces. If the basement is considered outside the conditioned living space, close the door between basement and upstairs living spaces and open a basement window.
3. Turn furnace off at the thermostat or main switch. Remove furnace filter, and tape filter slot if one exists. Ensure that all grilles, registers, and dampers are fully open.
4. Temporarily seal any outside fresh-air intakes to the duct system. Seal supply registers in zones that are not intended to be heated – an uninhabited basement or crawl space, for example.
5. Open attics, crawl spaces, and garages as much as possible to the outside so they don't create a secondary air barrier.
6. Connect hose between pressure pan and the input tap on the digital manometer. Leave the reference tap open.
7. With the blower door at –25 pascals, place the pressure pan completely over a grille or register to form a tight seal. Leave all other grilles and registers open. Record the reading, which should be a positive pressure.
8. If a grille is too large or a supply register is difficult to access (under a kitchen cabinet, for example), seal the grille or register with masking tape. Insert a pressure probe through the masking tape and record reading. Remove the tape and test the next over-sized registers in the same way.

9. Repeat this test for each register and grille in a systematic fashion.

### Pressure-Pan Duct Standards

If the ducts are perfectly sealed with no leakage to the outside, no pressure difference (0 pascals) is measured during a pressure-pan test. The higher the measured pressure-pan reading, the more connected the duct is to the outdoors. Readings greater than 1.0 pascal merit investigation and sealing of the leaks that are causing the reading.

Pay particular attention to registers connected to ducts that are located in areas outside the conditioned living space. These spaces include attics, crawl spaces, garages, and unoccupied basements as described previously. Also test return registers attached to stud cavities or panned joists used as return ducts. Leaky ducts located outside the conditioned living space may show pressure-pan readings of up to 25-to-50 pascals if they have large leaks.

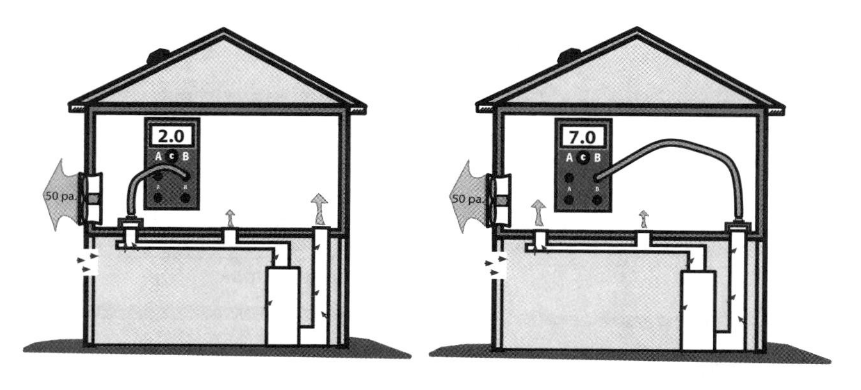


**Pressure-Pan Test:** A pressure-pan reading of 2 indicates moderate duct air leakage in the supply ducts.

**Problem Return Register:** A pressure reading of 7 pascals indicates major air leakage near the tested register.

## 4.14.2 Measuring House Pressure Caused by Duct Leakage

The following test measures pressure differences between the main body of the house and outdoors, caused by duct leakage. Pressure difference greater than +2.0 pascals or more negative than –2.0 pascals should be corrected because of the shell air leakage they create. The following procedure is quick and easy. It is useful for both testing in and testing out.

1. Set-up house for winter conditions. Close all windows and exterior doors. Turn-off all exhaust fans.
2. First, open all interior doors, including door to basement.
3. Turn on air handler.
4. Measure the house-to-outdoors pressure difference. This test indicates dominant duct leakage as shown here.

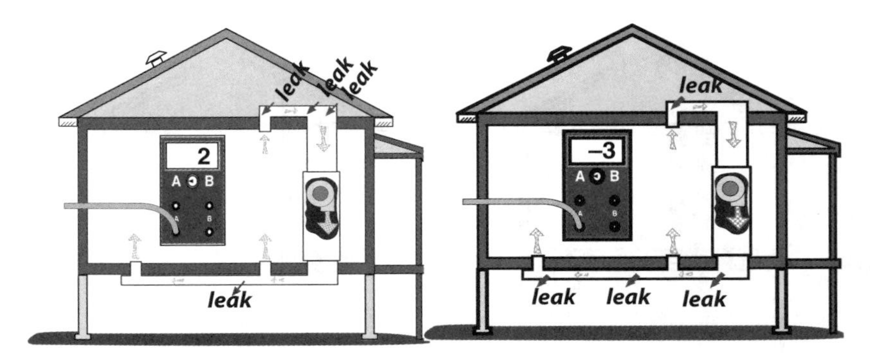


**Dominant Return Leaks:** When return leaks are larger than supply leaks, the house shows a positive pressure with reference to the outdoors.

**Dominant Supply Leaks:** When supply leaks are larger than return leaks, the house shows a negative pressure with reference to the outdoors.

A positive pressure indicates that the return ducts (which pull air from leaky intermediate zones) are leakier than the supply ducts. A negative pressure indicates that the supply ducts (which push air into intermediate zones through their leaks) are leakier than return ducts. A pressure at or near zero indicates equal supply and return leakage or else little duct leakage.

## 4.14.3 Duct Air-Tightness Standards

Duct leakage may or may not be a significant energy and comfort problem, depending on where the ducts are located. If the ducts are located completely within the conditioned living space of a home, duct leakage is probably not a significant energy problem. An example would be a two-story home where every square foot of enclosed space is heated and cooled. (Even though duct leakage itself may not be a problem, the pressures created by duct leakage or unbalanced airflow can drive air leakage through the building shell.)

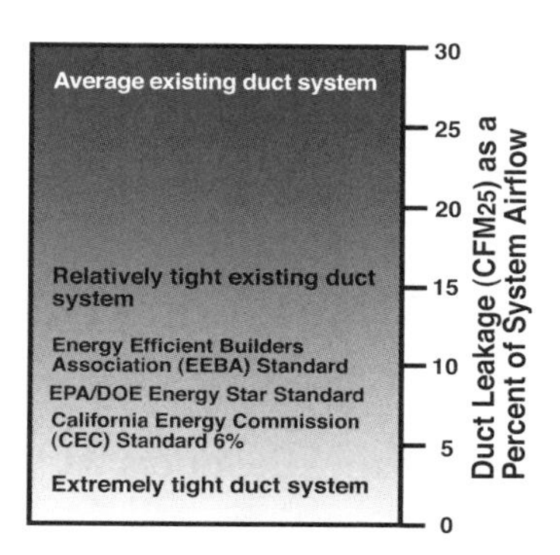


**Duct Leakage Standards:** Dividing the tested duct leakage in $CFM_{25}$ by the assumed system airflow of 400 CFM per ton provides the most common type of duct-leakage standard.

If existing ducts are located outside the home's thermal boundary, it's a safe bet that sealing their leaks will be cost-effective, assuming technicians don't have to perform demolition to find them. You can either assume high typical air leakage and begin sealing the system's leaks, working from the air handler out to the extremities, using touch and sight to find the leaks. Or you can test existing ducts to measure the quantity of air leakage and determine how much effort and money sealing requires. Testing also helps measure success and gives technicians valuable feedback.

There are two common ways of rating duct systems for air leakage.

1. Divide duct leakage by rated or measured system airflow to get a percentage.

2. Divide duct leakage by heated/cooled floor space to get a percentage.

**Table 4-23: Total Duct Air Leakage Standards for Homes**

| | $CFM_{50}$ | $CFM_{25}$ |
|---|---|---|
| **Existing Homes** | 10% of floor area | 6% of floor area |
| **New Homes** | 6% of floor area | 3.5% of floor area |

From Delta-T Inc. and Oregon Department of Energy

## 4.14.4 Measuring Duct Air Leakage with a Duct Blower

Pressurizing the ducts with a duct blower measures total duct leakage. The duct blower is the most accurate common testing device for duct air leakage. It consists of a fan, a digital manometer or set of analog manometers, and a set of reducer plates for measuring different leakage levels. Using a blower door with a duct blower, you can measure leakage to outdoors.

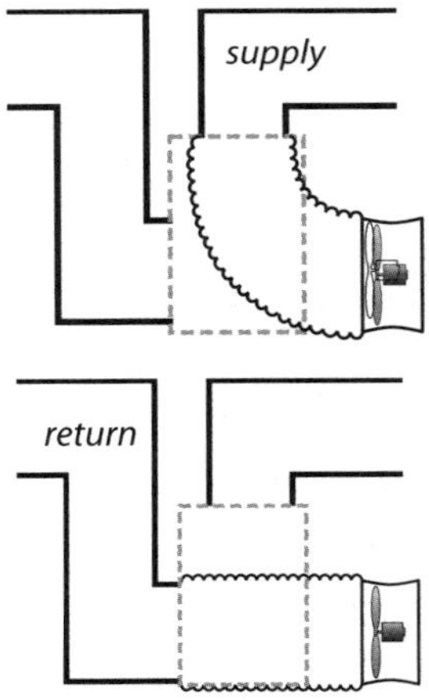

**Testing Ducts Before Air-Handler Installation:** If the ducts are installed prior to the air handler, as with a furnace replacement, the duct blower can test first supply then return ducts for airtightness.

### Measuring Total Duct Leakage

The total duct leakage test measures leakage to both indoors and outdoors. The house and intermediate zones should be open to the outdoors by way of windows, doors, or vents. Opening the intermediate zones to outdoors insures that the duct blower is measuring only the ducts' airtightness – not the airtightness of ducts combined with other air barriers such as roofs, foundation walls, or garages.

Supply and return ducts can be tested separately, either before the air handler is installed in a new home or when an air handler is removed during replacement.

Follow these steps when performing a duct airtightness test.

1. Install the duct blower in the air handler or to a large return register, either using its connector duct or simply attaching the duct blower itself to the air handler or return register with cardboard and tape.
2. Remove the air filter(s) from the duct system.
3. Seal all supply and return registers with masking tape or other non-destructive sealant.
4. Open the house, basement or crawl space, containing ducts, to outdoors.
5. Drill a $^{1}/_{4}$ or $^{5}/_{16}$-inch hole into a supply duct a short distance away from the air handler and insert a manometer hose. Connect a manometer to this hose to measure *duct WRT outdoors*. (Indoors, outdoors, and intermediate zones should ideally be opened to each other in this test).
6. Connect an airflow manometer to measure *fan WRT the area near the fan.*

Check manometer(s) for proper settings. Dial-and-needle manometers may need warm-up and calibration. Digital manometers require your choosing the correct mode, range, and fan-type settings.

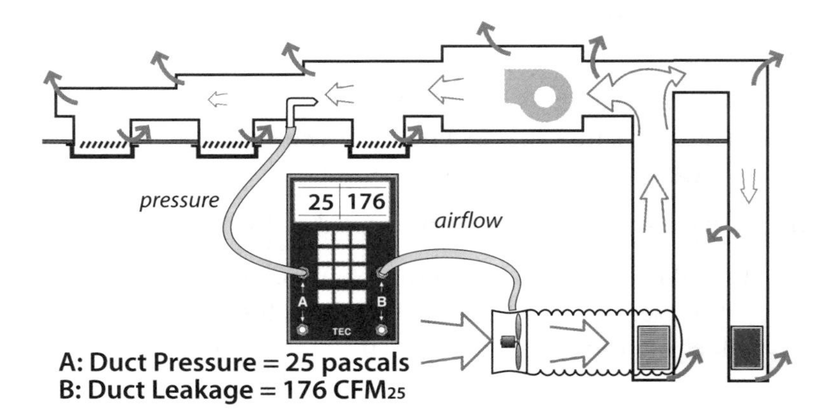


**Total Duct Air Leakage Measured by the Duct Blower:** All registers are sealed except the one connecting the duct blower to the system. Pressurize the ducts to 25 pascals and measure airflow.

1. Turn on the duct blower and pressurize the ducts to 25 pascals.
2. Record duct-blower airflow.
3. While the ducts are pressurized, start at the air handler and move outward feeling for leaks in the air handler, main ducts, and branches.
4. After testing and associated air-sealing are complete, restore filter(s), remove seals from registers, and check air handler.

## Measuring Duct Leakage to Outdoors

Measuring duct leakage to outdoors gives you a duct-air-leakage value that is directly related to energy waste and the potential for energy savings.

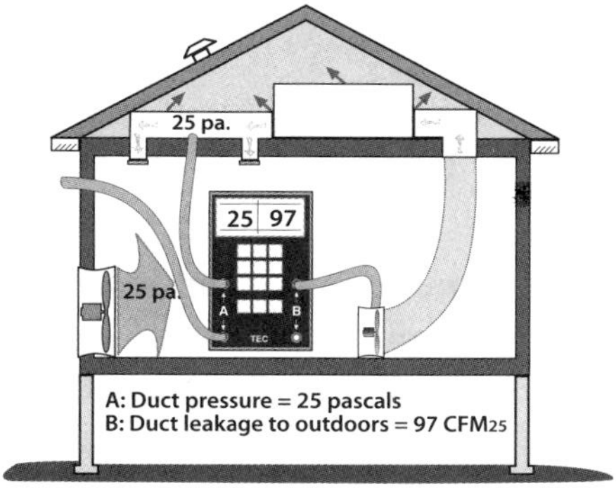

**Measuring Duct Leakage to Outdoors:** Using a blower door to pressurize the house with a duct blower to pressurize the ducts measures leakage to the outdoors – a smaller number and a better predictor of energy savings. This test is the preferred for evaluating duct leakage for specialists in both shell air leakage and duct air leakage whenever a blower door is available.

1. Set up the home in its typical heating and cooling mode with windows and outside doors closed. Open all indoor conditioned areas to one another.
2. Install a blower door, configured to pressurize the home.
3. Connect the duct blower to the air handler or to a main return duct.
4. Pressurize the ducts to +25 pascals by increasing the duct blower's speed until this value is reached.
5. Pressurize the house until the pressure difference between the house and duct is 0 pascals (*house WRT ducts*).
6. Read the airflow through the duct blower. This value is duct leakage to outdoors.

# 4.14.5 Typical Duct Leak Locations

Ducts located outside the thermal boundary or in an intermediate zone like a ventilated attic or crawl space should be sealed. The following is a list of duct-leak locations in order of their relative importance. Leaks nearer to the air handler see higher pressure and are more important than leaks further away. Follow the duct pathways from every register back to the air handler examining every joint and transition.

- ✔ All return leaks within the combustion zone should be sealed to prevent this leakage from depressurizing the combustion zone and causing backdrafting.
- ✔ Plenum joint at air handler: These joints may have been difficult to fasten and seal because of tight access. Seal these thoroughly even if it requires cutting an access hole in the plenum. (Prefer silicone caulking or foil tape to mastic and fabric mesh here for possible future modifications – furnace replacement, for example.)
- ✔ Joints at branch takeoffs: Seal these with a thick layer of mastic. Fabric mesh tape provides reinforcement to prevent cracking.
- ✔ Transitions between panned return sections and the ducted main return drops to the air handler.
- ✔ Tabbed sleeves: Attach the sleeve to the main duct with 3-to-5 screws and apply mastic abundantly.
- ✔ Seal leaky joints between building materials composing cavity-return ducts, like panned floor joists and furnace-return platforms.
- ✔ Joints in sectioned elbows: Known as gores, these are usually leaky.
- ✔ Flexduct-to-metal joints: Clamp the flexduct's inner liner with a plastic strap, using a strap tensioner. Clamp the insulation and outer liner with another strap.
- ✔ Support ducts and duct joints with duct hangers where needed. Install duct hangers approximately every 24 inches.

- ✔ Deteriorating ductboard facing: Replace ductboard, preferably with metal ducting when the facing deteriorates because this condition leads to massive air leakage.

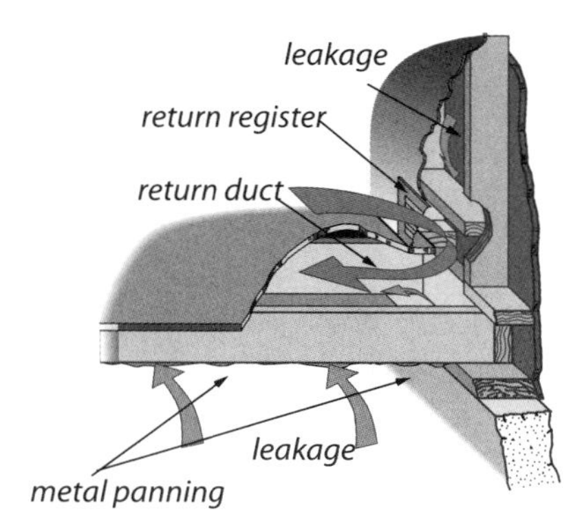


**Panned Floor Joists:** These return ducts are often very leaky and may require removing the panning to seal the cavity.

- ✔ Seal leaky joints between supply and return registers and the floor, wall, and ceiling to which they are attached to reduce shell air leakage.

## Materials for Duct Air-Sealing

Duct mastic is the preferred duct-sealing material because of its superior durability and adhesion. Apply at least $^1/_{16}$-inch thick and use reinforcing mesh for all joints wider than $^1/_8$-inch or joints that may experience some movement.

Joints should rely on mechanical fasteners to prevent joint movement or separation. Tape should never be expected to hold a joint together nor expected to resist the force of compacted insulation or joint movement. Aluminum foil or cloth duct tape are not good materials for duct sealing because their adhesive often fails. Tape should be covered with mastic to prevent its adhesive from drying out and failing.

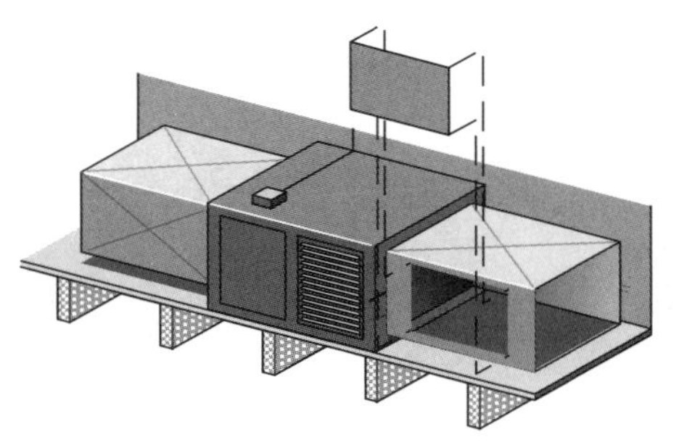

**Plenums, Poorly Sealed to Air Handler:** When air handlers are installed in tight spaces, plenums may be poorly fastened and sealed. Cutting a hole in the duct may be the only way to seal this important joint.

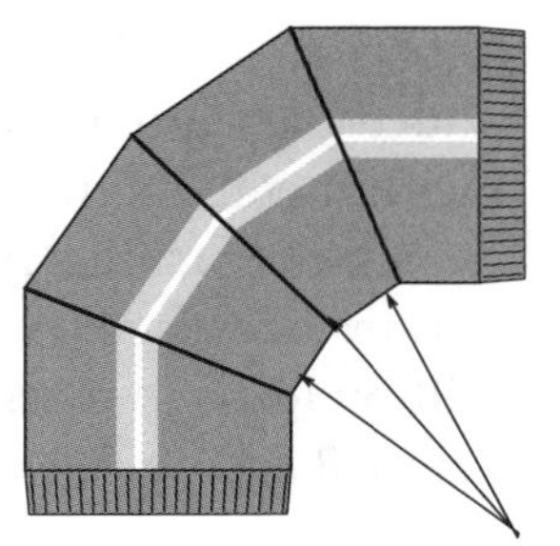

**Sectioned Elbows:** Joints in sectioned elbows known as gores are usually quite leaky and require sealing with duct mastic.

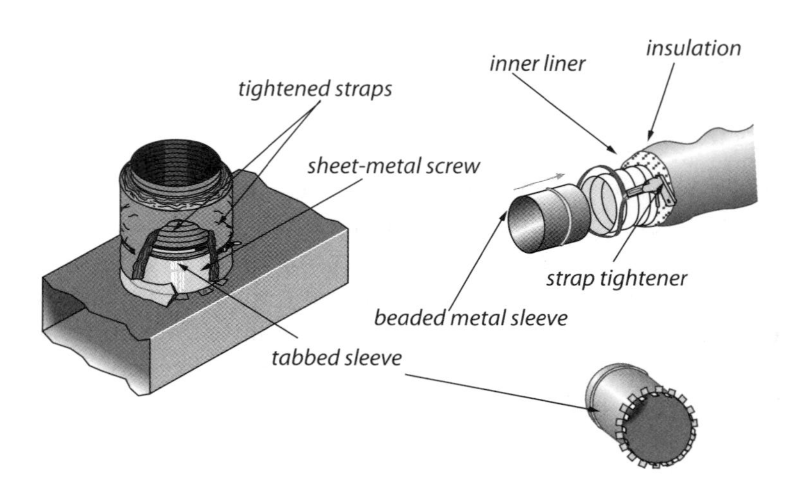


**Flexduct Joints:** Flexduct itself is usually fairly airtight, but joints, sealed improperly with tape, can be very leaky. Use methods shown here to make flexduct joints airtight.

# 4.15 Duct Insulation

Specify insulation for supply ducts that run through unconditioned areas outside the thermal boundary such as crawl spaces, attics, and attached garages with a minimum of R-6 vinyl-faced or foil-faced duct insulation. Don't insulate ducts that run through conditioned areas unless they cause overheating in winter or condensation in summer. Follow the best practices listed below for installing insulation.

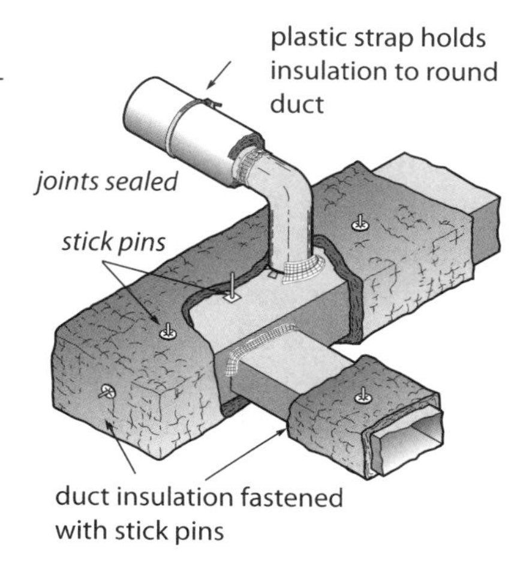


**Duct Insulation:** Supply ducts, located in unheated areas, should be insulated to a minimum of R-6.

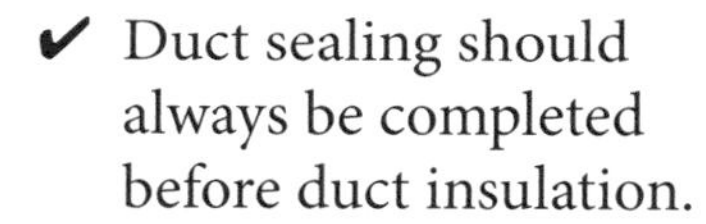

- ✔ Duct sealing should always be completed before duct insulation.
- ✔ Insulation should cover all exposed supply ducts, without significant areas of bare duct left uninsulated.
- ✔ Specify fastening insulation with mechanical means such as stick pins, twine, or plastic straps. Note: Tape can be effective for covering joints in the insulation to prevent air convection, but tape fails when expected to resist the force of the insulation's compression or weight. Outward clinch staples can help hold the insulation facing and tape together.

# 4.16 Hot-Water Space-Heating Distribution

Hot-water heating is generally a little more efficient than forced-air heating and considerably more efficient than steam heating. The most significant energy wasters in hot-water systems are poor steady-state efficiency, off-cycle flue losses robbing heat from stored water, and boilers operating at too high a water temperature. For information about boiler installation, *see page 97.*

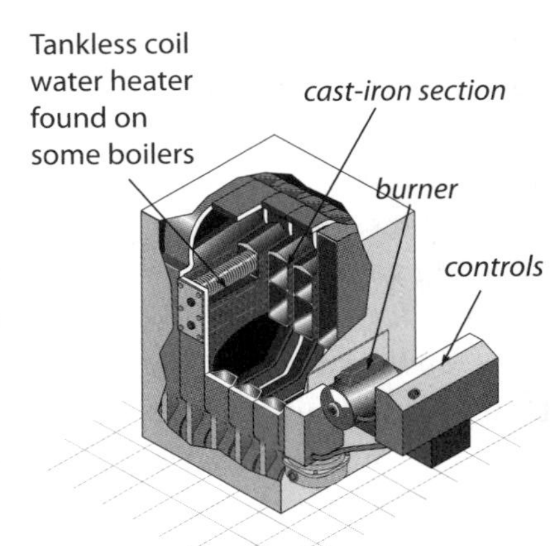


**Cast-Iron Sectional Boilers:** The most common boiler type for residential applications.

## 4.16.1 Boiler Efficiency and Maintenance

Boilers can maintain good performance and efficiency for many years if they are regularly maintained and tuned-up. Boiler performance and efficiency improve after effective maintenance and tune-up procedures. There are more ways for performance and efficiency to deteriorate in boilers compared to furnaces. Specifically these are:

- ✔ Corrosion, scaling, and dirt on the water side of the heat exchanger.
- ✔ Corrosion, dust, and dirt on the fire side of the heat exchanger.
- ✔ Excess air during combustion from air leaks and incorrect fuel-air mixture.
- ✔ Off-cycle air circulation through the firebox and heat exchanger, removing heat from stored water.

### Boiler Efficiency Improvements

Consider specifying the following maintenance and efficiency improvements for both hot-water and steam boilers based on boiler inspection.

- ✔ Check for leaks on the boiler, around its fittings, or on any of the distribution piping connected to the boiler.
- ✔ Clean fire side of heat exchanger of noticeable dirt.
- ✔ Drain water from the boiler drain until the water flows clean.

## 4.16.2 Distribution System Improvements

Hydronic distribution systems consist of the supply and return piping, the circulator, expansion tank, air separator, air vents, and heat emitters. A properly designed and installed hydronic distribution system can operate for decades without service. However, many systems have installation flaws or need service.

> **Note:** You can recognize a hot-water boiler by its expansion tank, located somewhere above the boiler. The expansion tank provides an air cushion to allow the system's water to expand and contract as it is heated and cooled without creating excessive pressure in the boiler and piping and discharging through the pressure-relief valve.

### Safety Checks and Improvements

Work with contractors and technicians to specify and verify the following safety and efficiency tests and inspections.

- ✔ Confirm the existence of a 30-psi-rated pressure-temperature (P&T) relief valve. The P&T relief valve should have a drain pipe that terminates 6 inches from the floor. Replace a malfunctioning valve or add one if none exists. Note signs of leakage or discharges. Direct technicians to find out why the relief valve is discharging.
- ✔ Verify that the expansion tank isn't waterlogged or sized too small for the system. This could cause the pressure-relief valve to discharge. Test expansion tank for correct air pressure — typically one (1) psi per 2.3 feet of the system's height.
- ✔ If you observe rust in venting, ask technicians to verify that return water temperature is warmer than 140° F for gas and warmer than 130° F for oil, to prevent acidic condensation.
- ✔ Verify that high-limit control deactivate burner at a water temperature of 200° F or less.
- ✔ Lubricate circulator pump(s) if necessary.

## Efficiency Improvements

Work with contractors and technicians to implement the following energy-efficiency improvements.

- ✔ Repair water leaks in the system.
- ✔ Remove corrosion, dust, and dirt on the fire side of the heat exchanger.
- ✔ Check for excess air during combustion from air leaks and incorrect fuel-air mixture.
- ✔ Consider operating the boiler without a low-limit control for maintaining a minimum boiler-water temperature, unless the boiler is heating domestic water in addition to space heating. Technicians must verify that the boiler won't be operating at too low a flue-gas temperature after removing low-limit control.

**Expansion Tank, Air Separator, and Vent:** Preventing excessive pressure and eliminating air from the systems are important for hydronic distribution systems.

**Zone Valves:** Separate thermostats control each zone valve. Zone valves have switches that activate the burner.

- ✔ Bleed air from radiators and piping through air vents on piping or radiators. Most systems have an automatic fill valve. If there is a manual fill valve for refilling system with water, it should be open to push water in and air out, during air purging.

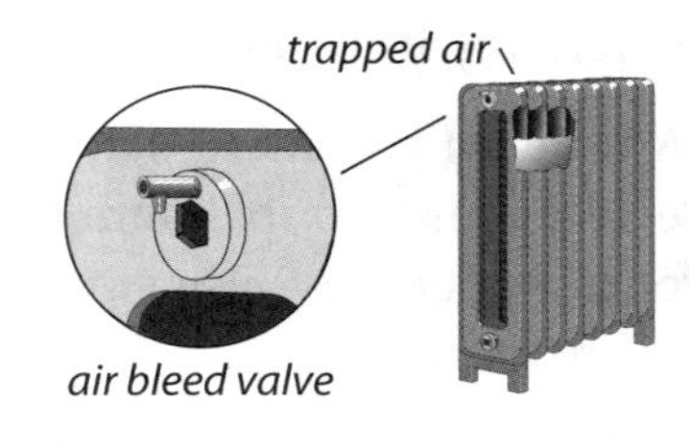


**Purging Air:** Trapped air collects at the hot-water system's highest parts. Bleeding air from radiators fills the radiator and gives it more heating surface area.

- ✔ Install outdoor reset controllers on larger boilers to regulate water temperature, depending on outdoor temperature.
- ✔ After control improvements like two-stage thermostats or reset controllers, verify that return water temperature is high enough to prevent condensation and corrosion in the chimney as noted previously.
- ✔ Vacuum and clean fins of fin-tube convectors if you notice dust and dirt there.
- ✔ Insulate all supply and return piping, passing through unheated areas, with foam pipe insulation, at least one-inch thick, rated for temperatures up to 200° F.
- ✔ Install electric vent dampers on atmospheric gas- and oil-fired high-mass boilers.

## 4.17 Steam Heating and Distribution

Steam heating is less efficient than hot-water heating because steam relies on higher temperatures than hot water. Higher temperature heating systems are less efficient than lower temperature ones. A steam boiler heats water to its boiling point before making steam or providing any heat to the building. Steam boilers are also more hazardous because of the steam pressure. For these reasons heating-system replacement with a hot-water or forced-air system should be considered, depending on the boiler's operating efficiency after a tune-up.

**Note:** You can recognize a steam boiler by its sight glass, which indicates the boiler's water level. Notice that the water doesn't completely fill the boiler, but instead allows a space for the steam to form above the boiler's water level.

If the steam-heating system must remain, operate it at the lowest steam pressure that still heats the building adequately. Two psi on the boiler-pressure gauge is a practical limit for many systems although most systems can operate at pressures down to a few ounces per square foot of pressure. Traps and air vents are crucial to operating at a low steam pressure. Electric vent dampers reduce off-cycle losses for both gas- and oil-fired systems.

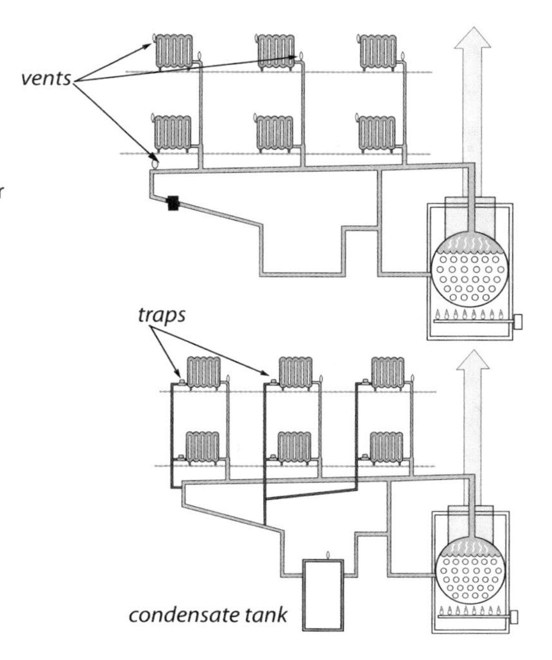


**One-Pipe and Two-Pipe Steam Systems:** Still common in multifamily buildings, one-pipe steam works best when very low pressure steam can drive air out of the piping and radiators quickly through plentiful vents. Vents are located on each radiator and also on main steam lines.

**Two-Pipe Steam Systems:** Radiator traps keep steam inside radiators until it condenses. No steam should be present at the condensate tank.

## 4.17.1 Steam System Maintenance

Specify the following safety and maintenance checks on steam systems.

- ✔ Verify that steam boilers are equipped with high-pressure limits and low-water cut-off controls.
- ✔ Verify that flush valves on low water cutoffs are operable and do not leak.
- ✔ On steam boilers with externally mounted low water cut-offs, verify the function of the control by flushing the low water cutoff with the burner operating. Combustion must cease when the water level in the boiler drops below the level of the float.
- ✔ Ask owner about instituting a schedule of blow-down and chemical-level checks.
- ✔ Specify that technicians drain mud legs on return piping.

## 4.17.2 Steam System Energy Conservation

Specify the following efficiency checks and improvements for steam systems.

- ✔ Verify that high-pressure limit control is set at or below 1 (one) psi or as low as acceptable in providing heat to the far ends of the building.
- ✔ Inspect return lines and condensate receiver for steam coming back to the boiler. Check radiator and main line traps.
- ✔ Verify steam vents are operable and that all steam radiators receive steam during every cycle. Unplug vents or replace malfunctioning vents as necessary. Add vents to steam lines and radiators as needed to achieve this goal.
- ✔ Check steam traps with a digital thermometer or listening device to detect any steam escaping from radiators

through the condensate return. Replace leaking steam traps or their thermostatic elements.

- ✔ Consider installing remote sensing thermostats that vary cycle length according to outdoor temperature and include night-setback capability.
- ✔ Repair leaks on the steam supply piping or on condensate return piping.
- ✔ Consider a flame-retention burner and electric vent damper as retrofits for steam boilers.
- ✔ Clean fire side of heat exchanger of noticeable dirt.
- ✔ All steam piping that passes through unconditioned areas should be insulated to at least R-3 with fiberglass or specially designed foam pipe insulation rated for steam piping.

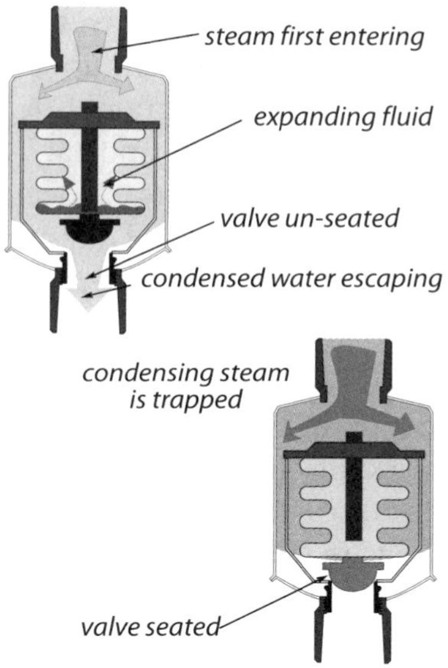

*steam first entering*
*expanding fluid*
*valve un-seated*
*condensed water escaping*
*condensing steam is trapped*
*valve seated*

**Steam Traps:** Steam enters the steam trap heating its element and expanding the fluid inside. The expanded element plugs the steam's escape with a valve.

## 4.18 Programmable Thermostats

A programmable thermostat may be a big energy saver if the building occupant understands how to program it. A programmable thermostat won't save any energy if occupants already control day and night temperatures effectively.

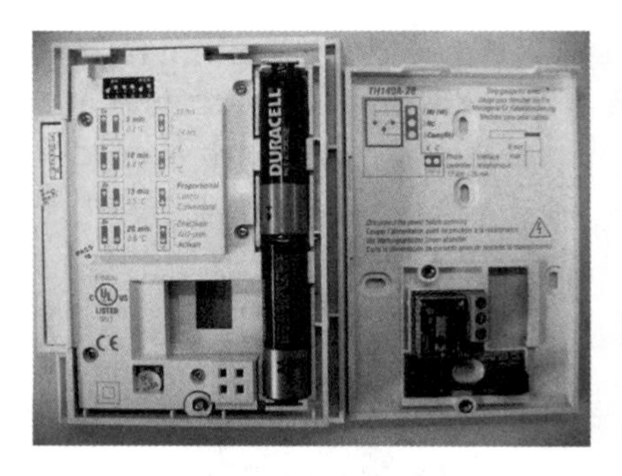


**Inside a Programmable Thermostat:** In addition to the instructions on the exterior of this thermostat are instructions inside for setting the heat anticipator.

If the existing thermostat is replaced as a part of weatherization or home performance work, discuss programmable thermostats with occupants. If they are willing to use a programmable thermostat, proceed with the installation. Train occupants on the use of the thermostat and leave a copy of manufacturers directions with them.

Many models of programmable thermostats have settings that are selected from inside the thermostat. These include the heat anticipator setting, which adjusts the cycle length of the heating or cooling system.

## 4.19 Electric Heat

Electricity is a more convenient form of energy than gas or other fuels, but it is considerably more expensive. Electric heaters are usually 100% efficient at converting the electricity to heat in the room where they are located. However, coal- or oil-generated electricity converts only about 30% of the fuel's potential energy to electricity.

All electric space heaters convert electricity to heat at the same efficiency — 100%. Miracle space heaters, advertised in the media, are no more efficient than those bought at your local store. However, there are comfort and delivery issues that do constitute important differences between electric resistance heaters.

### 4.19.1 Electric Baseboard Heat

Electric baseboard heaters are zonal heaters controlled by thermostats within the zone they heat. Electric baseboard heat can result in relatively lower energy costs in many homes, if residents take advantage of the ability to zone.

Baseboard heaters contain electric resistance heating elements encased in metal pipes. These pipes extend the length of the unit and are surrounded by aluminum fins to aid heat transfer. As air within the heater is heated, it rises into the room. This draws cooler air into the bottom of the heater.

- ✔ Make sure that the baseboard heater sits at least an inch above the floor to facilitate good air convection.
- ✔ Clean fins and remove dust and debris from around and under the baseboard heaters as often as necessary.
- ✔ Avoid putting furniture directly against the heaters. To heat properly, there must be space for air convection.

There are two kinds of built-in electric baseboard heaters: strip-heat and liquid-filled. Strip-heat units are less expensive than liquid-filled, but they don't heat as well. Strip-heat units release heat in short bursts, as the temperature of the heating elements rises to about 350°F. Liquid-filled baseboard heaters release heat more evenly over longer time periods, as the element temperature rises only to about 180°F.

The line-voltage thermostats used with baseboard heaters sometimes do not provide good comfort. This is because they allow the temperature in the room to vary by 2°F or more. Newer, more accurate thermostats are available. Programmable thermostats for electric baseboard heat employ timers or a resident-activated button that raises the temperature for a time and then automatically returns to setback. Some baseboard systems use low-voltage thermostats connected to relays that control baseboard heaters in rooms.

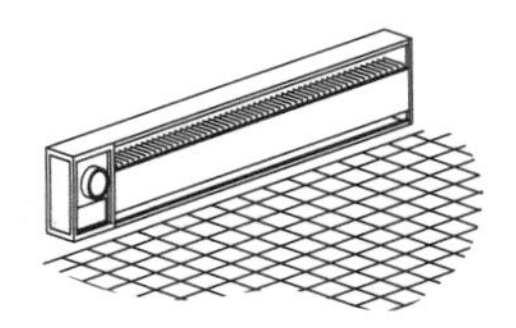

**Electric Baseboard:** Electric baseboard is more efficient than an electric furnace and sometimes even outperforms a central heat pump because it is easily zoneable. The energy bill is determined by the habits of the occupants and the energy efficiency of the building.

## 4.19.2 Electric Furnaces

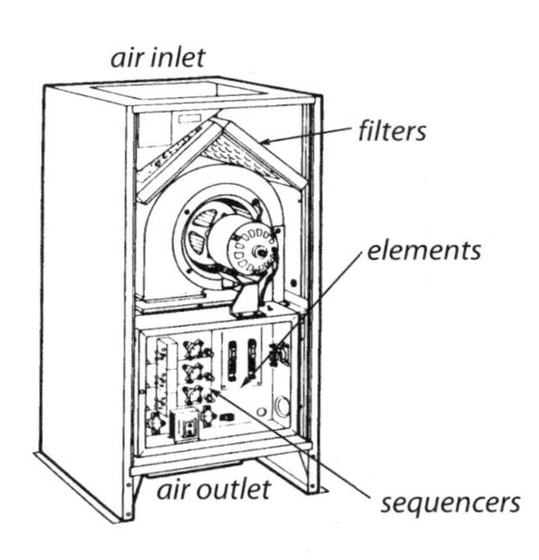


**Electric Furnace:** A squirrel-cage blower blows air over 3 to 6 electric resistance coils and down into the plenum below the floor.

Electric furnaces are the most expensive way to heat a building, combining the most expensive energy source with an often inefficient ducted air distribution system. Electric furnaces heat air moved by its fan over several electric-resistance heating elements. Electric furnaces have three to six elements — 3.5 to 7 kW each — that work like the elements in a toaster. The 24-volt thermostat circuit energizes devices called sequencers that bring the 240 volt heating elements on in stages when the thermostat calls for heat. The variable speed fan switches to a higher speed as more elements engage to keep the air temperature stable. Electric furnaces are obsolete and should be replaced.

### 4.19.3 Electric Radiant Heat

Electric radiant panels can be an appropriate way to heat very energy-efficient homes. They are available in ceiling- and wall-mount panels, as well as ceiling cove and baseboard cove units. These radiant heaters have a number of advantages

- Ability to heat part of a home (zoning).
- Ability to deliver comfort faster and at a lower wattage, thereby saving electricity.

### 4.19.4 Central Heat-Pump Energy Efficiency

An air-source heat pump is almost identical to an air conditioner, except for a reversing valve that allows refrigerant to follow two different paths, one for heating and one for cooling. Heat pumps move heat with refrigeration rather than converting it from the chemical energy of a fuel.

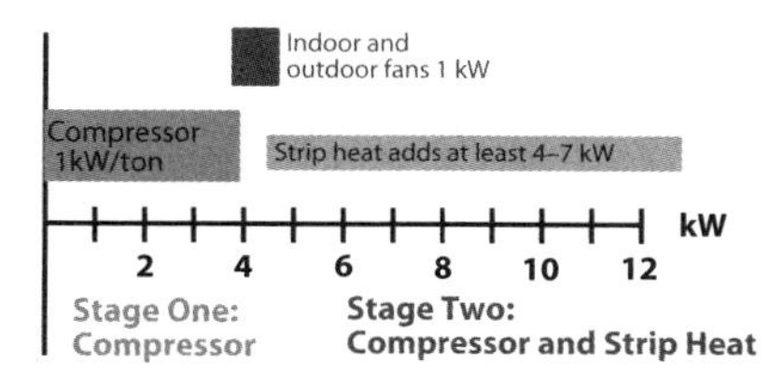


**Is Strip Heat Activated?** Using an ammeter and the nameplate data on the heat pump, a technician can know when and if the strip heat is activated.

Like air conditioners, air-source heat pumps are available as centralized units with ducts or as room units. Heat pumps are 1.5 to 3 times more efficient than electric furnaces. Heat pumps can provide competitive comfort and value with combustion furnaces, but they must be installed with great care and planning.

Heat pumps are also equipped with auxiliary electric resistance heat, called strip heat. The energy efficiency of a heat pump is largely determined by how much of the heating load can be handled by the compressor without the aid of the strip heat.

## Evaluating Heat Pumps During the Heating Season

Testing central heat pumps during the summer follows the same procedures as testing central air conditioners and described on *page 200*. Testing heat pumps in the winter is more difficult and some specifications follow.

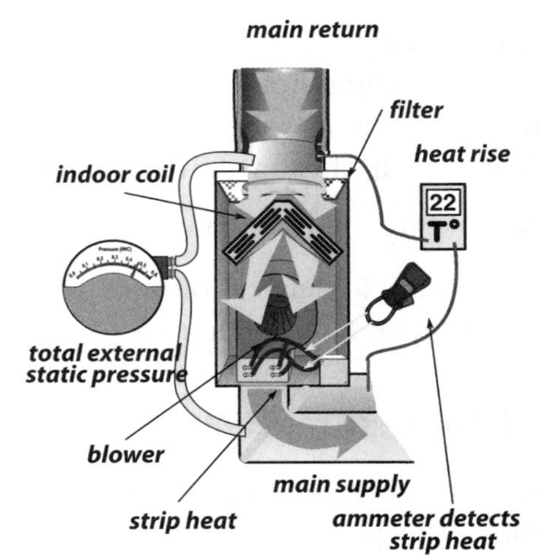


**Heat Pump:** The air handler contains a blower, indoor coil, strip heat, and often a filter. Static pressure and temperature rise are two indicators of performance.

- ✔ Look for a temperature rise of around half the outdoor temperature in degrees Fahrenheit.
- ✔ Check for strip heat operation with an ammeter, using the chart shown here. Heat pumps should have two-stage thermostats designed for heat pumps. The first stage is compressor heating and the second stage is the strip heat.
- ✔ External static pressure should be 0.5 IWC (125 pascals) or less for older, fixed-speed blowers and less than 0.8 IWC (200 pascals) for variable-speed and two-speed blowers. Lower external static pressure is better.
- ✔ Supply ducts should be sealed and insulated after the airflow has been verified as adequate. Return ducts should be sealed too.

Most residential central heat pumps are split systems with the indoor coil and air handler indoors and outdoor coil and compressor outdoors. Individual room heat pumps are more efficient since they have the advantage of no ducts and are factory-charged with refrigerant. The illustrations show features of an energy-efficient heat pump installation.

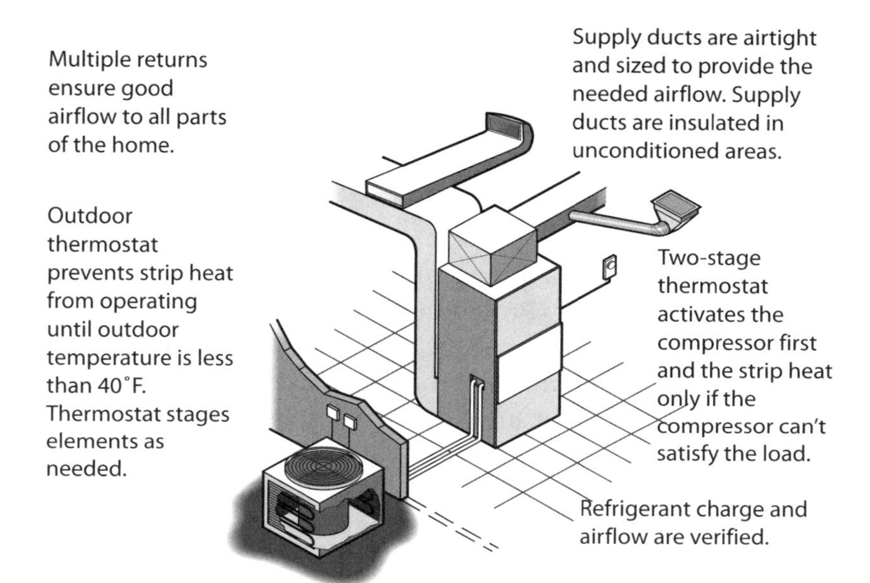


Coil is cleaned every year. Weeds, grass and shrubs are not allowed to grow within 3 feet on all sides. Verify that no airflow restrictions exist above the condenser.

## 4.19.5 Room Heat Pumps

Room heat pumps can provide all or part of the heating and cooling needs for small homes. These one-piece room systems (also known as terminal systems) look like a room air conditioner, but provide heating as well as cooling. They can also provide ventilation air when neither heating nor cooling are required. They mount in a window or through a framed opening in a wall.

Room heat pumps can be a good choice for replacing existing un-vented gas space heaters or obsolete central heating systems. Their fuel costs may be somewhat higher than oil or gas furnaces, though they are safer and require less maintenance than combustion appliances. Room heat pumps also gain some overall efficiency because they heat a single zone and don't have the delivery losses associated with central furnaces and ductwork. If they replace electric resistance heat, they consume only one-half to one-third the electricity to produce the same amount of heat.

Room heat pumps have a coefficient of performance (COP) comparable to the best new window air conditioners, which is more than 2.5. They operate at up to twice the efficiency of older air conditioners.

Room heat pumps draw a substantial electrical load, and may require 240-volt wiring. Provide a dedicated circuit that can support the equipment's rated electrical input. Insufficient wiring capacity can result in dangerous overheating, tripped circuit breakers, blown fuses, or motor-damaging voltage drops. In most cases a licensed electrician should confirm that the house wiring is sufficient. Don't run portable heat pumps or any other appliance with extension cords or plug adapters.

## 4.20 Evaluating Central Air-Conditioning Systems

Problems with air conditioning often go hand in hand with problems with the building shell. An energy-efficient home shouldn't need more than a ton of air-conditioning capacity for every 1000 square feet of floor space. Window shading, attic insulation, and air-leakage should be evaluated together with air-conditioner performance.

1. *See "Window Shading" on page 223.*
2. *See "Evaluating Attic or Roof Insulation" on page 48.*
3. *See "Air-Leakage Testing" on page 65.*

The following four installation-related problems are characteristic of central air conditioning systems.

1. Inadequate airflow.
2. Duct air leakage.
3. Incorrect charge.

4. Oversizing.

Refrigerant-charge testing and adjustment should be done after airflow measurement and improvement and after duct testing and sealing. The logic behind this sequence is that airflow should be adequate before duct sealing is done in case you have to add or enlarge ducts. Manufacturers recommend that adequate airflow be verified before charge is checked and adjusted.

**Table 4-24: Compiled Research Results on HVAC Performance[a]**

| Installation-Related Problem | %[b] | Savings Potential |
|---|---|---|
| Duct air leakage (Ave. 270 $CFM_{25}$)[c] | 70% | 17% Ave. |
| Inadequate airflow | 70% | 7% Ave. |
| Incorrect charge | 74% | 12% Ave. |
| Oversized by 50% or more | 47% | 2–10% |

a. Report sponsored by Environmental Protection Agency (EPA) and compiled from research from Multiple Field Studies
b. Percent of tested homes found with a significant problem.
c. The number of homes of the duct-leakage studies was around 14,000; the number for the other problems was over 400 each.

## 4.20.1 Central Air-Conditioner Inspection

Air conditioners move vast amounts of air, and the air contains dust. The filter in the air handler is supposed to catch all the dust, but depending on how good the filter and its mounting assembly are, some dirt gets through or around the filter. The condenser coil outdoors isn't protected by a filter and is usually quite dirty.

✔ Inspect the condenser coil and know that it is probably dirty even if it looks relatively clean on the outside. Take a flat toothpick and shove it in between the fins to the other side. Can you scrape dirt out from between the fins? Can you push the toothpick through the dirt?

- ✔ Specify cleaning the condenser with either with a biodegradable coil cleaner or by special high-pressure spray, used by professional coil cleaning contractors.
- ✔ Inspect the filter slot in the air handler or the filter grille in a the return air registers. Do the filters completely fill their opening? Is the filter dirty?
- ✔ Inspect the blower in the air handler after disconnecting power to the unit. Can you remove significant dirt from one of the blades with your finger? If the blower is dirty, then the evaporator coil is also dirty.

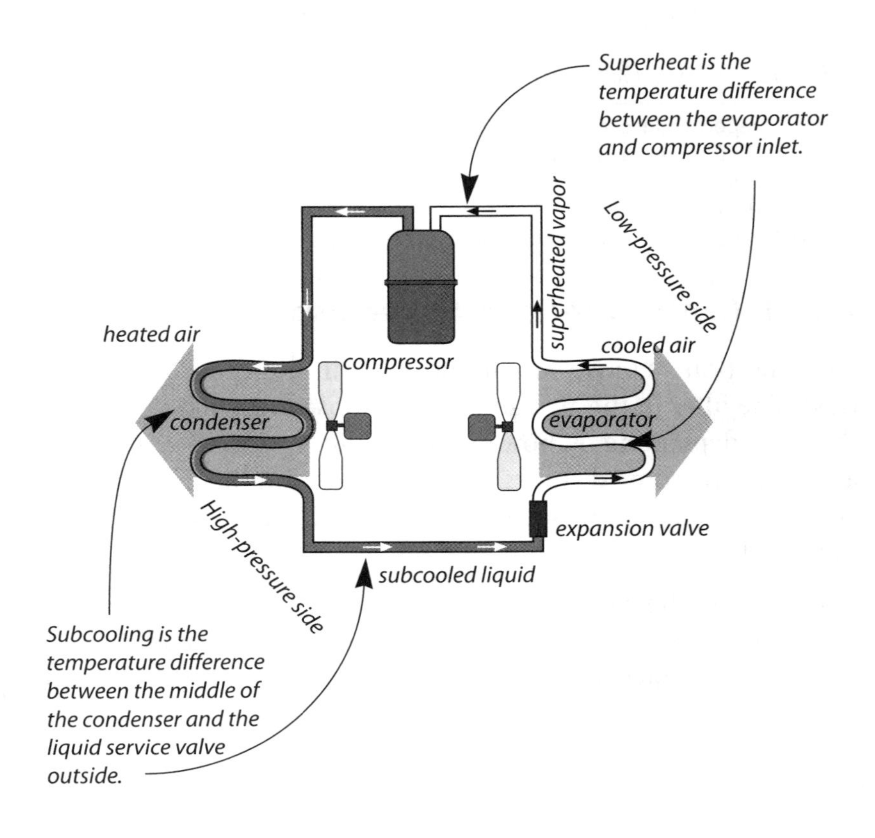

✔ Insist that the blower and evaporator be thoroughly cleaned. Technicians should use an indoor coil cleaner if a cleanser is used.

## 4.20.2 Air-Conditioner Sizing

Correct sizing is accomplished through sizing calculations, typically performed by an auditor or HVAC specialist using a computer sizing program.

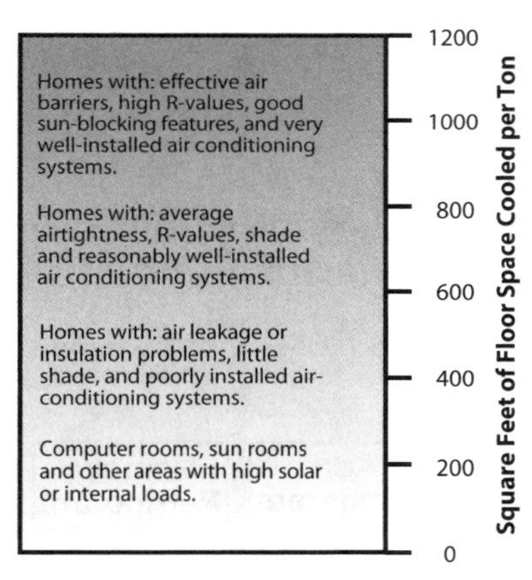


**Air-Conditioner Sizing:** An energy-efficient home shouldn't need more than a ton of air-conditioner capacity per 1000 square feet of floor area.

The number of square feet of floor space that can be cooled by one ton of refrigeration capacity is a measure of the home's energy efficiency. Air-conditioners provide cooling most cost-effectively when they are sized accurately and run for long cycles. The auditor's cooling-cost reduction strategy should focus on making the home more energy efficient and making the air conditioner work more efficiently. Making the home more efficient would involve shading, insulation and air-leakage reduction. Making the air conditioner more efficient would involve either service or repair to remove installation-related flaws.

## 4.20.3 Duct Leakage and System Airflow

Duct leakage and poor airflow afflict most air-conditioning systems unfortunately. The testing and mitigation of these problems was covered earlier.

1. *See "Evaluating Duct Air Leakage" on page 171.*
2. *See "Ducted Air Distribution" on page 150.*

## 4.20.4 Air-Conditioner Charge Checking

HVAC technicians check charge by two common methods depending on what type of expansion valve the air conditioner has. If the expansion valve has a fixed orifice, the technician performs a superheat test and if the valve is a thermostatic expansion valve (TXV), the technician performs a subcooling test.

These two tests indicate whether the amount of refrigerant in the system is correct or whether there is too much or too little refrigerant. The amount of refrigerant is directly related to the efficiency of the air-conditioning system.

Charge-checking is performed after the airflow tests and repairs and after duct testing and sealing. These tests must be done during the cooling season while the system is operating. Specify charge-checking as part of any complete weatherization or home-performance job.

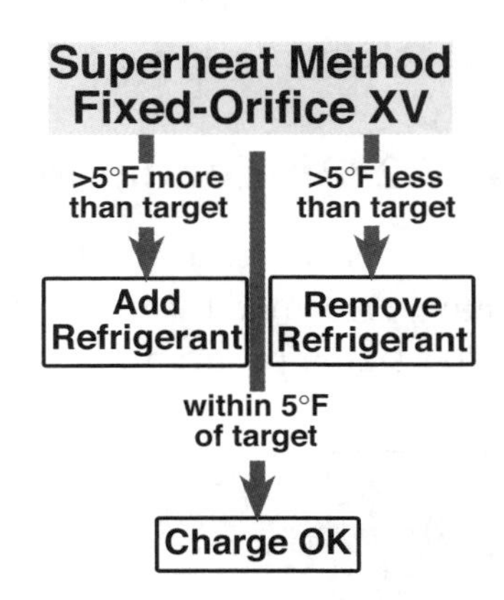


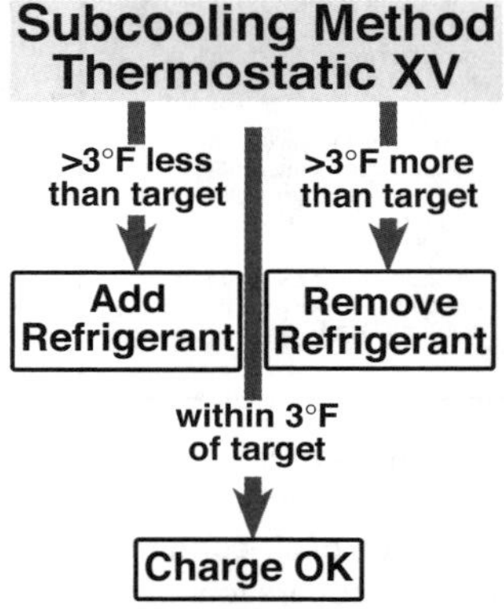


**Charge-Checking:** Two methods help technicians judge whether charge is correct. The remedy for incorrect charge is to either add or remove refrigerant.

# CHAPTER 5: BASELOAD MEASURES

Baseload energy consumption—water heating, refrigeration, lighting, clothes drying, and plug loads—accounts for a large part of the energy use in most homes. In mild climates, baseload consumption may be larger than heating and cooling combined. Water heating, refrigerators, and lighting are discussed in this chapter.

## 5.1 WATER-HEATING ENERGY SAVINGS

The most important tasks in evaluating hot water energy savings are determining the water heater's insulation level, measuring the shower's flow rate, and measuring the hot-water's temperature.

### 5.1.1 Determining the Water Heater's Insulation Level

Common storage water heaters consist of a tank, insulation surrounding the tank, and an outer shell. There is typically either 1 or 2 inches of insulation surrounding the tank. The insulation is either fiberglass, if the water heater was manufactured before 1991, or polyisocyanurate if it was manufactured after 1991.

Follow this procedure to determine the water heater's insulation level.

- ✔ Look for a listing of R-value on a label on the water heater.
- ✔ Find a hole in the outer shell where the flue pipes emerges or where plumbing connects. Look around the hole for either fiberglass or polyisocyanurate insulation.
- ✔ If the hole isn't large enough, on an electric water heater, try the access panel for the heating element after disconnecting power from the unit.

- ✔ You may just be able to see the gap between the tank and outer shell. If you can't see this gap, use a ruler or probe to push through the insulation along side of a pipe connecting to the tank until the probe hits the steel tank to determine thickness. Make sure that the probe is against the tank and not against a nut welded to the tank.
- ✔ If the existing water heater has less than R-10 insulation, specify a water-heater blanket for the unit.

**Identifying Tank Insulation**

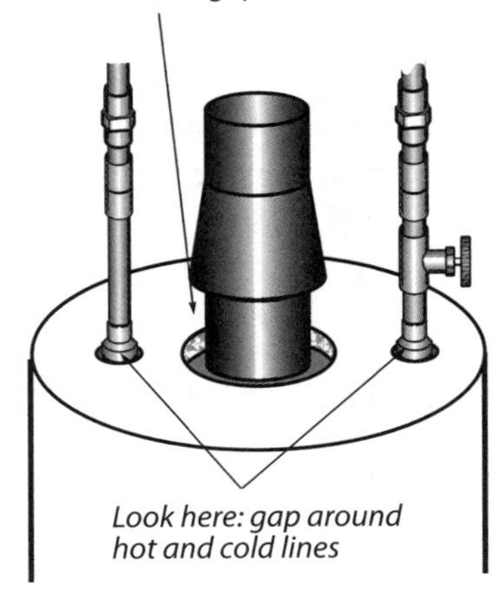


**Table 5-1: Insulation R-Values**

| Insulation/thickness | R |
|---|---|
| Fiberglass 1 inch | 3 |
| Fiberglass 2 inches | 6 |
| Isocyanurate 1 inch | 6.5 |
| Isocyanurate 2 inches | 13 |
| Isocyanurate 3 inches | 19.5 |

## 5.1.2 Water Heater Blankets

Install an insulation blanket on all heaters that are outside the heated space, unless the manufacturer's label prohibits it. Follow these guidelines to avoid fire hazards and to simplify future service.

### Gas Water Heaters

- ✔ Keep insulation at least 2 inches away from the gas valve and the burner access panel. Do not install insulation below the burner access panel.
- ✔ Don't cover the pressure relief valve.

- ✔ Don't insulate the tops of gas- or oil-fired water heaters to avoid obstructing the draft diverter.

### Electric Water Heaters

- ✔ Cut the blanket around the thermostat and heating element access plates, or cover the plates and mark their location on the insulation facing.
- ✔ Don't cover the pressure relief valve.
- ✔ Cover the top of the water heater with insulation if it doesn't obstruct the pressure relief valve.

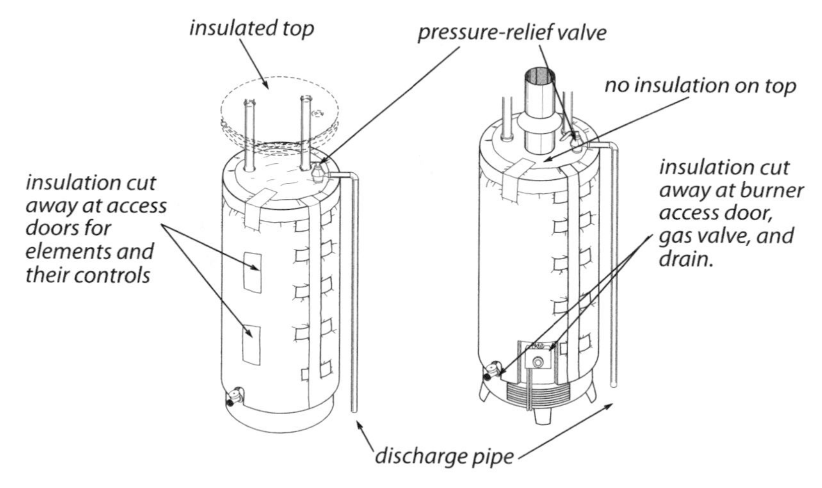


**Water Heater Insulation:** Insulation should be installed carefully so it doesn't interfere with the burner, elements, draft diverter, or pressure relief valve.

## 5.1.3 Measuring and Adjusting Hot Water Temperature

- ✔ Measure the water heater's water temperature at the nearest faucet to the water heater, and reduce the temperature to 120° F with the customer's permission.

- ✔ Make a mark at the current setting and move the control to a lower temperature. Note the difference between electric and gas controls shown here.
- ✔ Set both upper and lower thermostats to the same temperature on electric water heaters. Shut off power to the water heater before opening thermostat access panels.

**Setting Hot-Water Temperature:** Getting the temperature correct can take a few measurements and re-adjustments.

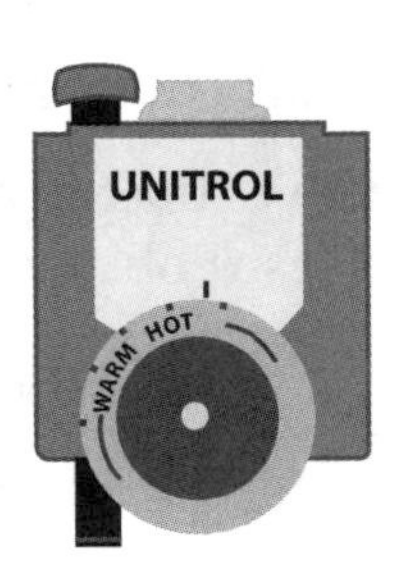


*Gas water heater control*

*Electric water heater control*

## 5.1.4 Water-Heater Pipe Insulation

Perform this measure to slow convection of hot water into the water lines near the tank.

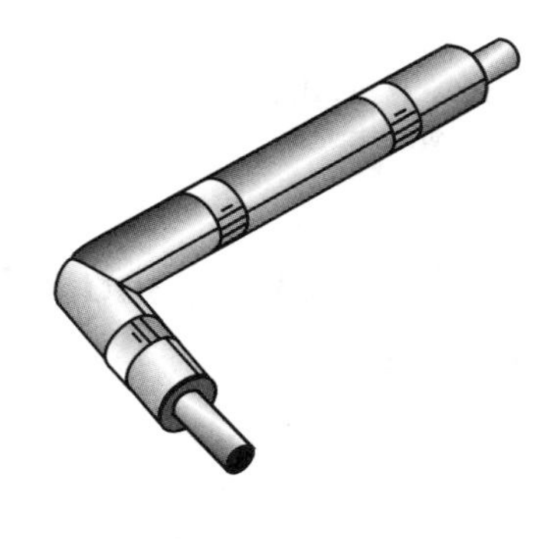

- ✔ Insulate at least the first 6 feet of the cold water pipe from the water heater. Insulate all exposed hot water pipes. With a boiler-and-sidearm heater, insulate all pipes on the circulating loop.

- ✔ Use pipe wrap with a R-value of at least 2. Cover elbows, unions and other fittings to same thickness as pipe.
- ✔ Keep pipe insulation at least 3 inches away from combustion vent pipe.
- ✔ Use the correct diameter of insulation sleeve so it fits tightly.
- ✔ Fasten with zip ties or wire.

## 5.1.5 Water-Saving Shower Heads

Most families use more hot water in the shower than for any other use. A low-flow shower head reduces this consumption.

Replace high-flow shower heads with a water-saving shower head rated for a flow of 1.5 to 2.0 gallons per minute. Avoid installing the cheapest shower heads as they often provide a less satisfying shower and are prone to clogging.

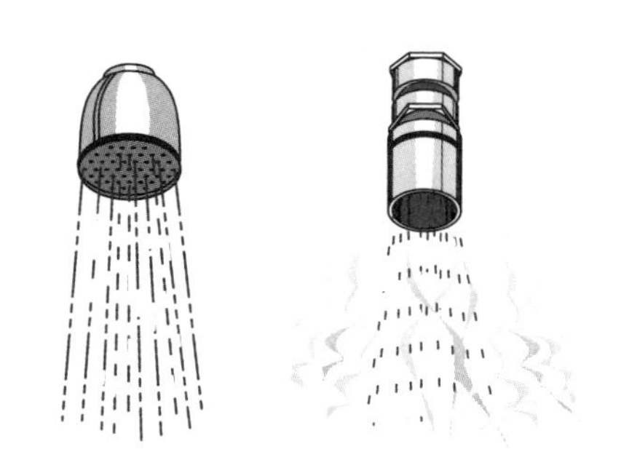

**Water-Saving Shower Heads:** Two styles of water-saving shower heads give consumers a choice between steamy showers and less steamy ones.

Use caution in removing the existing shower head from old, fragile plumbing systems. To be safe, do not attempt to remove the neck that connects the shower head to the fitting inside the wall, but replace just the showerhead itself.

### Measuring Shower Flow Rate

You can determine flow rate by measuring the time it takes to fill a one-gallon plastic milk jug. If the jug fills in less than 20 seconds, your flow rate is more than 3 gallons per minute.

- ✔ Cut a large round hole in the top of the jug.

- ✔ Start the shower and set it to your judgement of a normal showering rate.
- ✔ Start a stopwatch at the same time you move the jug underneath the shower, capturing its entire flow.
- ✔ Note the number of seconds and divide 60 by that number to find gallons per minute.

**Measuring Shower Flow Rate:** If you divide 60 by the number of seconds needed to fill a gallon jug, you will calculate flow in gallons per minute.

$$\frac{1 \text{ gal}}{15 \text{ sec}} \times \frac{60 \text{ sec}}{1 \text{ min}} = 4 \frac{\text{gal}}{\text{min}}$$

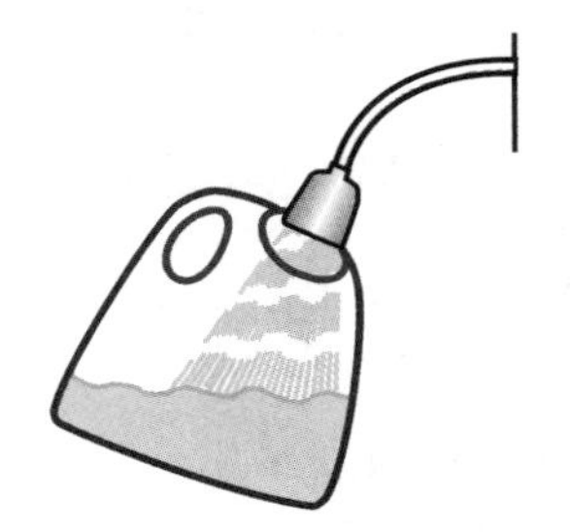

## 5.2 Water-Heater Replacement

Water heating is one of the greatest energy uses in any home. Unfortunately, standard storage water heaters are a primitive and inefficient technology. Tankless heaters offer efficiency benefits, but their initial costs are greater. Solar water heating systems offer a low-emission and sustainable alternative, though their costs are still high.

### 5.2.1 Gas Storage Water Heaters

When evaluating gas storage water heaters, be aware of these problems.

- ✔ Because of their weak draft, gas storage water heaters often spill and backdraft in response to small air-pressures inside homes. This creates a hazard for the occupant and a stringent testing requirement for the energy auditor.
- ✔ Storage water heaters are very inefficient. The most efficient ones, which are insulated with 2 inches of foam, manage to use a little over 60% of the potential energy in

the natural gas. The units with only one inch of insulation are much more popular than the better ones and are often the only ones in stock. This whole technology is obsolete but still widely accepted in North America.

- ✔ The fan-assisted and sealed-combustion gas water heaters may solve the safety problem but don't solve the efficiency problem.
- ✔ High-efficiency gas tankless water heaters are an option but they are still quite expensive. Specify sealed-combustion tankless water heaters to avoid combustion-air and drafting problems.

**Standard Gas Water Heater:** This open combustion appliance is often troubled by spillage and backdrafting.

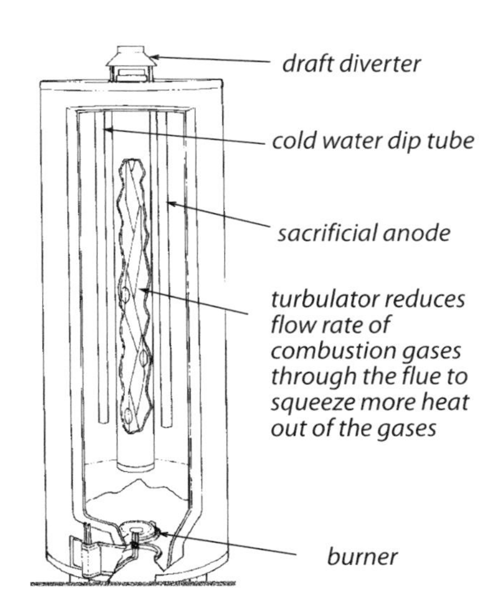

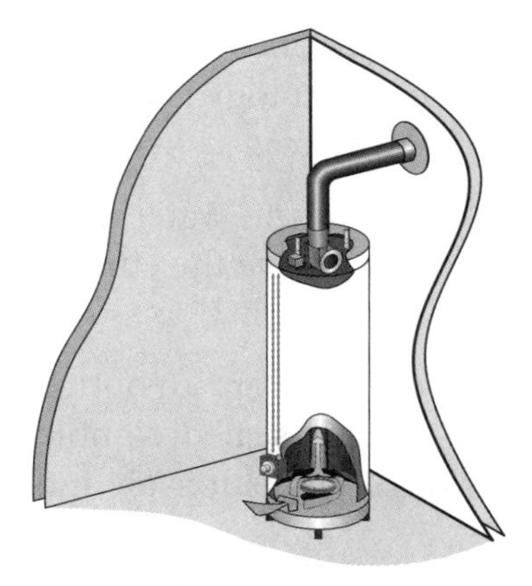

**Fan-Assisted Water Heater:** The fan allows horizontal venting but does nothing to improve efficiency.

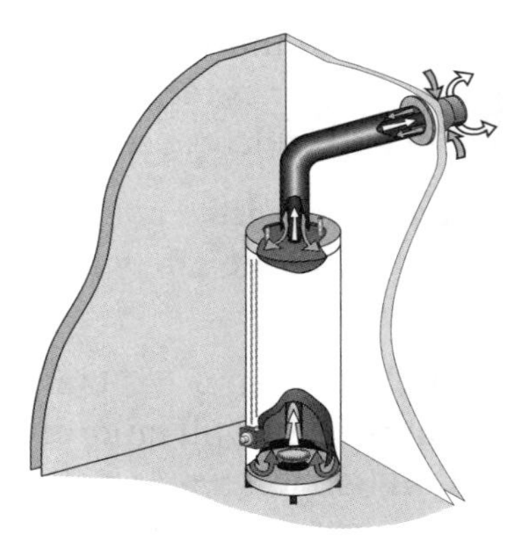

**Sealed-Combustion Water Heater:** Moves combustion air and flue gases through a concentric pipe system without a draft fan.

## 5.2.2 Water-Heater Replacement Decisions

Existing gas water heaters typically use 200 to 400 therms per year. New gas water heaters us as little as 175 therms per year, resulting in a savings of around 75 therms per year. Consider the following recommendations for specifying water heaters.

- ✔ Any replacement gas storage water heater should have an energy factor of at least 0.61 and be insulated with at least 2 inches of foam insulation.
- ✔ In tight homes or homes where the mechanical room is located in living areas, replacement gas water heaters should be either power-vented or sealed-combustion.
- ✔ Insist on sealed-combustion water heaters in tight homes when the water heater is installed in a living space.
- ✔ If people have the money and want a permanent solution, suggest solar water heating.

### 5.2.3 Tankless Gas Water Heaters

Compared to storage water heaters, tankless gas water heaters reduce energy consumption substantially by both increasing water-heating efficiency and eliminating the standby losses of the storage tank. But choosing the right technology is complicated since there are four generations of tankless water heaters. Also a customer should plan for replacement before the existing water heater fails because the modern models, described below, may not be stock items.

1. Open-combustion tankless water heaters with a draft diverter. This unit is more efficient than most storage water heaters, but not any safer in terms of draft.
2. Open-combustion fan-assisted tankless water heaters. Slightly better than choice 1 in both efficiency and safety.
3. Sealed-combustion fan-assisted tankless water heaters (non-condensing). Solves the draft-safety problem with the same efficiency as choice 2.
4. Sealed-combustion, fan-assisted, condensing water heaters. Solves the draft-safety problem and nearly optimizes efficiency.

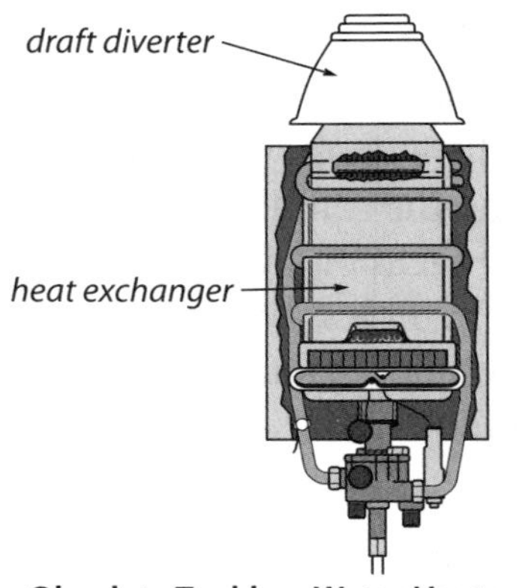


**Obsolete Tankless Water Heater:** These older units may have a standing pilot, which negates some of the savings compared to storage water heaters.

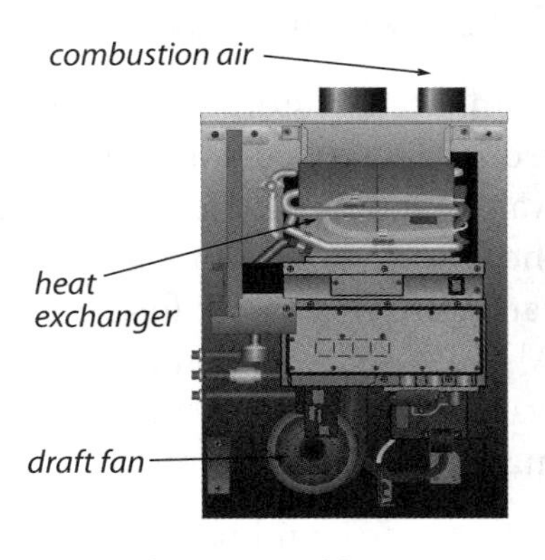


**Sealed-Combustion Tankless Water Heater:** These expensive water heaters have a tiny market share and save around one-third of energy used by the best storage water heaters.

## 5.2.4 Solar Hot-Water System Design

Almost all North American climates require freeze protection for solar collectors. Two common designs provide reliable freeze protection using off-the-shelf components. These are the drain-back system and the closed-loop anti-freeze system. Both systems have five components in common with each other: solar collectors, heat exchangers, storage tank, circulators, and control system.

- The heat exchangers can have integral heat exchangers that surround the tank, heat exchangers immersed in the tank, or external heat exchangers.
- Storage tanks should be insulated to at least R-19.
- Pumps for drainback systems must overcome the static head of the system on startup, but pumps for closed-loop antifreeze systems must only overcome the system's friction head.
- Both systems should use an appropriate mix of propylene glycol and water for the heat-transfer fluid.

### Drainback Systems

Drainback systems are more efficient, reliable, and durable than closed-loop antifreeze systems if installed properly. They have fewer components and the heat-transfer fluid won't stagnate because it drains back to a drainback tank when the high limit control deactivates the circulator.

- ✔ The pump must be sized to overcome the static head between the tanks and the collectors.
- ✔ The collector loop runs through a drainback tank where the heat-transfer fluid returns by gravity when the pump is deactivated.
- ✔ The heat exchanger can be integral to the storage tank, immersed in the storage tank, immersed in the drainback tank, or external to both tanks.
- ✔ All piping to and from the collectors must slope at least 10° and be a minimum of 3/4-inch diameter.

### Closed-Loop Antifreeze Systems

Closed-loop antifreeze systems use a mixture of propylene glycol and water for the heat-transfer fluid.

The system must be pressurized according to the height of the collectors above the lowest point in the system.

- ✔ A check valve must stop water from circulating through the collectors at night and wasting heat.
- ✔ The system must be protected from overheating and damaging the glycol and collectors by the use of a photovoltaic-powered circulator to keep water circulating or some other means.
- ✔ The system must be equipped with an expansion tank and a 75 psi pressure-relief valve.

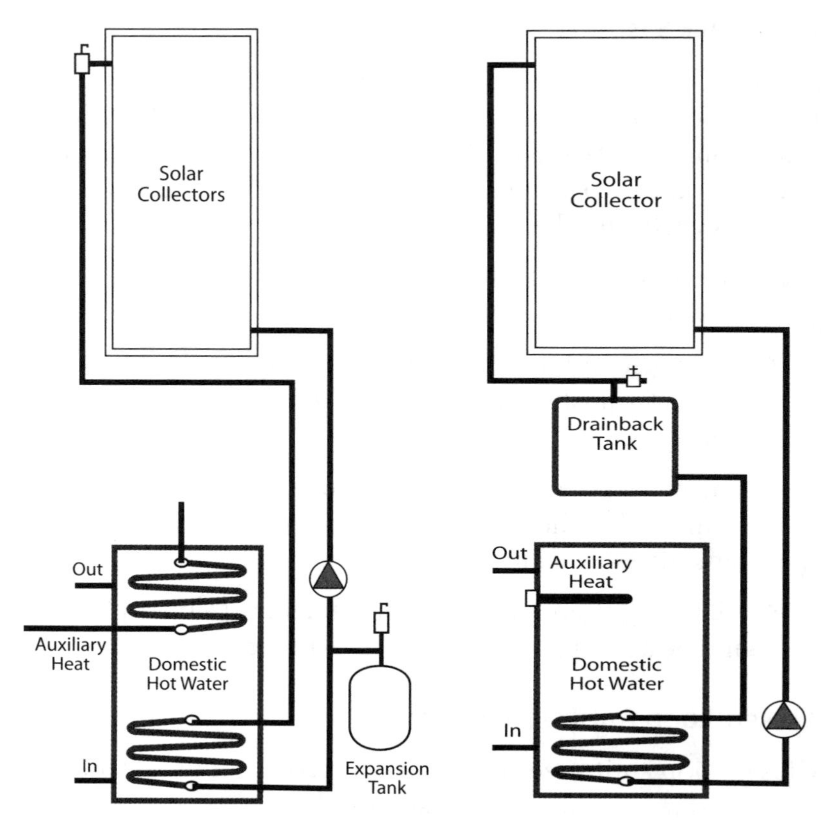


**Closed Loop Antifreeze System:** The most popular freeze protection.

**Drainback System:** Simple freeze protection with a minimum of valves and hardware.

## 5.3 Refrigerator Evaluation

There are two common options for evaluating refrigerator energy consumption for replacement. The first option is to use the resources included in the *Refrigerator Guide* on the WAP-TAC website (www.waptac.org). These resources include a database of refrigerators by model with approximate electricity usage and a refrigerator analysis tool. The second option is to follow the metering procedure presented here.

Refrigerators built after 1993 use less than refrigerators built before that year and another efficiency increase occurred in 1999. To simplify evaluation some energy programs simply replace refrigerators built before 1993 or 1999, depending on the cost of electricity. Refrigerators that are replaced should be taken to a facility that is licensed to reclaim their refrigerant and recycle the refrigerator's parts.

The use of multiple refrigerators in homes is common and has a significant effect on electricity usage. Energy auditors should inform customers about the use of more than one refrigerator and suggest consolidating food storage into a large single refrigerator.

### 5.3.1 Refrigerator Metering Protocol

Older refrigerators use from 1000 to 2000 kWh per year. Newer ENERGY STAR refrigerators use less than 500 kWh per year. This difference presents a good opportunity to significantly reduce electricity consumption.

At least two hours are needed to accurately measure refrigerator energy consumption. A recording watt-hour meter is used to measure consumption.

A number of unusual circumstances could affect the accuracy of the metering, including the following.

- A quantity of warm food recently placed in the refrigerator.
- Abnormally high or low ambient temperature. For example: refrigerators in garages during the summer or winter or refrigerators in vacant homes where heating or cooling systems aren't operating.

**Recording Watthour Meter:** Measures energy consumption over time. The better units can also calculate monthly consumption, or record maximum current draw to help identify the defrost cycle.

If the refrigerator is an automatic defrost model, an inaccurate reading could result if the unit goes into the electric defrost mode during the test period. This test protocol includes provisions to account for this defrost mode.

1. Determine if the refrigerator is equipped with automatic defrost. This is usually stated on the manufacturer's data plate or on the outside of the unit. If it is *not* so equipped (manual defrost), proceed to step 3.
2. If the unit is equipped with automatic defrost, follow this sub-procedure.

    a. Locate the defrost timer. This small electrical box is usually located behind the front kick-plate, though you may need to move some wires and use a flashlight to see it. It may also be located on the rear of the unit or inside the main compartment behind the lighting panel.

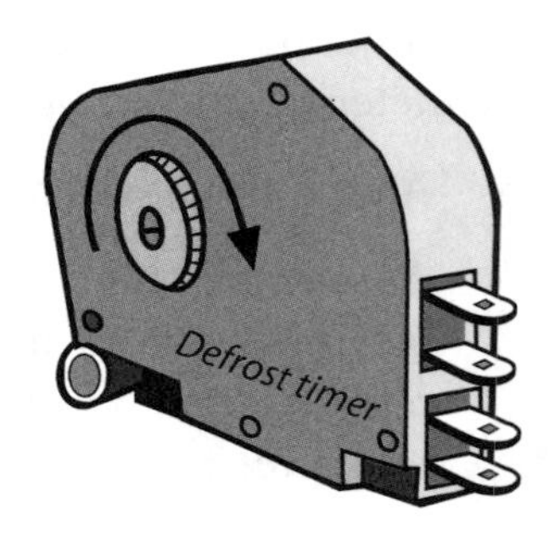


    b. Open the defrost timer and locate the advance pinion. This shaft usually has a screwdriver slot to allow you to manually advance the timer.

c. Turn the timer clockwise (you can break the timer if you turn counter-clockwise) until you hear a loud click. This turns the defrost heaters on. Turn it 10-20 degrees further until it clicks loudly again, turning the heaters off.

d. You can now perform your measurement since the timer won't call for defrost heat again for several hours.

3. Connect the refrigerator to a recording watt-hour meter. Run the test for at least two hours. You don't need to stop at exactly two hours, and a longer measurement is O.K. During the test, avoid opening the refrigerator, or do so briefly.
4. At the end of the test, read the kilowatt/hours of consumption measured by the meter. Divide this number by the number of hours in the test. This gives you the number of kilowatts consumed each hour. Multiply this number times the total number of hours in a year (8760 hours per year). The product of this calculation is the annual kilowatt-hours expected to be consumed by the unit.
5. **Plug the refrigerator back into its outlet.**

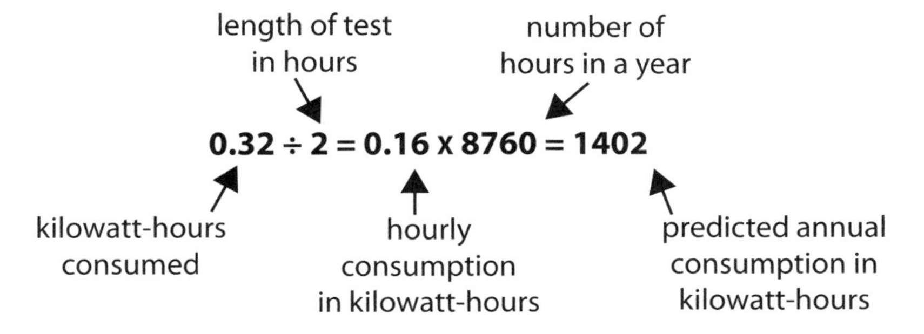


**Refrigerator Consumption Example:** In this example, a 2-hour measurement was performed. During this time, the appliance consumed 0.32 kilowatt-hours of electricity, or 0.16 kilowatt-hours for every hour. The annual total of 1402 kilowatt-hours is well beyond the 450 kilowatt-hours per year consumed by today's most efficient refrigerators.

## 5.4 Lighting Improvements

Most homes have 6 to 12 lamps that burn for more than two hours per day. These should be considered for retrofit by more-efficient compact fluorescent lamps (CFLs). This easy retrofit has as good an economic return as any home performance measure.

- ✔ Ask the customer about their lighting usage, and explain the electrical savings potential for switching to compact fluorescent lamps (CFLs).
- ✔ Demonstrate a CFL bulb to the customer if they are unsure about replacing their incandescent light bulbs.
- ✔ Select the type of CFL and its wattage, according to its use and the light level to which the customer is accustomed.
- ✔ Turn each CFL on after installation to ensure that it operates. Make sure that the customer is satisfied with the lighting level.
- ✔ Replace halogen torchieres with fluorescent torchieres.
- ✔ Inform customers about proper recycling of fluorescent bulbs by stores, municipal waste departments, or other recycling organizations.

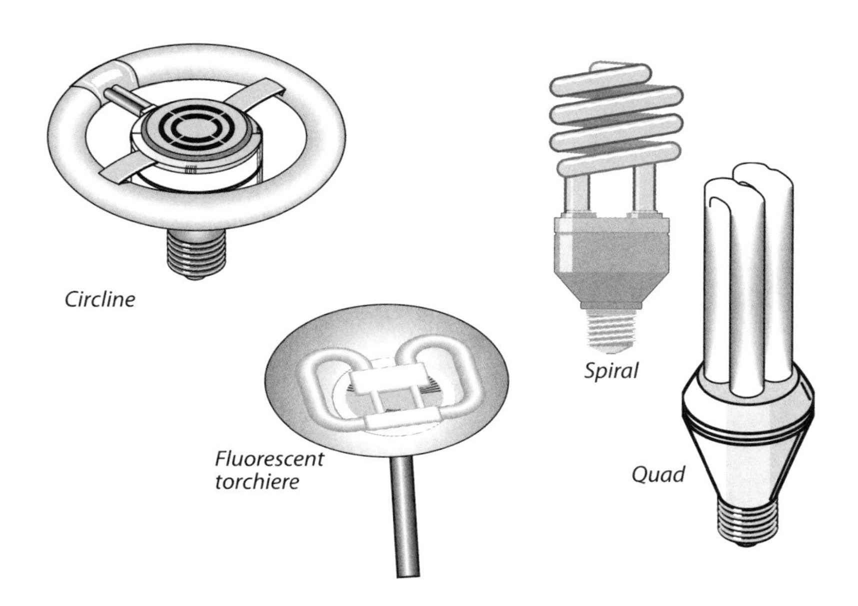


**Compact Fluorescent Lamps:** These advanced lamps use about one-third of the electricity of the incandescent lamps they usually replace, and they last about ten times as long.

# CHAPTER 6: WINDOWS, DOORS, AND EXTERIOR INSULATION

This chapter discusses these topics that relate to energy and repair measures.

- Window shading for low-cost cooling.
- Storm windows.
- Doubling of primary windows.
- Weatherstripping and repair of windows and doors.
- Window replacement.
- Window and door replacement with exterior insulation.

If windows and doors are in poor condition, their repair is often essential for a building's survival even if it's not an energy-saving measure. All tasks relating to window and door repair should be accomplished using lead-safe repair methods.

## 6.1 WINDOW SHADING

Much of the solar energy that strikes a home's windows passes through the glass and enters the living space. This solar heat accounts for up to 40% of summer overheating in many homes. It's better to block solar heat before it enters the home than to cool the home after the sun overheats it.

Window shading increases comfort and reduces the cost of cooling. Window shading is one of the most cost-effective weatherization measures in hot climates. Not all windows cause overheating, so you should direct your suggestions and specifications towards windows where the most solar heat enters.

- Windows that face east or west
- Windows that face south and have no effective roof overhang.

- Large windows.
- Skylights or other sloping glass.

## 6.1.1 Exterior Window Shading Treatments

Sun screens, made of mesh fabric, which is stretched over an aluminum frame, are one of the most effective window-shading options. They absorb or reflect a large portion of the solar energy that strikes them, while allowing a view through the window.

Sun screens are installed on the outside of the window, and work well on fixed, double-hung, or sliding windows. For casement and awning windows, the sun screen should be mounted on the movable window sash rather than on the window frame.

Awnings, exterior venetian blinds, and exterior rolling shades and shutters are also very effective but are more expensive than sun screens.

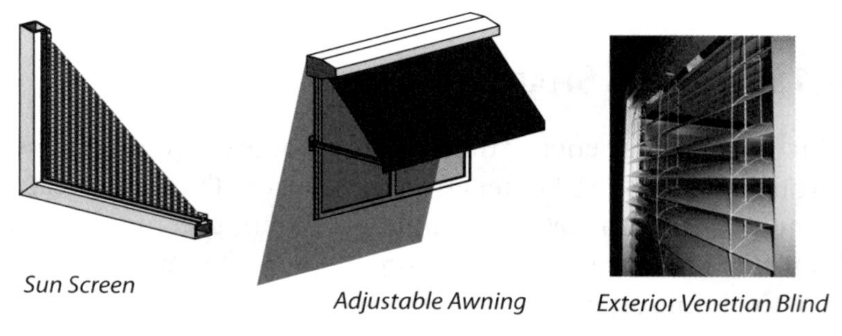


**Exterior Shading:** Installed on the window's exterior, these devices absorb or reflect solar heat before it enters the home. This strategy is superior to interior window treatments, which reflect heat back after it has entered.

## 6.1.2 Interior Window Shading Treatments

Interior shades or curtains are not as effective as exterior shades because they allow solar energy to enter the home. A significant portion of this heat remains inside the home.

Venetian blinds or opaque roller shades with bright white or metallic surfaces facing the exterior can block considerable solar heat.

Avoid translucent or light-admitting shades and blinds because they allow more heat to enter the home. Purchase window shades in the standard sizes that fit most windows since custom-sized shades are considerably more expensive.

Good management of window shades improves their effectiveness. Discuss these principles with the customers.

- ✔ Close window shades in the morning before the home begins to heat up. Also close the windows.
- ✔ Open shades in the evening to help cool the home. Also open the windows.
- ✔ Open south-facing shades all day during winter to allow solar heat to enter the home.

Metalized window films are applied to the inside of existing single- and double-pane windows. Non-metalized window films aren't appropriate for effective window shading. Highly reflective window films have shading coefficients as low as 0.30.

### 6.1.3 Landscaping for Shade

Trees and bushes can provide shade for windows, walls, and roofs. They also cool the air around the home with shade and moisture evaporating from their leaves. Well-planned landscaping can reduce an un-shaded home's air-conditioning costs by up to 50% while adding value to the home and neighborhood.

The best plan for cool landscaping includes tall deciduous trees on the south side of the home to block high mid-day sun. Shorter trees or bushes on the east and west block morning and afternoon sun.

Suggest planting deciduous trees that loose their leaves in the autumn to admit winter sun. Choose types that are quick-growing and easy to care for in your region. Advise customers to check with a local nurseryman to determine the best type of trees, when to plant, and method of planting.

**Trees for Shade:** Landscaping is a good long-term investment for residences. Tall deciduous trees on the south block high summer sun while allowing lower winter sun to reach the home. Shorter trees or bushes provide protection from low-angle sun on the east and west.

## 6.2 Exterior Storm Windows

Storm windows can preserve old worn primary windows and save energy. Storm windows are cheaper than replacing the primary windows. Aluminum storm window are the best choice if they are well designed and installed properly.

- Frames should have sturdy corners so they don't rack out-of-square during transport and installation.
- Sashes must fit tightly in their frames.
- The window should be sized correctly and fit tightly in the opening.

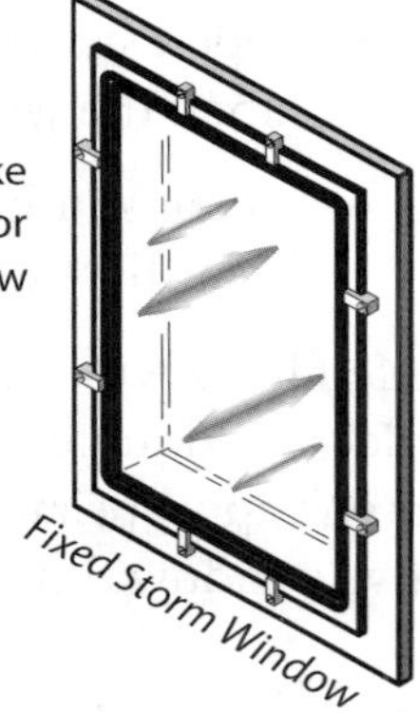


**Clip-on Storm Window:** Storms like this can be clipped or screwed into window sashes or frames.

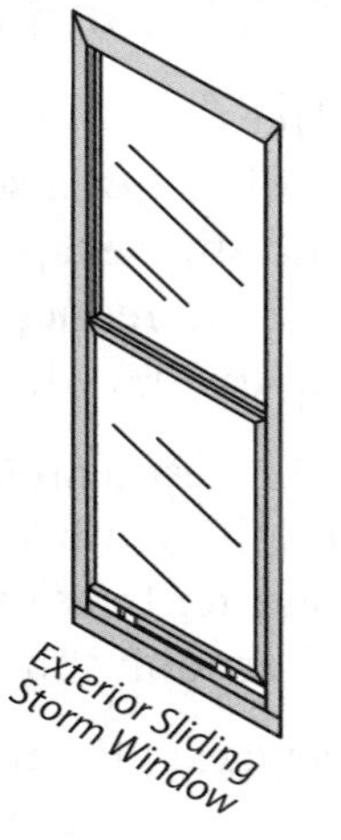


**Exterior Sliding Storm Windows:** These old favorites are still relevant to weatherization and home performance.

## 6.3 Double Windows

Installing new sliding windows on the interior or exterior of existing horizontal or vertical sliding windows is also an option for improving existing windows that are in good condition.

In fact, many aluminum prime single-pane windows are in good condition and might last many more years. Consider specifying another single-pane or double-pane prime window that fits over the existing window.

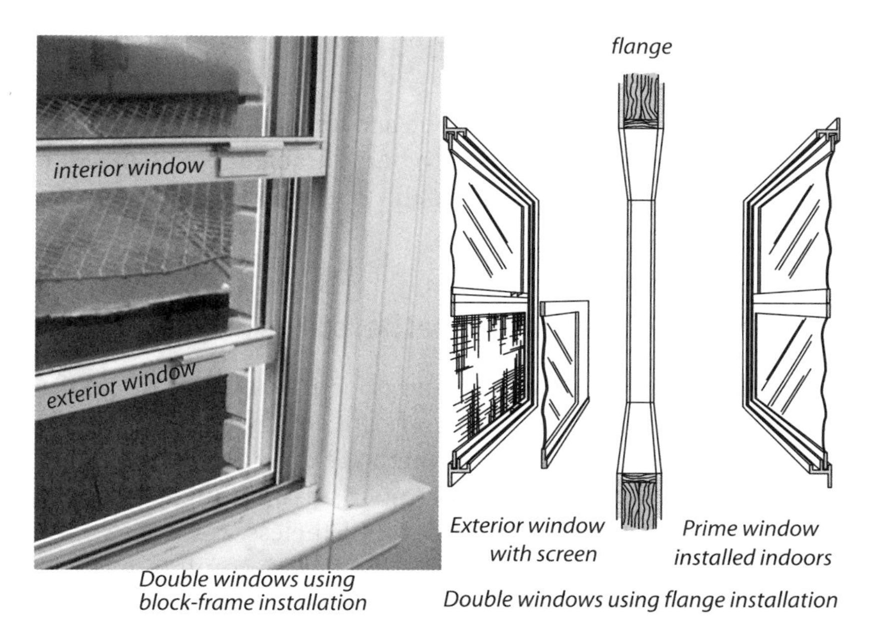


*Double windows using block-frame installation*

*Double windows using flange installation*

**Doubling Windows:** This is an economical alternative to tearing our the existing window and replacing it with another. If the existing window is single-pane, specify a double-pane window indoors for cold and temperate climates.

## 6.4 Window and Door Repair

Customers appreciate good window and door repair and weatherstripping. It takes a skilled technician to do a good job at these tasks. Make sure that the technicians you work with are capable of high-quality work before specifying these tasks.

Windows and doors were once thought to be a major air-leakage problem. However, the widespread use of blower doors has shown that windows and doors don't tend to be the home's largest air leaks.

### 6.4.1 Window Repair and Weatherstrip

With the exception of broken glass or missing window panes, windows are rarely the major source of air leakage in a home although the leaks may affect comfort. However, window weatherstripping can be effective at saving a little energy and reducing comfort complaints.

Re-glazing wood windows must be accompanied by thorough scraping, priming, and painting to be a durable repair. Consider specifying the following basic repairs to extend the life span and airtightness of existing windows.

### 6.4.2 Door Repair and Weatherstrip

Doors have a small surface area and door air leakage is more of a local comfort problem than a significant energy problem most of the time. Heat conduction through the door and thermal bridging through the structural lumber surrounding it are the most significant energy problems. Nevertheless, customers value door repair and weatherstripping for the comfort and security these measures deliver. Counsel technicians that they should repair the door to operate well before weatherstripping it. Consider the following measures as possible specifications for improving doors.

- ✔ Replace missing or inoperable lock sets.
- ✔ Reposition the lock set and strike plate.
- ✔ Reposition stops if necessary.
- ✔ Seal gaps between the stop and jamb with caulk.
- ✔ Install door-jamb weatherstrip.

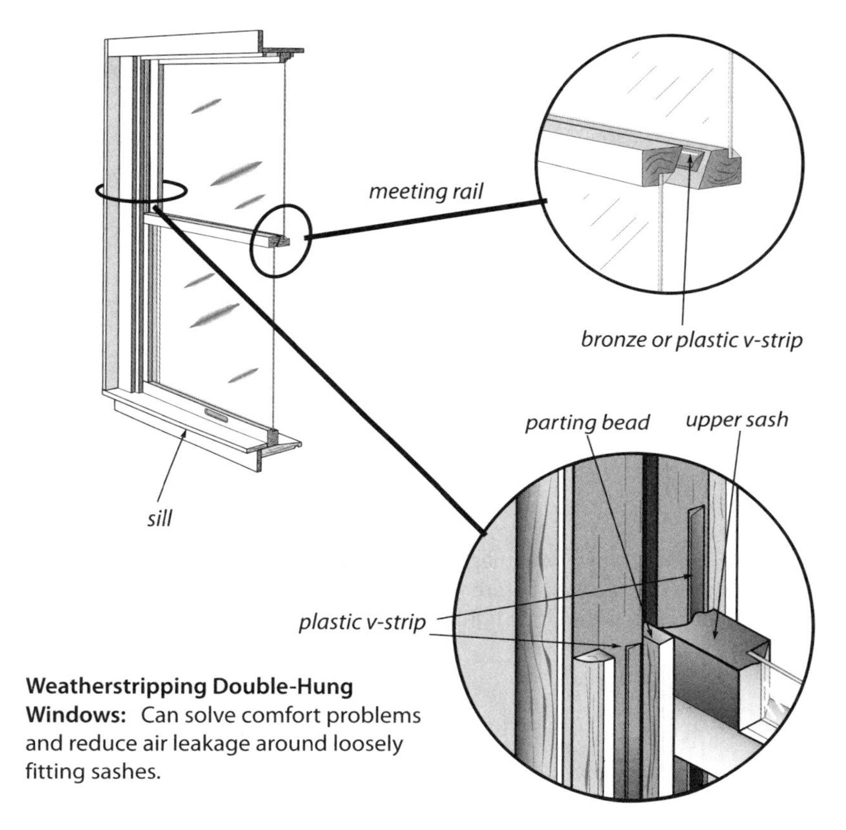


**Weatherstripping Double-Hung Windows:** Can solve comfort problems and reduce air leakage around loosely fitting sashes.

- ✔ Install or reposition threshold.
- ✔ Install a door shoe if needed to repair damage.

The gap at the bottom of the door is usually the door's biggest air leak. Install a sweep or a door bottom to seal the door to its threshold. A sweep is easier to install, but it hangs below the door and may drag on the floor covering if the threshold is not high enough. A door bottom only needs to meet the threshold and does not hang below it, so it is less likely to drag on the floor. Door bottoms usually get less wear and tear and last longer.

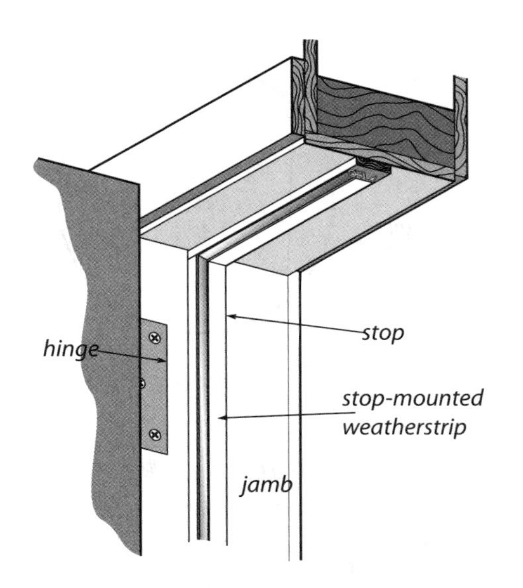


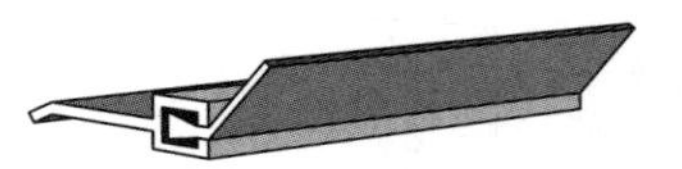

*Vinyl flap weatherstrip is particularly flexible, allowing the door to remained sealed with seasonal movements of the door.*

*Silicone bulb weatherstrip is much more flexible than vinyl bulb and therefore seals better.*

**Weatherstripping Doors:** Weatherstripping doors is mainly a comfort retrofit. The door should be repaired before weatherstripping by tightening hinges and latches. The door stop should fit tightly against the door when it is closed.

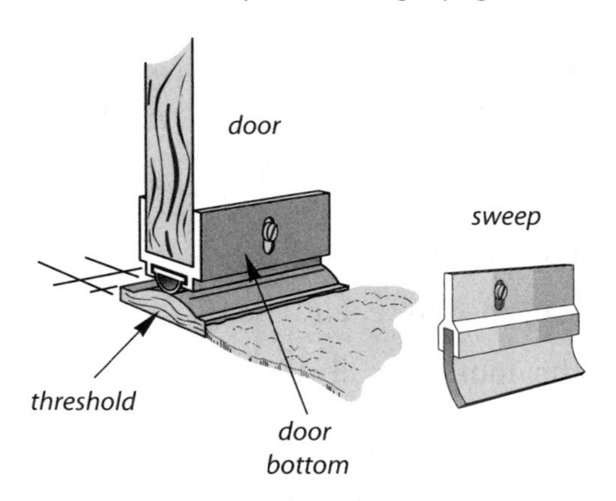


**Threshold and Door Bottom:** Door bottoms are superior to sweeps because they allow more clearance at the floor. Sweeps are easier to install, however.

**Minor Door Repair:** Tightening and adjusting locksets, strike plates, and hinges helps doors work better and seal tighter.

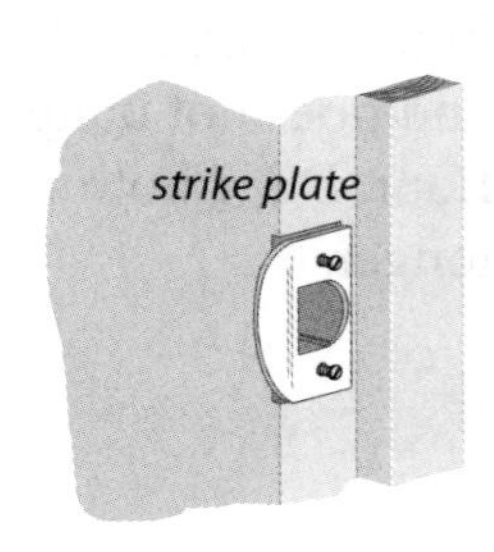

## 6.5 Window Replacement

The big challenge for an energy auditor is to help the homeowner, contractor, and energy program make the right decision about windows, siding, and exterior insulation. In many cases, it may be better to do nothing than to perform a quick and poorly planned window replacement because a homeowner or contractor believes window replacement saves a lot of energy. Many window replacements have resulted in unsatisfactory window performance and customer dissatisfaction.

The purpose of these recommendations is to guide energy auditors in making decisions about replacement windows. Improper window installation can cause air leakage, sound leakage, and water leakage. Water leakage is a serious concern because it deteriorates building components around the window. Existing window openings may have moisture damage and air leakage. These conditions require repair during the window replacement process.

Wood-frame walls have a weather-resistant barrier, which is a waterproof membrane behind the siding that prevents rain water from wetting the sheathing, framing, and insulation. This weather barrier sometimes also serves as the wall's air barrier if it is sealed air tight at its seams. Sealing the weather barrier against water intrusion at joints around windows and doors is the most important requirements for window, door, and siding replacement.

## 6.5.1 Replacement Window Specifications

New windows, installed by weatherization and home-performance contractors, must be energy-efficient.

- Replacement windows should have a U-factor less than or equal to 0.32. Lower is better, especially in cold climates.
- Replacement windows, facing east or west in air-conditioned homes, should have a solar heat-gain coefficient (SHGC) of less than or equal to 0.35. Lower is better, especially in hot climates.

**NFRC label:** The key selection criteria for window shopping is displayed on the NFRC label.

## 6.5.2 Window-Replacement Options

Consider the following three options for replacing windows in homes with membrane-drainage systems, which utilize a weather-resistant barrier (such as Tyvek or asphalt felt) behind the siding.

The existing condition of the window and siding are the most important consideration for selecting one of the three options below. The third option is acceptable, the second is better, and the first is the best.

1. Ideally, windows should be replaced during siding replacement so that the flashing can be integrated perfectly with the wall's weather-resistant barrier.
2. If the existing window is moisture-damaged or has other problems, the existing window should be completely removed to expose the rough opening.

3. A replacement window may be installed within the existing window jambs and sill, when the existing window frame is undamaged by moisture and well integrated into the building exterior.

The option chosen for replacement-window installation also depends on these concerns.

- Annual rainfall
- Window orientation with reference to wind, rain, and sun
- The distance of the window's head jamb from a horizontal protective roof overhang

The more exposed the window is to weather, the more effort is merited to optimize its waterproofing.

### Installing Replacement Windows: Existing Frame

When evaluating window replacement, consider the following specifications.

- Measure the diagonals of the old window frame. If the diagonals are equal the window frame is square. If not, make allowances by ordering a slightly smaller window so that installers can install the window squarely.
- Measure the window width and height and subtract $^3/_4$ inch from each dimension to allow room for shimming, backer rod, and caulking.

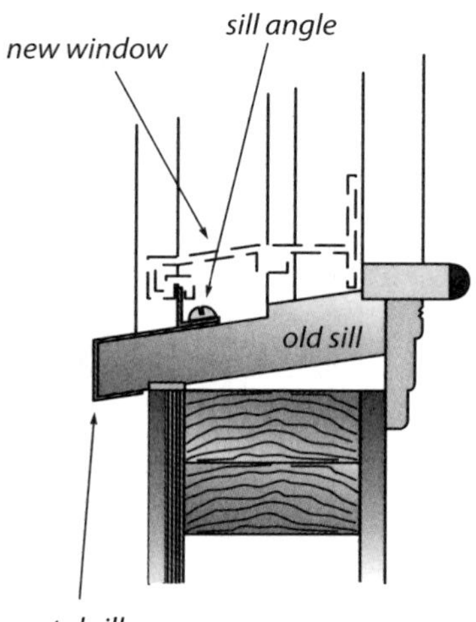


**Replacement Window and Sill Angle:** The sill angle supports the window level and the sill cap covers and protects the aged sill.

- Check with the installers about the method of measuring the window to ensure that they agree with your allowances.
- Present the dimensions to the supplier width first then height.
- Order window-installation accessories, such as sill angle, sill cap, flashing, backer rod, one-part foam, and caulking.

### Installing Windows Within the Rough Opening

When the window jambs, sill, or exterior trim are weathered or moisture-damaged, the existing window should be removed and the new window installed in the rough opening.

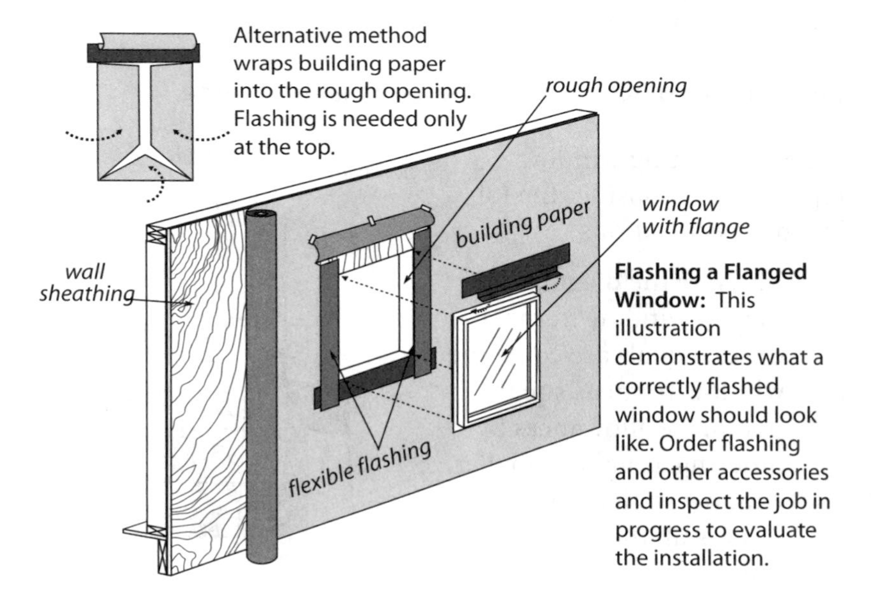


**Flashing a Flanged Window:** This illustration demonstrates what a correctly flashed window should look like. Order flashing and other accessories and inspect the job in progress to evaluate the installation.

1. Take whatever steps are necessary to find the edges of the rough opening. This may involve removing a piece of interior trim.
2. Measure the width and height of the rough opening. Subtract approximately $1^1/_2$ inches from each dimension to size the window.

3. Check with the installers about the method of measuring the window to ensure that they agree with your allowances.
4. Provide the supplier the dimensions: width first then height.
5. Order flashing, caulking, roofing nails and other installation accessories.

## 6.5.3 Window Safety

Windows have special requirements for fire escape and breakage-resistance in areas that are statistically prone to glass breakage. These specifications only apply during window replacement and major renovation.

### Windows Requiring Safety Glass

Safety glass must be used for window or glass replacement when the danger of breakage is high. Safety glass must be either laminated glass or tempered glass bearing a permanent label identifying it as safety glass.

Instead of safety glazing, glazed panels may have a protective bar installed on the accessible sides of the glazing 34 to 38 inches above the floor.Follow the general specifications shown in the illustrations below.

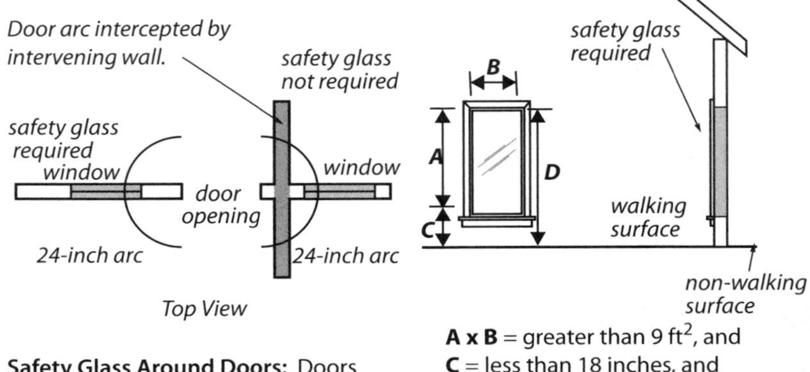


**Safety Glass Around Doors:** Doors create hazards for glass with the movement of people and things through them.

**A x B** = greater than 9 ft$^2$, and
**C** = less than 18 inches, and
**D** = more than 36 inches

**Windows Near Walking Surfaces:** Safety glass is required in areas where the activity level is high.

## Fire Egress Windows

Windows are the designated fire escape for many homes and should offer a minimum opening for a person's escape from a fire. Follow the general specifications shown in the illustration. The measurements shown are common among building codes and may differ by locality.

**Fire Egress Windows:** Windows for fire escape must be large enough and close enough to the floor that occupants may escape and firefighters may enter in case of fire.

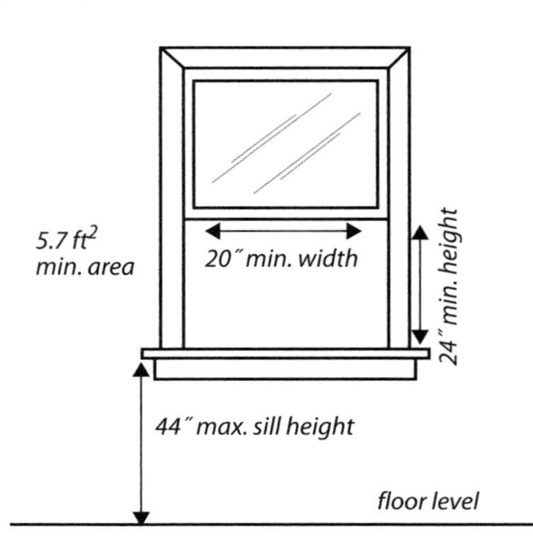

## 6.6 Exterior Insulation, Siding, and Windows

Siding, windows, and doors form the exterior finish and weather barrier of the walls. The biggest energy problems in walls are the windows' low thermal resistance and thermal bridging through solid framing members. Thermal bridging is rapid heat transfer through non-insulating materials. Thermal bridging is a particular problem around windows and doors. The authors believe that it makes economic sense to replace windows and siding at the same time and to add insulation to the exterior wall surface to achieve a high whole-wall R-value.

Infrared scanning, wall-cavity insulation, and associated repairs should also be part of this type of major exterior renovation. Replacing siding at one time and windows at another makes the integration of exterior insulation and weather-barrier complex, expensive, and sometimes impossible. We believe that the disappointing energy savings of typical of window replacement indicate that the two logical consumer choices are to either do a more serious and comprehensive exterior energy retrofit, or else do nothing to windows, doors, and siding until a comprehensive retrofit can be undertaken.

**Exterior Foam Insulation:** A flange window is mounted to 1-by-4 nailers, which fasten one or two sheets of 2-inch foam to the exterior wall.

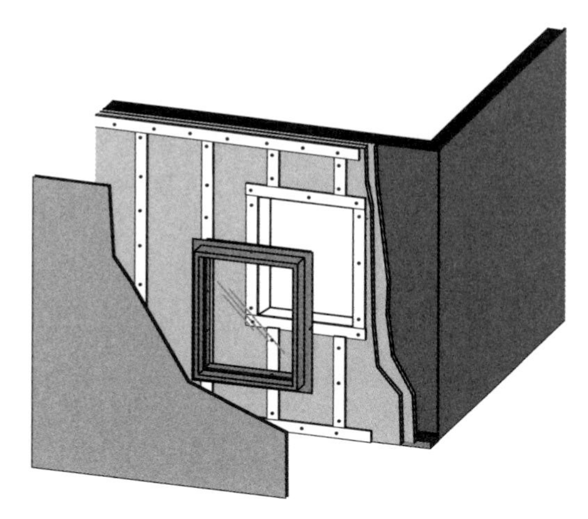

# CHAPTER 7: HEALTH AND SAFETY

This chapter introduces some of the most pressing hazards that customers face in their homes. Major hazards and potentially life-threatening conditions should be corrected before installers begin work in the dwelling unless the installers are making the corrections as part of their work. Among the most important pollutants are air pollutants. Source control is the best strategy for reducing indoor air pollution. In airtight homes, whole house ventilation systems are necessary to assure good indoor air quality.

## 7.1 POLLUTANT SOURCE CONTROL

The control of pollutants such as moisture and volatile organic compounds becomes more important as homes become more airtight.

Controlling pollutants at the source is always the best solution, especially in tighter homes. Mechanical ventilation can help remove and dilute pollutants, but ventilation isn't the first choice for pollutant control.

Auditors should survey the home for pollutants before weatherization or home performance work and to specify the following measures if needed.

- ✔ Repair roofs and plumbing leaks.
- ✔ Install a ground-moisture barrier over any bare soil in crawl spaces or basements.
- ✔ Vent clothes dryers and exhaust fans directly to the outdoors and not to attics or crawl spaces.
- ✔ Confirm that combustion-appliance vent systems operate properly.
- ✔ Replace unvented space heaters with vented appliances.

The home's occupants have control over the introduction and spread of many home pollutants. Educate residents about minimizing pollutants in their homes.

## 7.1.1 Carbon Monoxide (CO)

The EPA's suggested maximum 8-hour exposure is 9 ppm in room air. CO at or above 9 ppm is often linked to malfunctioning combustion appliances within the living space, although cigarette smoking or automobile exhaust are also common CO sources.

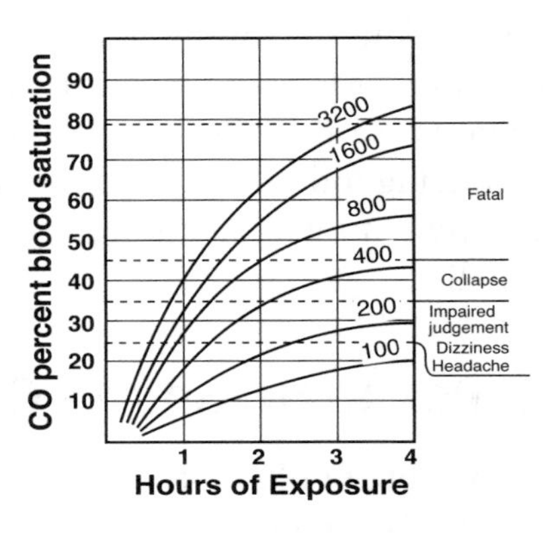


**Effects of CO:** This graph's 6 curves represent different exposure levels in parts per million.

### Causes of Carbon Monoxide

CO is often linked to unvented gas space heaters, kerosene space heaters, backdrafting vented space heaters, gas ranges, leaky wood stoves, and motor vehicles idling in attached garages or near the home. Central furnaces and boilers that backdraft may also lead to high levels of CO.

CO is normally tested near the flame or at the exhaust port of the heat exchanger. CO is usually caused by one of the following.

- ✔ Gas appliances that are overfired for their rated input.
- ✔ Backdrafting of combustion gases smothering the flame.
- ✔ Flame interference by an object (a pan over a gas burner on a range top, for example).
- ✔ Inadequate combustion air.
- ✔ Flame interference by rapidly moving air.
- ✔ Misalignment of the burner.

- ✔ Blockage in the flue or heat exchanger.

Appliance service technicians should strive to identify and correct these problems.

### Testing for Carbon Monoxide

The most common CO-testing instruments are electronic sensors with a digital readout in parts per million (ppm). Follow the manufacturer's recommendations on zeroing the meter – usually by exposing the meter to clean air. CO testing equipment usually needs to be re-calibrated every 6 months or so, using factory-specified procedures.

## 7.1.2 Gas Range and Oven Safety

Test gas ranges and ovens after all other vented appliances have been tested. Range top burners must be tested as measured (in ambient air without adjustment for oxygen content). Follow this procedure.

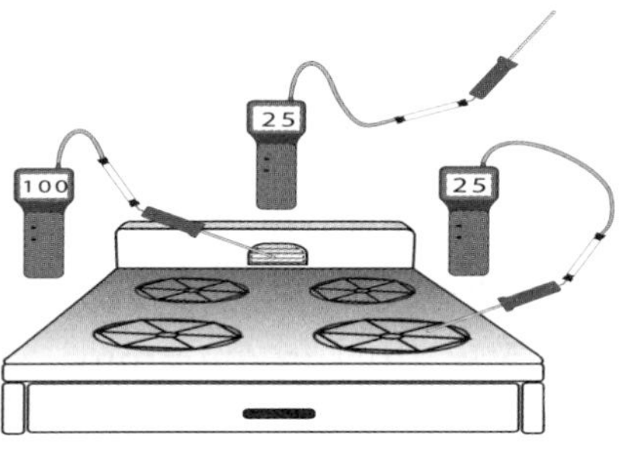

**CO from Range and Oven:** Measure CO at burners from 6" away. Measure CO at oven in undiluted flue gases.

1. Remove all pots and foil from the burner area.
2. Turn each range top burner on high and allow to warm.
3. Test burner combustion gases 6 inches above the flame.
4. Test the oven with the probe inside the oven vent.

Note: To protect both yourself and the customer, continually monitor ambient space around oven during testing. The ambient air should not exceed 9ppm for any 8-hour period.

### CO Mitigation

When the measured CO level is between 100 and 300 parts per million (ppm), measured at the oven vent while the oven is lit or one foot above the burners while they are lit, the following two steps are required.

1. Make adjustments to reduce the CO level, or recommend a service call by a gas combustion specialist to mitigate the CO problem.
2. Install a CO alarm in the kitchen.

In the case of CO greater than 300 ppm, arrange an immediate service call to identify and correct the cause of CO production. Install an exhaust fan with a capacity of 100 cubic feet per minute (cfm) in the kitchen.

Kitchen exhaust fans installed as part of weatherization or home-performance work must vent to outdoors and be equipped with the following.

- Solid metal ducting to the outdoors.
- A weatherproof termination fitting.
- A backdraft damper, installed in the fan housing or termination fitting.
- Two speeds so that the lower speed can be used for continuous ventilation if needed.
- Noise rating of less than 2 sones.

**Advanced 4-Speed Range Fan:** Lower speeds for continuous ventilation and higher ones for spot

## 7.1.3 Smoke and Carbon Monoxide Alarms

All homes should have at least one smoke alarm on each level, including one near the combustion zone and at least one near the bedrooms. Carbon monoxide (CO) alarms are appropriate whenever the CO hazard is considered a likely occurrence.

Customers should be educated about the purpose and features of the alarms and what to do if an alarm sounds. Follow these specifications when installing CO alarms and smoke alarms.

### CO Alarms

Specify CO alarms in all homes with an atmospherically drafting heating system or water heater or a gas range/oven.

Observe these specifications when installing CO alarms.

- ✔ Install according to the manufacturer's instructions.
- ✔ Leave instructions with customer and educate them about battery replacement.

Don't specify CO alarms in these cases.

- ✔ In a room that may get too hot or cold for alarm to function properly.
- ✔ Within 5 feet of a combustion appliance, vent, or chimney.
- ✔ Within 5 feet of a storage area for vapor-producing chemicals.
- ✔ Within 12 inches of exterior doors and windows.
- ✔ Within a furnace closet or room.
- ✔ With an electrical connection to a switched circuit.
- ✔ With a connection to a ground-fault interrupter circuit (GFCI).

### Smoke Alarms

Observe these specifications when installing smoke alarms.

- ✔ Install according to manufacturer's instructions.
- ✔ If mounted on a wall, mount from 4 to 12 inches from the ceiling.

- ✔ If mounted on a ceiling, mount at least 6 inches from the nearest wall.

Don't install smoke alarms in these cases.

- ✔ Within 12 inches of exterior doors and windows.
- ✔ With an electrical connection to a switched circuit, if hard-wired.
- ✔ With a connection to a ground-fault interrupter circuit (GFCI).

### 7.1.4 Moisture Problems

Moisture causes billions of dollars worth of property damage and high energy bills each year in American homes. Water damages building materials by dissolving glues and mortar, corroding metal, and nurturing pests like mildew, mold, termites, and dust mites. These pests, in turn, cause many cases of respiratory distress.

Water reduces the thermal resistance of insulation and other building materials. The most common sources of moisture are leaky roofs and damp foundations. Other critical moisture sources include dryers venting indoors, showers, cooking appliances, and unvented gas appliances like ranges or decorative fireplaces.

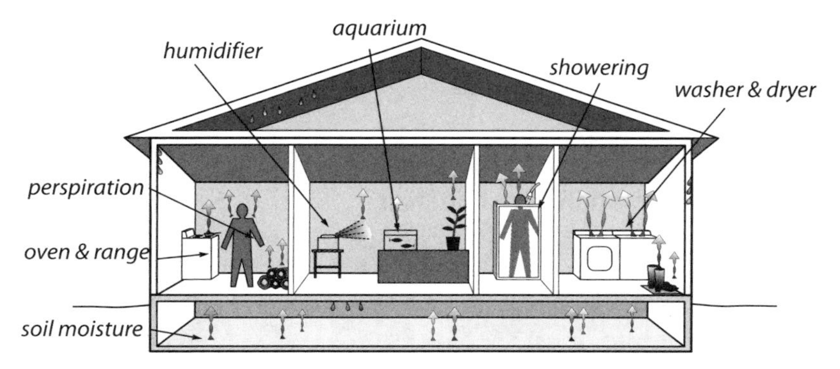


**Moisture Sources:** Household moisture can often be controlled at the source by informed and motivated occupants. Indoor relative humidity should be between 30% and 50%.

Climate is also a major contributor to moisture problems. The more rain, extreme temperatures, and humid weather a region has, the more its homes are vulnerable to moisture problems.

Reducing sources of moisture is the first priority for solving moisture problems. Next most important are air and vapor barriers to prevent water vapor from migrating through building cavities. Relatively airtight homes may need mechanical ventilation to remove accumulating water vapor.

Relative humidity is a measurement of the percent that air is saturated with moisture. Air at 100% relative humidity (rh) is saturated. Air below 30% rh is uncomfortably dry for many people. Air above 50% rh is a threat to cause condensation on cold interior surfaces and in building cavities during winter.

Table 7-1: Moisture Sources and Their Potential Contributions

| Moisture Source | Potential Amount Pints |
|---|---|
| Ground moisture | 0–105 per day |
| Seasonal evaporation from materials | 6–19 per day |
| Dryers venting indoors | 4–6 per load |
| Dishwashing | 1–2 per day |
| Cooking (meals for four) | 2–4 per day |
| Showering | 0.5 per shower |

### Symptoms of Moisture Problems

Condensation on windows, walls, and other surfaces signals high relative humidity and the need to find and reduce moisture sources. During very cold weather or rapid weather changes, condensation may occur. This occasional condensation isn't a major problem. However, if window condensation is a persistent problem, reduce moisture sources, add insulation, or consider other remedies that lead to warmer interior surfaces. The colder the outdoor temperature, the more likely condensation is to occur. Adding insulation helps eliminate cold areas where water vapor condenses.

Moisture problems arise when the moisture content of building materials reaches a threshold that allows pests like termites, dust mites, rot, and fungus to thrive. Asthma, bronchitis and other respiratory ailments can be exacerbated by moisture problems because mold, mildew, and dust mites are potent allergens.

- ✔ Rot and wood decay indicate advanced moisture damage. Unlike surface mold and mildew, wood decay fungi penetrate, soften, and weaken wood.

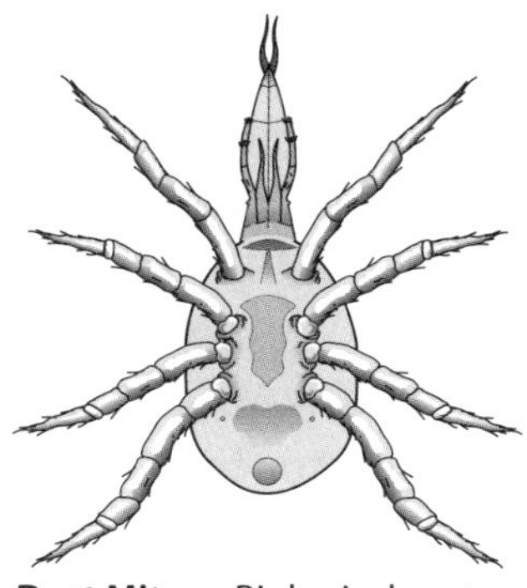

**Dust Mites:** Biological pests create bioaerosols that can cause allergies and asthma.

- ✔ Peeling, blistering or cracking paint may indicate that moisture is moving through a wall, damaging the paint and possibly the building materials underneath.
- ✔ Corrosion, oxidation and rust on metal are unmistakable signs that moisture is at work. Deformed wooden surfaces may appear as damp wood swells and then warps and cracks as it dries.
- ✔ Concrete and masonry efflorescence often indicates excess moisture at the home's foundation. Efflorescence is a white, powdery deposit left by water that moves through masonry and leaves minerals from mortar or the soil behind as it evaporates.

## 7.1.5 Crawl Space Moisture Control

A surprising number of moisture problems in the living space or attic are caused by ground-moisture sources. Moisture that enters the home through foundations and crawl spaces can be a substantial contributor to indoor humidity even when no wet ground is apparent. Moisture, from a wet crawl space or basement, moves easily through the home, driven by stack effect and by wicking through permeable wood and concrete. Other unhealthy gases, such as radon move readily through loose soils like sand and gravel.

Cover the floor in all crawl spaces with ground-moisture barriers that are sealed at the seams and at the foundation walls. For extremely wet crawl spaces more drastic measures are needed. A sump pump can remove bulk water, or powered fans can remove moisture-laden air, but the cost of installation and maintenance are high for both. Passive methods of moisture control are preferable to these active solutions.

If a home has an inaccessible crawl space, avoid air sealing and negative pressure indoors, which could bring moisture into the home and concentrate it then.

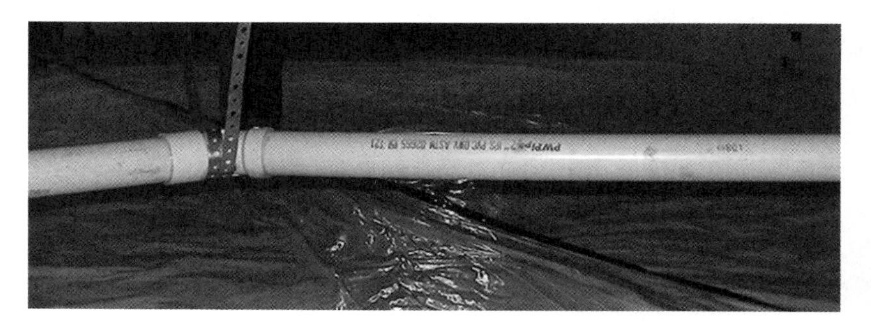

**Well Sealed Crawl Spaces:** The dirt floor in this crawl space is covered with a well-sealed cross-linked polyethylene ground moisture barrier.

## Crawl-Space Ventilation

Install crawl space ventilation when a the floor has been insulation and it is required by local codes. Follow the code guidance for the installation of ventilation. The floor should be thoroughly air-sealed before any ventilation openings are added.

## Ground-Moisture Barriers

Air, moisture, and pollutants can move through soil and into crawl spaces and dirt-floor basements. Even soil that seems dry at the surface can release a lot of moisture into the home.

Specify airtight polyethylene ground covers in crawl spaces to control the movement of moisture and soil gases.

- ✔ The ground should be covered completely with a ground-moisture barrier such as six-mil cross-laminated polyethylene.
- ✔ The barrier should run up the foundation wall several inches. The barrier should be attached by a wood strip and be sealed there with polyurethane caulking.
- ✔ The seams should be sealed with polyurethane caulking or contractor's tape to create an airtight seal.
- ✔ Standard polyethylene plastic is acceptable for a ground-moisture barrier, but cross-laminated high-density polyethylene is better. This tough moisture barrier won't tear when workers or homeowners crawl around on it. If the ground moisture barrier is installed in a little-used basement, install walk boards to prevent residents from slipping.

In basements with concrete slabs, use a commercial deep-penetrating vapor-proofing to stop vapor from dampening carpets and ruining tile. Concrete vapor-proofing prevents the passage of water vapor which raises indoor humidity and causes a variety of moisture problems. Be sure to read the material safety data sheet and follow precautions to the letter.

### 7.1.6 Lead-Safe Weatherization

Lead-safe weatherization (LSW) is a group of safe practices used by weatherization technicians when they suspect or confirm the presence of lead paint. LSW practices focus on rigorous dust-prevention and housekeeping precautions. Lead-safe weatherization is required when workers will disturb painted surfaces by cutting, scraping, drilling, or other dust-creating activities. Workers must be trained in lead-safe work practices.

Lead dust is dangerous because it damages the neurological systems of people who ingest it. Children are more vulnerable than adults because of their common hand-to-mouth behavior.

Lead paint was commonly used in homes built before it was outlawed in 1978. Weatherization or home-performance auditing activities that could disturb lead paint and create lead dust include the following.

- ✔ Drilling holes in the interior or exterior of the home for checking insulation levels.
- ✔ Removing siding for checking insulation levels.

## 7.2 ELECTRICAL SAFETY

Electrical safety is a basic housing need affecting home weatherization and repair. Observe the following specifications for electrical safety in existing homes.

- ✔ Evaluate the overload protection provided by fuses and circuit breakers. #14 copper or #12 aluminum wiring should be protected by a fuse or breaker rated for no more than 15 amps. #12 copper or #10 aluminum should be protected by a fuse or breaker rated at no more than 20 amps.

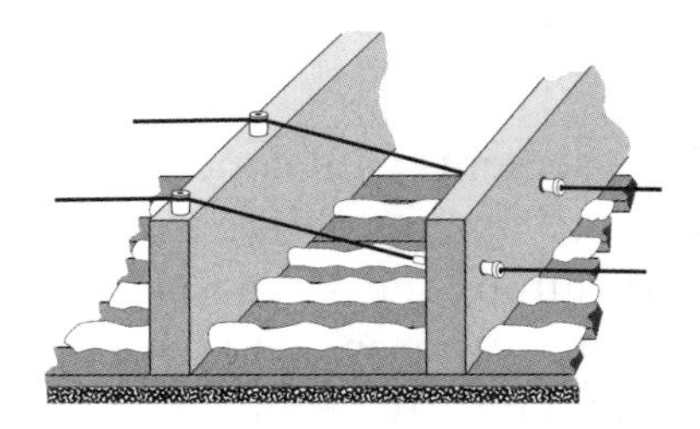

**Knob-and-Tube Wiring:** Prior to insulating around knob-and-tube wiring in attics, barriers must be installed to keep insulation at least 3 inches from the wires. Better yet, replace knob-and-tube wiring before installing attic insulation.

- ✔ Ensure that there is no bare wiring and that wiring splices are enclosed in metal or plastic electrical boxes that are fitted with cover plates.
- ✔ Don't specify insulation for wall cavities containing knob-and-tube wiring.
- ✔ Knob-and-tube wiring in attics may be isolated by building a barricade around it with R-30 unfaced batts. Keep the batts at least 3 inches away from the knob-and-tube wiring. Note: Verify that knob-and-tube wiring is live before

specifying a barricade. If it isn't live, just specify insulation around and over the wiring.

The best solution for knob-and-tube wiring is to replace it. Tenting over it is an less-than-satisfactory solution.

## 7.3 EVALUATING HOME VENTILATION

Most homes in North America rely on air leakage for ventilation, a practice which is considered by many to be inferior to installing a whole-house ventilation system. The American Society of Heating, Refrigeration, and Air Conditioning Engineers (ASHRAE) sets ventilation standards. There are two ASHRAE standards currently being used in North America: ASHRAE 62-1989 and ASHRAE 62.2-2007. Both standards are covered in this section.

These calculated ventilation rate, evaluated under these ASHRAE standards, are represented by a number of terms. We prefer and use the first term in this list.

- Minimum ventilation requirement (MVR)
- Minimum ventilation guideline (MVG)
- Building tightness limit (BTL)
- Building airflow standard (BAS)
- Minimum ventilation level (MVL)

The older standard, ASHRAE 62-1989, allows air leakage to serve as ventilation. Air leakage is measured by a blower door in CFM at 50 pascals ($CFM_{50}$). This standard is associated with the terms: building tightness limit (BTL) and building airflow standard (BAS) but the other terms above may also be used to describe ASHRAE 62-1989.

The newer standard, ASHRAE 62.2-2007, requires fan-powered ventilation in all but very leaky homes and homes in very mild climates. As homes are built with better air-sealing to cope with rising energy costs, they usually require mechanical ventilation systems under ASHRAE 62.2-2007.

The 2006 International Energy Conservation Code (IECC) requires the ASHRAE 62.2 procedure for sizing whole-house ventilation systems and the ASHRAE 62-1989 procedure (0.35 $ACH_n$) for verifying an adequate natural ventilation rate for homes without whole-house ventilation systems.

## 7.3.1 Control of Pollutants

Pollution control should be a priority for all homes. The importance of pollution control and whole-house ventilation depend on the following.

- Are sources of moisture like ground water, humidifiers, water leaks, or unvented space heaters causing indoor dampness, high relative humidity, or moisture damage? *See "Moisture Problems" on page 244.*
- Do occupants complain or show symptoms of building-related illnesses?
- Are there combustion appliances in the living space? *See also "Testing for Carbon Monoxide" on page 241.*
- Do the occupants smoke?

Technicians should survey the home for pollutants before performing air-sealing, and perform the following pollutant control measures if needed.

✔ Repair roof and plumbing leaks.

✔ Install a ground moisture barrier over any bare soil in crawl spaces or basements.

✔ Duct dryers and exhaust fans to the outdoors.

✔ Confirm that combustion appliance vent systems operate properly. Don't air seal homes, which contain unvented space heaters.

- ✔ Move paints, cleaning solvents, and other chemicals out of the conditioned space if possible.

The home's occupants have control over the introduction and spread of many home pollutants. Always educate the residents about minimizing pollutants in the home.

## 7.3.2 ASHRAE 62-1989: Minimum Ventilation Requirement (MVR)

Without fan-powered ventilation, air leakage is the home's only source of fresh air to dilute pollutants. According to ASHRA standard 62-1989 mechanical ventilation systems must provide fresh outdoor air when the home's natural air leakage is below the minimum ventilation requirement (MVR).

The MVR is calculated from the following two formulas, one based on the home's occupancy and the other on the home's volume. Calculate both and use the larger result as the home's MVR in cubic feet per minute under natural conditions ($CFM_n$).

**By Occupancy:** $CFM_N = 15 \text{ CFM} \times \# \text{ OCCUPANTS}^1$

**By Volume:** $CFM_N = 0.35 \times \text{VOLUME}^2 \div 60$

*1 Number of occupants is the greater of: a) actual number of occupants, or b) number of bedrooms plus one.*
*2 Volume of conditioned space.*

A blower door test measures the home's actual ventilation rate. A natural adjustment factor (n) converts the $CFM_{50}$ blower door measurement to $CFM_n$ and vice versa. The n-factor is derived from the home's zone, exposure, and height using the map and table below. Multiply the home's MVR ($CFM_n$) by the n-factor and compare the result to the home's $CFM_{50}$ blower door measurement to determine if mechanical ventilation is required.

$$\text{MVR } (CFM_{50}) = \text{MVR } (CFM_N) \times \text{N-FACTOR}$$

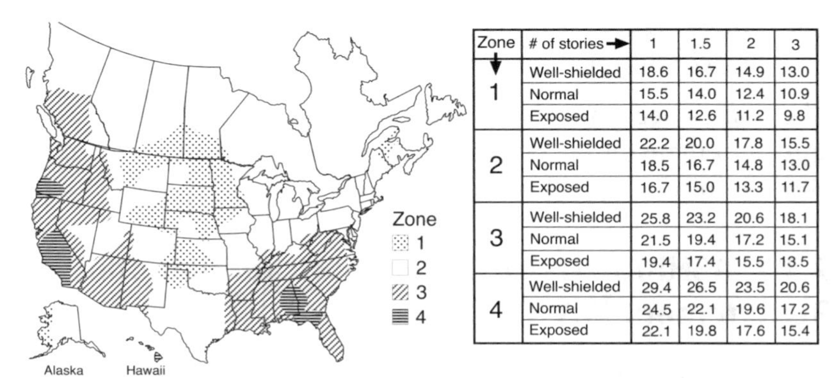


| Zone | # of stories → | 1 | 1.5 | 2 | 3 |
|---|---|---|---|---|---|
| 1 | Well-shielded | 18.6 | 16.7 | 14.9 | 13.0 |
| | Normal | 15.5 | 14.0 | 12.4 | 10.9 |
| | Exposed | 14.0 | 12.6 | 11.2 | 9.8 |
| 2 | Well-shielded | 22.2 | 20.0 | 17.8 | 15.5 |
| | Normal | 18.5 | 16.7 | 14.8 | 13.0 |
| | Exposed | 16.7 | 15.0 | 13.3 | 11.7 |
| 3 | Well-shielded | 25.8 | 23.2 | 20.6 | 18.1 |
| | Normal | 21.5 | 19.4 | 17.2 | 15.1 |
| | Exposed | 19.4 | 17.4 | 15.5 | 13.5 |
| 4 | Well-shielded | 29.4 | 26.5 | 23.5 | 20.6 |
| | Normal | 24.5 | 22.1 | 19.6 | 17.2 |
| | Exposed | 22.1 | 19.8 | 17.6 | 15.4 |

**Finding the N-Value:** Find your zone from the map. Pick the correct column by the number of stories in the building. Then decide how exposed the building is and find the n-value.

**Example home**: 1 story, 3 bedrooms, zone 2, normal exposure, 1200 $ft^2$, 8 foot ceilings.

OCCUPANCY: $CFM_N$ = 15 CFM X 4 = 60

VOLUME: $CFM_N$ = 0.35 X 9600 ÷ 60 = 56

**MVR ($CFM_{50}$) = 60 CFM X 18.5 = 1110 $CFM_{50}$**

## Local Ventilation: ASHRAE 62 –1989

Kitchens and bathrooms must have a source of ventilation either by an operable window or an exhaust fan.

1. Kitchens must have an exhaust fan capable of providing 100 CFM of intermittent ventilation or 25 CFM continuous ventilation. Alternatively, the kitchen may have a operable window.
2. Bathrooms must have an exhaust fan capable of providing 50 CFM of intermittent ventilation or 20 CFM continuous ventilation. Alternatively, the bathroom may have a operable window.

## 7.3.3 ASHRAE 62.2 – 2007 Ventilation Standard

To comply with ASHRAE 62.2 – 2007, you can use either the formula or the table below to determine the minimum requirements (MVR) in CFM of fan-powered airflow. ASHRAE 62.2-2007 doesn't consider air leakage, as is measured by a blower door in 62-1989, to compute the MVR. Under 62.2-2007, ventilation is provided by a whole-house ventilation fan or fans. The MVR is measured in CFM, and this determines the airflow of the required fans. Note that under 62.2-2007, the n-factor is not used to convert to $CFM_{50}$ blower door readings.

Follow these steps to determine the MVR under 62.2-2007.

1. Determine the number of occupants by both of the following methods and choose the larger of the two: a) actual number of occupants, or b) number of bedrooms plus one.
2. Determine the floor area of the conditioned space of the home in square feet.
3. Insert these numbers in the formula below, or use *Table 7-2.*

**MVR (CFM) = (7.5 CFM X # OCCUPANTS) + (0.01 X FLOOR AREA)**

**Table 7-2: Fan Sizes for Homes with Average Air Leakage**

| Floor Area ($ft^2$) | No. of Bedrooms | | | | |
|---|---|---|---|---|---|
| | 0-1 | 2–3 | 4–5 | 6–7 | >7 |
| < 1500 | 30 | 45 | 60 | 75 | 90 |
| 1501–3000 | 45 | 60 | 75 | 90 | 105 |
| 3001–4500 | 60 | 75 | 90 | 105 | 120 |
| 4501–6000 | 75 | 90 | 105 | 120 | 135 |
| 6001–7500 | 90 | 105 | 120 | 135 | 150 |
| > 7500 | 105 | 120 | 135 | 150 | 165 |

Fan flow in CFM. From ASHRAE Standard 62.2-2007

## Exceptions to ASHRAE 62.2 – 2007

Whole-house ventilation systems aren't required for homes in International Energy Conservation Code (IECC) Zones 3B and 3C, or in homes without mechanical cooling in IECC Zones 1 and 2, or in homes that are conditioned for less than 876 hours per year.

Apply infiltration credits to reduce whole-house mechanical ventilation requirements as appropriate. ASHRAE Standard 62.2-2007 allows for a reduction of the whole-house ventilation requirements, determined by the formula or table shown previously. The ventilation credit is determined by information contained in ASHRAE Standard 62.2-2007 and ASHRAE Standard 136, A Method of Determining Air Change Rates in Detached Dwellings. These infiltration-credit calculations are incorporated into several software packages, which are available commercially.

## Local Ventilation According to ASHRAE 62.2 – 2007

Specify local ventilation for kitchens and bathrooms according to ASHRAE Standard 62.2 – 2007.

1. Specify that bathrooms have a minimum of 50 CFM of intermittent ventilation or 10 CFM of continuous ventilation, supplied by either a bathroom exhaust fan or central ventilator.
2. Specify that kitchens have a minimum of 100 CFM of intermittent ventilation or 5 air changes per hour (ACHn), supplied by either a kitchen exhaust fan or central ventilator.
3. You can reduce the required ventilation rate for kitchens and bathrooms by 20 CFM each, if these rooms have opening windows.

## 7.4 Whole-House Ventilation Systems

This section discusses three options for design of whole-house ventilation systems.

- Exhaust ventilation.
- Supply ventilation.
- Balanced ventilation.

### Exhaust Ventilation

Exhaust ventilation systems use an exhaust fan to remove indoor air, which is replaced by infiltrating outdoor air. Better air distribution is achieved by using a remote fan that exhausts air from several rooms through small (3-to-4 inch) diameter ducts.

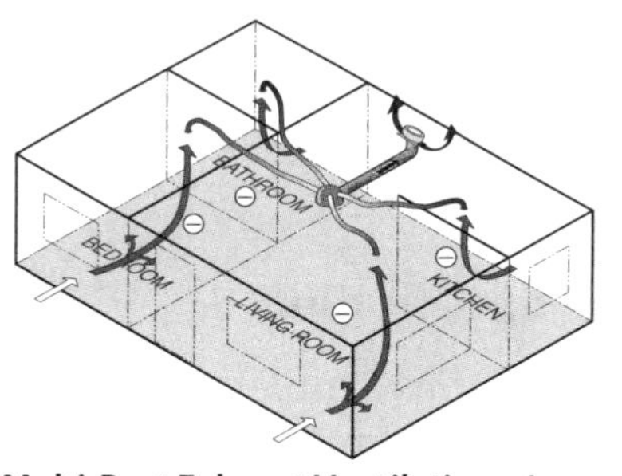


**Multi-Port Exhaust Ventilation:** A multi-port ventilator creates better fresh-air distribution than a single central exhaust fan.

In smaller homes, it is adequate to install a high-quality ceiling exhaust fan, preferably in a central location. For simplicity, the central ventilation fan should run continuously, and local exhaust fans should be employed as usual, to remove moisture and odors as needed. Continuous ventilation allows for a small fan size that will minimize the depressurization compared to intermittent ventilation with a larger fan.

To replace a bathroom exhaust fan with an exhaust ventilation fan, the new fan should run continuously on low speed for whole-house ventilation. This fan should also have a high speed that occupants can use to remove moisture and odors from the bathroom quickly.

Exhaust ventilation systems are inexpensive and easy to install, but it isn't possible to recover heating and cooling energy or to control the source of incoming air. Since most exhaust ventilation systems don't have filters, dust collects in the fan and ducts and must be cleaned out every year or so to preserve the design airflow. Exhaust ventilation systems create negative pressure so they aren't appropriate for homes with fireplaces or other open-combustion appliances.

Exhaust systems create negative pressure within the home, drawing air in through leaks in the shell. This keeps moist indoor air from traveling into building cavities, reducing the likelihood of moisture accumulation in cold climates during the winter months. In hot and humid climates, however, this depressurization can draw outdoor moisture into the home. Therefore pressurized ventilation is recommended for mixed and hot climates.

## Fan Specifications

Continuous ventilation is highly recommended because it simplifies design and control and also minimizes depressurization by allowing selection of the minimum-sized fan. Exhaust fans, installed as part of weatherization or home-performance work must vent to outdoors and include the following.

**Specifying Exhaust Fans:** Specify quiet energy-efficient fans.

1. The ENERGY STAR® seal.
2. A weatherproof termination fitting.
3. A backdraft damper, installed in the fan housing or termination fitting.
4. Noise rating and ventilation efficacy as specified.

Table 7-3: **Fan Capacity, Maximum Noise Rating, & Efficacy**

| Fan Capacity | Noise Rating (sones) | Efficacy cfm/Watt |
|---|---|---|
| <50 CFM | ≤1 sone | ≥2.8 |
| 50–100 CFM | ≤1.5 sones | ≥2.8 |
| >100 CFM | ≤2.0 sones | ≥2.8 |

## Supply Ventilation

Supply ventilation uses your furnace or heat pump as a ventilator. A 5-to-10 inch diameter duct is connected from outdoors to the furnace's main return duct. This outdoor-air supply duct often has a motorized damper that opens when the air-handler blower operates. This outdoor air is then heated or cooled by the furnace before its delivery into the living space.

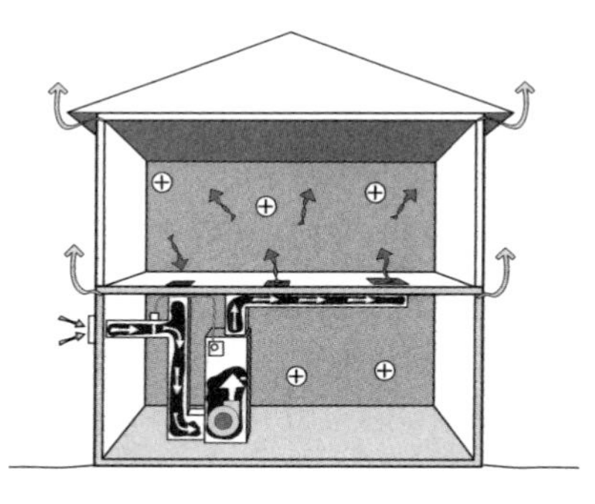

**Supply Ventilation:** A furnace or heat pump is used for ventilation with a control that ensures sufficient ventilation.

At least one manufacturer makes a control for running the furnace blower and damper for ventilation. The control activates both the damper and blower as necessary to provide sufficient ventilation.

Supply ventilation is never used with continuous operation as with exhaust ventilation because the blower is too large and would over-ventilate the home. Supply ventilation isn't appropriate for very cold climates because it pushes indoor air through exterior walls, where moisture can condense on cold surfaces.

## Balanced Ventilation

Balanced ventilation systems exhaust stale air and provide fresh air through a ducted distribution system. Of all the ventilation schemes, they do the best job of controlling pollutants in the home.

Balanced systems move equal amounts of air into and out of the home. Most balanced systems incorporate heat recovery ventilators that reclaim some of the heat and/or moisture from the exhaust air stream. Simple mixing boxes are occasionally used to temper incoming air by mixing it with exhaust air, but their cost approaches that of heat recovery ventilators.

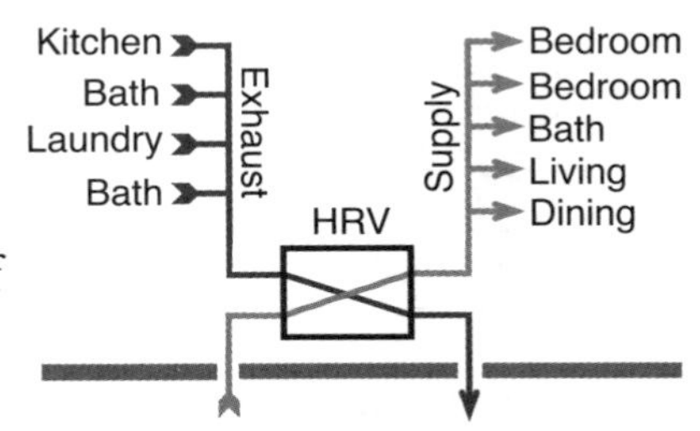


**Centralized Balanced Ventilation:** Air is exhausted from areas most likely to contain pollution and fresh air is supplied to living areas.

Balanced systems, when operating properly, reduce many of the safety problems and moisture-induced building damage that is possible with unbalanced ventilation. They are not trouble-free, however, and there are many homes with "balanced" ventilation systems that experience pressure imbalances and poor air quality due to poor design, installation, or maintenance.

These complicated systems can improve the safety and comfort of home, but a high standard of care is needed to assure that they operate properly. Testing and commissioning is vital during both the initial installation and periodic service calls.

### Heat- and Energy-Recovery Ventilators

The difference between heat recovery ventilators (HRVs) and energy recovery ventilators (ERVs) is that HRVs transfer heat only, while ERVs transfer both sensible and latent heat (moisture) between airstreams.

Heat recovery ventilators are often installed in conjunction with balanced whole-house ventilation systems. The HRV core is usually a *flat-plate* aluminum or polyethylene air-to-air heat exchanger in which the supply and exhaust airstreams pass one another with minimal mixing.

Heat travels through the core, by conduction, from the warmer to the cooler airstream. In heating climates this means that heat contained in the exhaust air warms the incoming supply air. In cooling climates, the heat of the incoming supply air is passed to the outgoing exhaust. Energy recovery reduces the costs of conditioning ventilation air, and the greater the difference in temperature (or moisture) between the airstreams, the more energy is recovered.

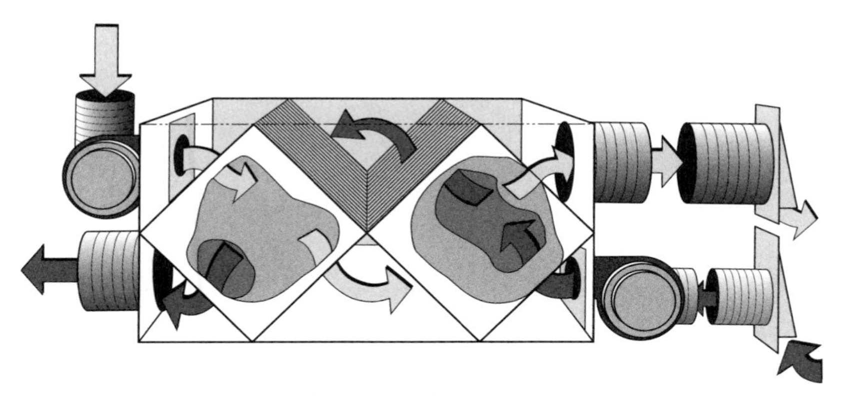

**Heat-Recovery Ventilator:** Heat from the exhaust air heats a plastic or aluminum heat exchanger, which in turn heats the fresh intake air. Two matched fans provide balanced ventilation.

# CHAPTER 8: EVALUATING MOBILE HOMES

Mobile homes typically use more energy per square foot than site-built homes, but their consistent construction makes them more straightforward to weatherize. Insulation upgrades save the most energy in mobile homes, though sealing shell and duct air leaks are also excellent energy-saving opportunities. Mobile home heating-system replacement are often cost-effective when a customer's energy usage is high.

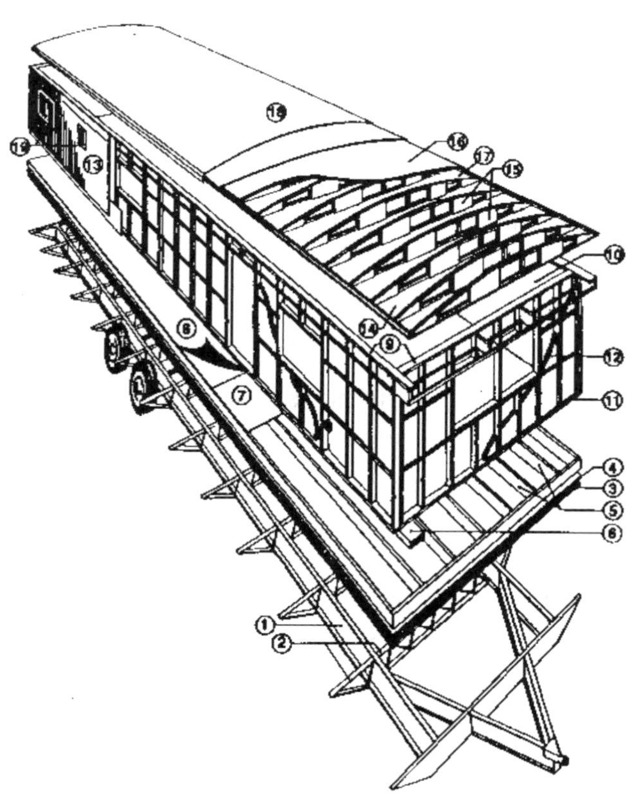

**Typical Components of a Mobile Home:** 1–Steel chassis. 2–Steel outriggers and cross members. 3–Underbelly. 4–Fiberglass insulation. 5–Floor joists. 6–Heating/air conditioning duct. 7–Decking. 8–Floor covering. 9–Top plate. 10–Interior paneling. 11–Bottom plate. 12–Fiberglass insulation. 13–Metal siding. 14–Ceiling board. 15–Bowstring trusses. 16–Fiberglass insulation. 17–Vapor barrier. 18–Galvanized steel one-piece roof. 19–Metal windows.

## 8.1 MOBILE HOME GENERAL AUDITING TASKS

Explain to the customer that you need access to all areas of the home including bedrooms, bathrooms, and closets.

Ask customers if they notice problems with the furnace, water heater, or any problems in the building shell.

Advise the customer that inspection holes may need to be drilled in inconspicuous locations in their home for auditing and inspection purposes.

Explain the general procedure of the audit and the weatherization process including the blower door test, health and safety tests, and inspection of insulation levels.

### 8.1.1 Health and Safety

Consider the following important health and safety issues, which are connected to mobile home weatherization.

- ✔ Check the furnace for cracks in the heat exchanger, gas leaks, carbon monoxide, flex connector, and venting.
- ✔ Check the water heater for carbon monoxide, spillage, venting, gas leaks, and adequate combustion air.
- ✔ Open-combustion furnaces and water heaters located in the living space should be replaced because open-combustion appliances are illegal and unsafe for mobile homes. New furnaces and water heaters must be sealed-combustion units, labeled and approved for mobile or manufactured homes.
- ✔ Check gas range and dryer gas line flex connector.
- ✔ Check dryer (gas or electric) for proper venting to outdoors.
- ✔ Look for rot in the rim joist and bottom of the wall.
- ✔ Look for signs that the home may not be level, such as window and door frames not being square.

- ✔ Check for mold and mildew especially at the bath and kitchen areas.
- ✔ Check for moisture problems that could degrade weatherization measures, such as plumbing leaks and roof leaks.

*See "Health and Safety" on page 239.*

### 8.1.2 Repair Work

Repairs are measures necessary for the effective performance or preservation of weatherization installations. Specify cost-effective repairs to the ceiling, sidewall and belly as necessary to prepare for retrofit insulation. Repairs are necessary to seal large air leaks. Repairs may also be necessary to solve health and safety problems. You may specify the following necessary repairs.

- ✔ Roof leaks and repairs.
- ✔ Moisture and drainage repairs.
- ✔ Ceiling panel repair and or replacement.
- ✔ Belly repairs.
- ✔ Plumbing supply leaks. Focus on hot water leaks that also waste fuel.
- ✔ Repair sewage leaks that present a health hazard.
- ✔ Ductwork repairs.
- ✔ Other structural repairs such as repairing rotted floors and walls.
- ✔ Repairing or replacing windows.
- ✔ Home re-leveling

## 8.2 Evaluating Mobile Home Insulation

Mobile homes require different auditing and installation procedures for insulation compared to site-built homes. Mobile-home roof insulation, belly insulation, and wall insulation are discussed here.

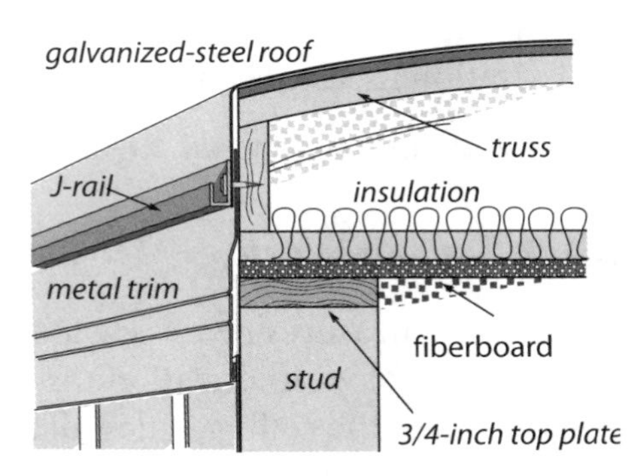


**Bowstring Roof Details:** Hundreds of thousands of older mobile homes were constructed with these general construction details.

### Evaluating Roof Insulation

Mobile home roof cavities are seldom insulated adequately. Fiberglass batts or blankets are usually present in the narrow roof cavity, but there is typically room for additional insulation. The space available varies from an inch or two at the edge to up to 10 inches in the center for homes with bowstring trusses. Lightweight sloped-roof trusses provide up to 3 inches at the edge and up to 2 feet at the center. Filling single-wide mobile home roof cavities doesn't interfere with roof-cavity ventilation because most single-wide mobile home roofs aren't ventilated.

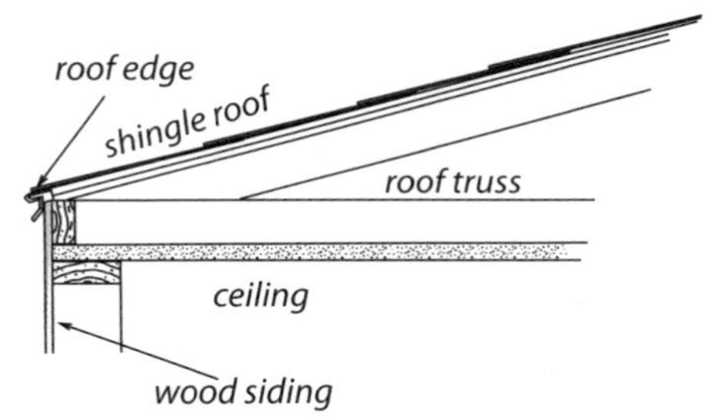


**Wall/Roof Details on Newer Homes:** Newer manufactured homes have wood siding and shingle roofs.

**Bowstring Roof Cavity:** Even with a 1- or 2-inch batt at the ceiling and roof, there is room for plenty more insulation.

Check the following areas to ensure that attic insulation is possible and practical.

- ✔ Measure the depth of the ceiling cavity at the center and the edge of the mobile home.
- ✔ Evaluate what repairs are necessary to ceiling and roof as part of the insulation job. Repairs to reinforce the ceiling are particularly important.
- ✔ Inspect the ceiling and roof condition to determine if installing insulation possible and cost-effective.

### 8.2.1 Evaluating Belly Insulation

Mobile homes normally have a barrier of fiberboard or tough fabric that protects the floor or belly from rodents and road dirt during transport. Damage to this barrier and resulting air leakage are common problems. Insulation is found between the rodent barrier and the bottom of the floor joists, meaning that the insulation is pinned to the floor joist by the rodent barrier. The floor cavity itself is usually empty of insulation.

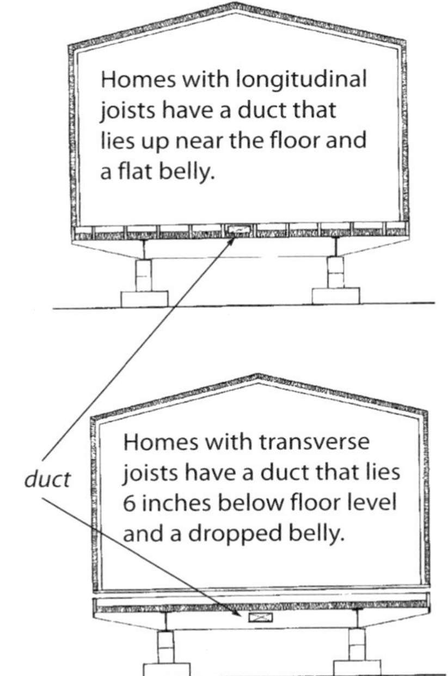


- ✔ Evaluate the belly condition, plumbing leaks, exposed ductwork, and necessary repairs.
- ✔ Water and sewer leaks must be repaired before insulating the floor cavity.

- ✔ Duct sealing must be completed before installing floor insulation.
- ✔ Specify installation of a ground moisture barrier. *See "Ground-Moisture Barriers" on page 248.*
- ✔ Measure the depth of the wing and center belly cavities in homes with dropped bellies.
- ✔ Estimate insulation needed. *See "Evaluating Mobile Home Insulation" on page 266.*

## 8.2.2 Evaluating Sidewall Insulation

The sidewalls of many mobile homes are not completely filled with insulation. This reduces the nominal R-value of the existing wall insulation because of convection currents and air leakage. Consider the following steps for determining the need and feasibility for additional wall insulation.

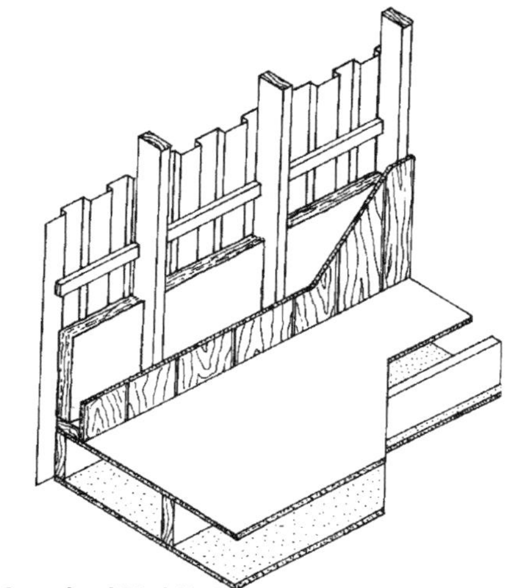

**Standard Mobile Home Construction:** 2-by-4 walls and 2-by-6 floor joists are the most common construction details.

Make sure customer is aware of any potential damage to walls before specifying more wall insulation.

Measure the wall cavity depth and also the batt size within the wall.

Inspect the electrical system to determine in the wiring and circuit break or fuse box are adequate. Check the area around wall switches and outlets to determine if there is evidence of past electrical problems.

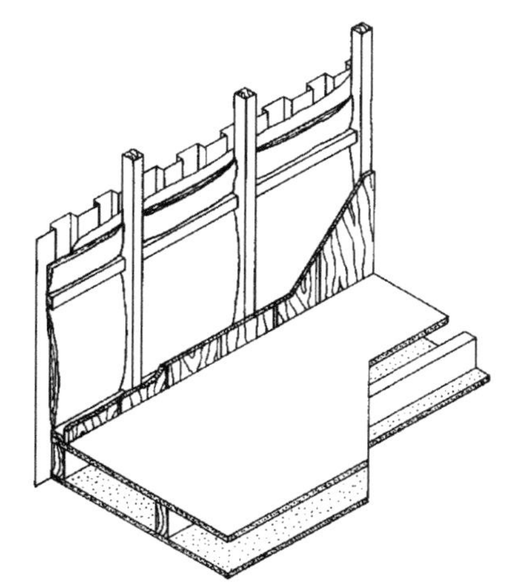

**Older Mobile Home Construction:** 2-by-2 walls and 2-by-4 floor joists are common in homes built before 1976.

- ✔ Check with the technicians you work with to find out whether they are experienced with blowing fiberglass insulation into partially insulated walls.

**Checking Walls:** Measure the cavity and the existing insulation level. Make sure wall outlets work before and after installation of retrofit insulation.

## 8.3 Specifying Furnace Replacement

When furnace replacements are required, use a Energy Star, sealed-combustion, downflow, condensing furnace, approved for use in mobile homes.

Conduct a combustion test and compare test results to the specifications in *"Combustion Standards for Gas Furnaces" on page 110*. Take action to correct non-conforming specifications.

## 8.4 Evaluating Duct Air Leakage

Mobile home ducts often leak significantly and present an excellent opportunity for savings through effective duct sealing. Duct-sealing work must be done prior to insulation or air sealing to the belly or floor.

Visually inspect ducts and registers with a mirror and flashlight.

Supply ducts should be tested for leakage, using a blower door and pressure pan or a duct blower.

Specify that supply ductwork be sealed so that the cumulative pressure-pan reading of all registers is 3 Pascals or less when the home is depressurized to 50 pascals by the blower door. Or, the duct blower air leakage should be less than 100 $CFM_{25}$.

- ✔ Evaluate slip joint connections, and crossover connections in doublewide units. Specify sealing, repair, or replacement as necessary.

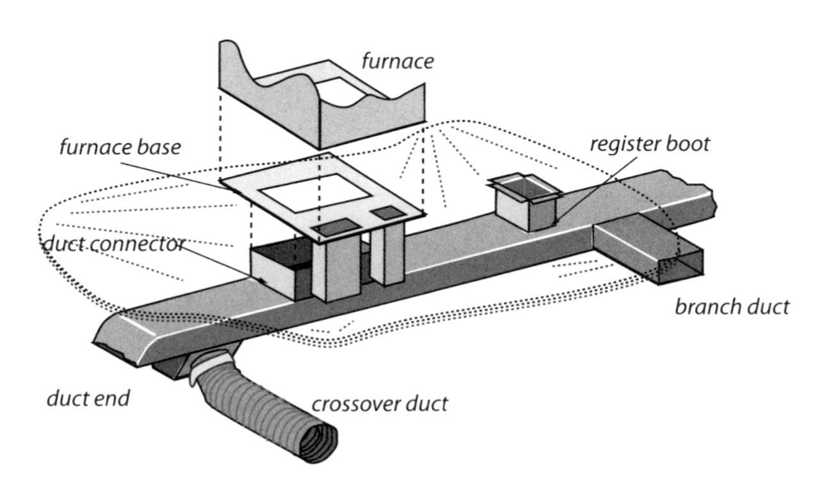


**Mobile Home Ducts:** Mobile home ducts leak at their ends and joints – especially at the joints beneath the furnace. The furnace base attaches the furnace to the duct connector. Leaks occur where the duct connector meets the main duct and where it meets the furnace. Branch ducts are rare, but easy to find, because their supply registers aren't in line with the others. Crossover ducts are found only in double-wide and triple-wide homes.)

## 8.4.1 Belly Return Air Systems

Floor and ceiling cavities used as return-air plenums should be eliminated in favor of return-air through the living spaces and into a large grille in the furnace-closet door.

- ✔ Specify a grille with at least 200 square inches of net free area to the furnace closet door or manufacturer's specifications, whichever is larger.
- ✔ Locate all floor return registers and all floor openings in the furnace closet.
- ✔ Combustion air inlets to the furnace must not be sealed.
- ✔ Measure the fan flow to assure that the airflow is within the manufacturer's specifications.

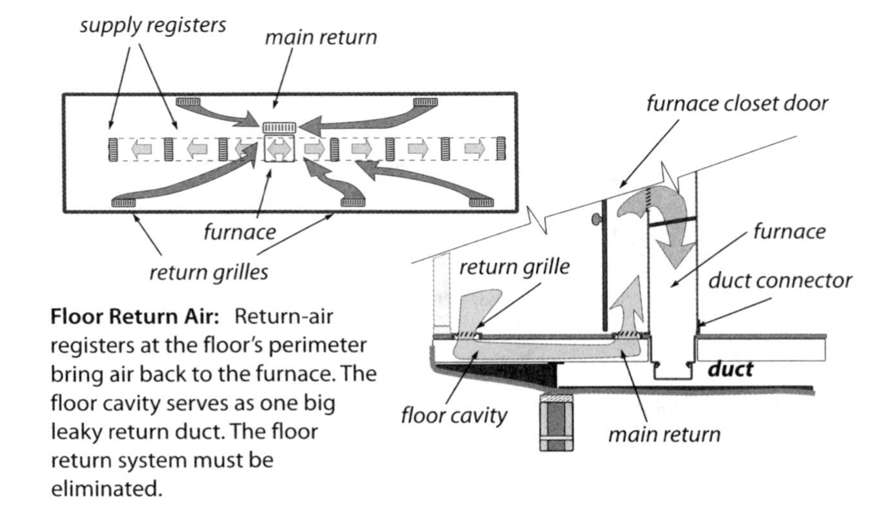


**Floor Return Air:** Return-air registers at the floor's perimeter bring air back to the furnace. The floor cavity serves as one big leaky return duct. The floor return system must be eliminated.

- ✔ Check the temperature rise of the furnace to ensure that the airflow is not restricted. The temperature rise should be within the range specified on the manufacturer's label or between 40° and 80° F.
- ✔ Inspect the plenum/furnace joint before measuring the temperature rise.

- ✔ Make sure all interior doors are open, except the furnace closet door.
- ✔ Close the furnace door and furnace closet door (if existing).
- ✔ Turn on the furnace and allow the temperature of the supply air to stabilize. Measure the supply-air temperature at the register closest to the furnace, making sure that the airflow to this register is not blocked and that there is no significant duct leakage between the furnace and your thermometer.
- ✔ Subtract the house air temperature from the supply air temperature. The difference is the temperature rise.
- ✔ If the temperature rise is greater than the recommended range the airflow may be restricted by one of the following:
- ✔ Undersized opening in the furnace closet door,
- ✔ Closed interior doors, or
- ✔ Another restriction in the ductwork.

### 8.4.2 Belly Pressure Test

Mobile home supply duct leaks tend to pressurize the belly cavity. This qualitative test can quickly detect duct leaks and indicate their general location. The belly must be repaired to a reasonably airtight state before this test is possible.

- ✔ Turn on the air handler at the furnace
- ✔ Insert a manometer hose into the belly through the rodent barrier and test the pressure with-reference-to (WRT) to the outdoors.
- ✔ Start near the furnace and work your way toward the ends alongside the trunkline. Pressure variations give you a rough idea of the location of leaks, size of leaks and the airtightness of the nearby rodent barrier.

✔ Repair the ductwork and re-test.

## 8.5 Evaluating Shell Air Leakage

Some mobile homes are quite leaky and some are tight. Perform blower-door tests on all homes. Choose between the following strategies.

1. Seal to 90% of the minimum ventilation requirement (MVR) as determined in *"ASHRAE 62.2 – 2007 Ventilation Standard" on page 255.*
2. Seal the home as tight as possible and install a continuous ventilation fan as specified in *"Fan Specifications" on page 258.*

### 8.5.1 Air-Leakage Locations

The following locations have been identified, by auditors and technicians using blower doors, as the most serious air-leakage sites.

Water-heater closets with exterior doors are particularly serious air-leakage problems, having large openings into the bathroom and other areas.

- Plumbing penetrations in floors, walls, and ceilings For example: behind washers and dryers.
- Torn or missing underbelly, exposing air leaks in the floor to outdoors.
- Large gaps around furnace and water heater chimneys.
- Severely deteriorated floors in water heater compartments.
- Gaps around the electrical service panel box, light fixtures, and fans.
- Joints between the halves of doublewide mobile homes and between the main dwelling and additions.

Window and door air leakage tends to be more of a comfort problem than a serious energy problem.

**Table 8-1: Air-Leak Locations and Typical $CFM_{50}$ Reductions**

| Leak to be Sealed | Expected Reduction |
|---|---|
| Sealing floor as return-air plenum | 300–900 |
| Sealing leaky water-heater closet | 200–600 |
| Sealing leaky supply ducts | 100–400 |
| Patching large air leaks in the floor, walls and ceiling | 200–700 |
| Caulking and weatherstripping | 50–150 |
| Installing tight interior storm windows | 100–250 |

## 8.6 Specifying Water-Heater Replacement

Specify a water-heater replacement as an energy conservation measure or as a health and safety measure based on combustion safety if it is leaking or if you find other safety defects.

- ✔ Inspect existing unit for defects such as a leaky storage tank.
- ✔ Perform combustion-safety testing.
- ✔ Inspect electrical connections for hazards.
- ✔ Note if an electrical outlet is near the water heater when the replacement unit requires an outlet to plug in motor.
- ✔ Measure length of gas piping to be installed when replacing an electric water heater with a gas water heater.

Replacement water heaters should be inspected to meet these standards at a minimum.

- ✔ Energy Factor of at least 0.60.

- ✔ Pressure and temperature relief valve should have a pipe extending it to within 12 inches of the floor.
- ✔ Check gas lines for leaks and the presence of a sediment trap.
- ✔ Examine venting for proper slope and terminations. Test the unit for carbon monoxide in the flue gases.
- ✔ Ensure proper electrical connections and wiring according to the *NEC*.
- ✔ No water pipe connections or the tank should be leaking.

## 8.7 Evaluating Interior Storm Windows

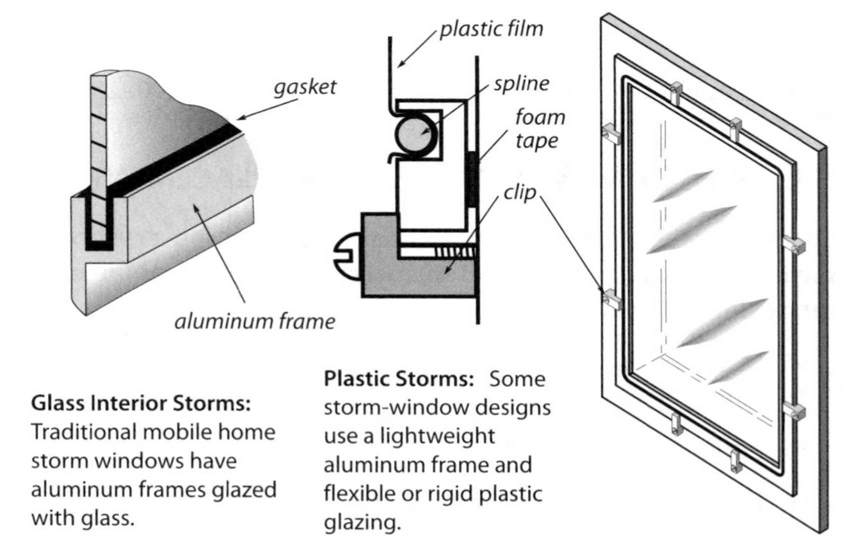


**Glass Interior Storms:** Traditional mobile home storm windows have aluminum frames glazed with glass.

**Plastic Storms:** Some storm-window designs use a lightweight aluminum frame and flexible or rigid plastic glazing.

Install insider storm windows on windows with primary single pane glass and no storm. Interior storm windows double the R-value of a single-pane window and reduce infiltration, especially in the case of leaky jalousie prime windows.

- ✔ Specify replacement of existing storm windows only when the existing storm windows can't be re-glazed or repaired.
- ✔ Specify interior storms where there is no storm present.

## 8.8 Considering Window Replacement

Replacement windows with an ENERGY STAR rating may be installed when existing windows are worn or damaged beyond repair.

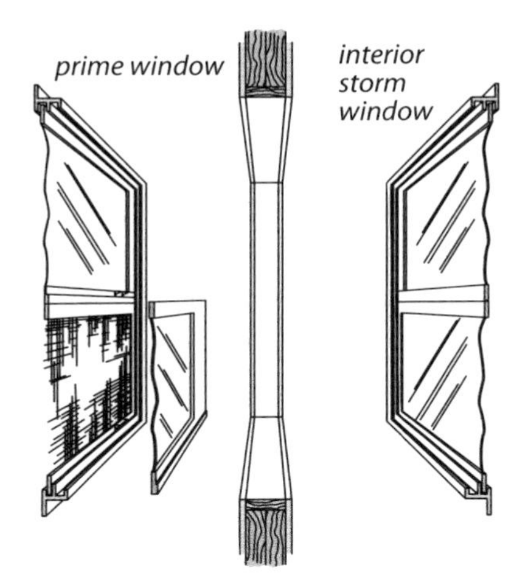


**Mobile-Home Double Window:** In mobile homes, the prime window is installed over the siding outdoors, and the storm window is installed indoors.

- ✔ Specify glass replacement with a window with a cracked or broken pane of glass, but where degradation isn't severe.
- ✔ Windows with broken cranks, deteriorated weatherstrip, and broken frames or sash may be replaced.
- ✔ Replacement windows should be designed for retrofit installation in mobile homes.
- ✔ Repairing existing moisture damage and preventing future moisture intrusion are the most important issues for window replacement.

## 8.9 Door Replacement Specifications

Mobile home doors come in two basic types: the mobile home door and the house-type door. Mobile home doors swing outwardly, and house-type doors swing inwardly.

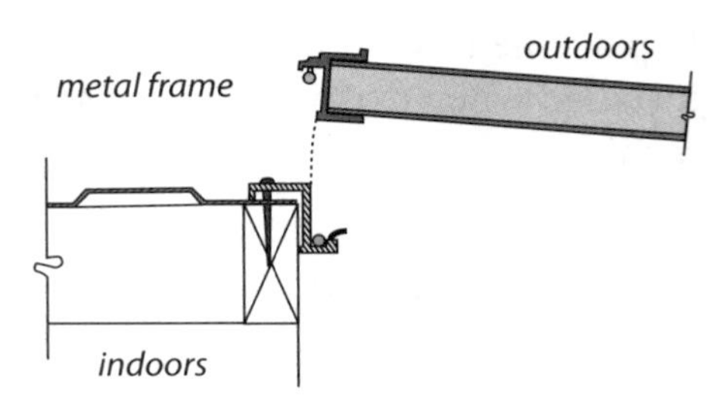


**Mobile-Home Door:** These older type mobile-home doors open outwardly. They are usually secondary doors.

Primary doors may be replaced following the conditions stated in protocols below, with ENERGY STAR qualified doors, if available. Replacement doors must be R-9 minimum, if available.

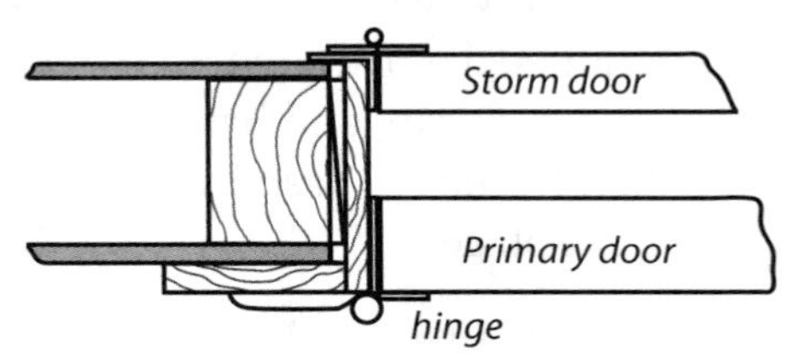


**Mobile-Home Double Door:** This type of mobile-home door is sold in one piece and contains a primary door opening inwardly and a storm door opening outwardly.

Specify exterior door replacement in the follow cases:

a. The existing door is damaged beyond repair and constitutes a severe air-leakage problem.

b. Moisture damage on either the door jamb or the door blank.

c. Large holes or cracks in the door jamb or door blank.

Note whether the door is hinged on the right or left when ordering. Mobile home doors are usually not standard heights.

# APPENDICES

## A–1 REQUIRED DIAGNOSTIC EQUIPMENT

### Minimum Equipment For Instrumented Air Sealing

- ✔ Fully instrumented and calibrated blower door, Minneapolis Model 3 or equivalent, capable of measuring $CFM_{50}$ (Cubic feet per minute at 50 Pascals).
- ✔ DG-3 or DG-700 handheld Digital Manometer, or equivalent.
- ✔ Smoke generating equipment.

### Minimum Equipment for Heating System Analysis

- ✔ Combustion analyzer.
- ✔ CO testing capacity.
- ✔ Draft gauge or manometer.
- ✔ Heat exchanger leakage testing equipment.
- ✔ Ammeter (sensitive enough to adjust thermostat anticipators).
- ✔ Gas leak detector.

# A–2 R-Values for Common Materials

| Material | R-value |
|---|---|
| Fiberglass or rock wool batts and blown 1″ | 2.8–4.0 |
| Blown cellulose 1″ | 3.0–4.0 |
| Vermiculite loose fill 1″ | 2.7 |
| Perlite 1″ | 2.4 |
| White expanded polystyrene foam (beadboard) 1″ | 3.9–4.3 |
| Polyurethane/polyisocyanurate foam 1″ | 6.2–7.0 |
| Extruded polystyrene 1″ | 5.0 |
| Sprayed 2-part polyurethane foam 1″ | 5.8–6.6 |
| Icynene foam 1″ | 3.6 |
| Oriented strand board (OSB) or plywood $^1/_2$″ | 1.6 |
| Concrete or stucco 1″ | 0.1 |
| Wood 1″ | 1.0 |
| Carpet/pad $^1/_2$″ | 2.0 |
| Wood siding $^3/_8$–$^3/_4$″ | 0.6–1.0 |
| Concrete block 8″ | 1.1 |
| Asphalt shingles | 0.44 |
| Fired clay bricks 1″ | 0.1–0.4 |
| Gypsum or plasterboard $^1/_2$″ | 0.4 |
| Single pane glass $^1/_8$″ | 0.9 |
| Low-e insulated glass (Varies according to Solar Heat Gain Coefficient (SHGC) rating.) | 3.3–4.2 |
| Triple glazed glass with 2 low-e coatings | 8.3 |

# A–3 Calculating Attic Insulation

Auditors and inspectors also help crews determine how much insulation is needed for ceilings and walls.

## Calculating Attic Loose-Fill Insulation

Loose-fill attic insulation should be installed to a uniform depth to attain proper coverage (bags per square foot) so it attains the desired R-value at the settled thickness. Follow the manufacturer's labeling in order to achieve the correct density to meet the required R-value. Attic insulation always settles: cellulose settles between 10% to 20% and fiberglass settles between 3% to 10%. For this reason, it's best to calculate insulation density in square feet per bag rather than installed thickness.

## Example: Insulation Calculations

### Table Appendices-2:Typical Table from Insulation Bag

| R-Value at 75° F mean Temperature | Minimum Thickness | Maximum Net Coverage | |
|---|---|---|---|
| Desired R-Value of Insulation | Minimum Insulation Depth | Maximum Coverage per Bag (sq. ft.) | Bags per 1000 sq. ft. |
| R-60 | 16.0 | 11.7 | 85.8 |
| R-50 | 13.3 | 14.0 | 71.5 |
| R-44 | 11.7 | 15.9 | 62.9 |
| R-40 | 10.7 | 17.5 | 57.2 |
| R-38 | 10.1 | 18.4 | 54.4 |
| R-32 | 8.5 | 21.6 | 45.8 |
| R-30 | 8.0 | 23.3 | 42.9 |
| R-24 | 6.4 | 29.1 | 34.3 |
| R-22 | 5.9 | 31.8 | 31.5 |
| R-19 | 5.1 | 36.8 | 27.2 |
| R-13 | 3.5 | 53.8 | 18.6 |
| R-11 | 2.9 | 63.6 | 15.7 |

**Insulation Coverage Table:** This table is provided by Weather Blanket Corporation. Coverage and other insulation characteristics will vary from manufacturer to manufacturer.

## Example: Calculating Number of Bags

*Step 1: Calculate area of attic*
Multiple length times width of the attic to get the area of attic.

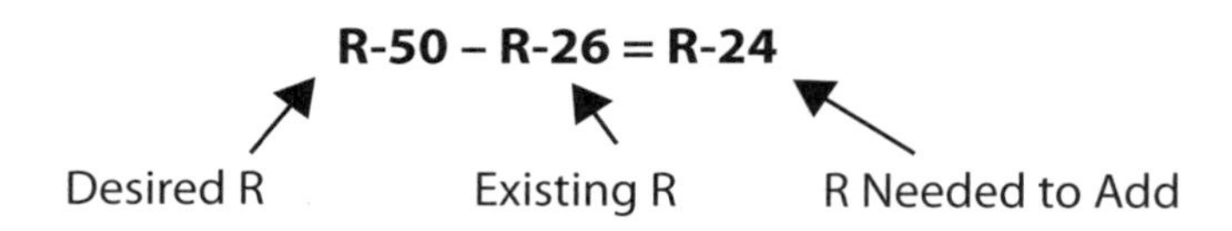


*Step 2: Calculate R-value that you need to add*
Subtract existing R from desired R to get the R-value you need to add.

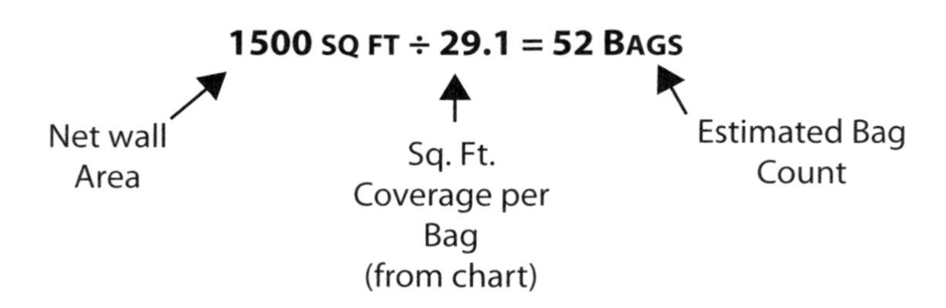


*STEP 3: Calculate bag count*
Divide area of attic by coverage per bag from the chart on the bag (number double circled in chart on *Table Appendices-2 on page 282*) to get your Estimated Bag Count.

## Example: Calculating Density of Attic Insulation

**1500 SQ FT X 6.4/12 FT= 800 CU FT**

Area — Depth in Inches — Inches per Foot — Volume of Insulation

*Step 1: Calculate volume of installed insulation*
Multiple area times depth of the attic insulation to get the volume of insulation.

**52 BAGS X 24 LBS/BAG = 1248 LBS**

Number of Bags — Weight of a Bag — Installed Weight

*Step 2: Calculate the weight of insulation you installed*
Take the number of bags times the weight per bag to get the total weight.

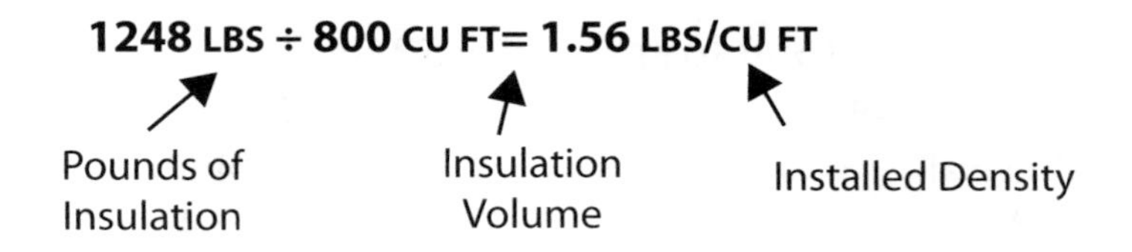


*STEP 3: Calculate density of installed insulation*
Divide pounds of insulation by cubic feet of insulation volume to get density.

*Note*
Density should be between 1.3 and 2.0 pounds per cubic foot or conform to manufacture's specifications for density, coverage, and bag count for the desired R-value.

# A–4 CALCULATING WALL INSULATION

Wall insulation should be installed to a density of 3.5 to 4.5 pounds per cubic foot. These calculations serve to calculate the number of bags necessary to insulate walls and to judge density after completing the wall-insulation job. Calculate the bag count based on information from the agency's insulation supplier.

## Example: Calculating Number of Bags for Wall Insulation

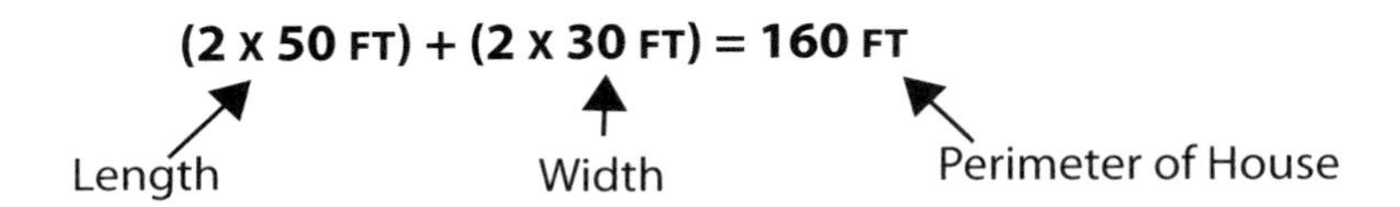


*STEP 1: Calculate perimeter of house*

Calculate the perimeter of the house. If the house is a simple rectangle or near a simple rectangle, use the formula above. If the house has numerous unequal sides, simply add the lengths together to find the perimeter.

*STEP 2: Calculate total wall area*

After calculating the perimeter of the house, multiply it times the wall height. This will give you the total wall area.

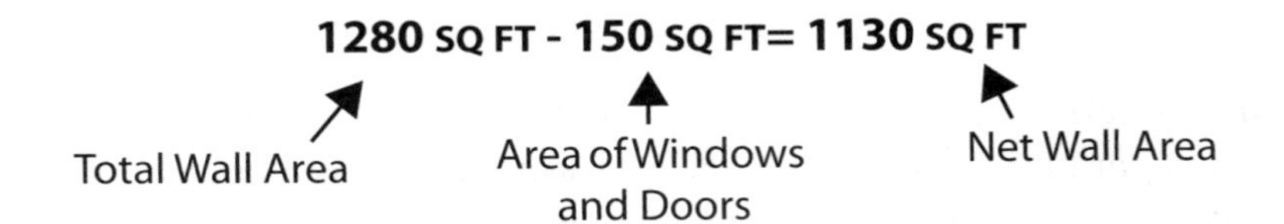


*STEP 3: Calculate net wall area*
Calculate the sum of the areas of windows and doors. Subtract them from the total wall area to get net wall area.

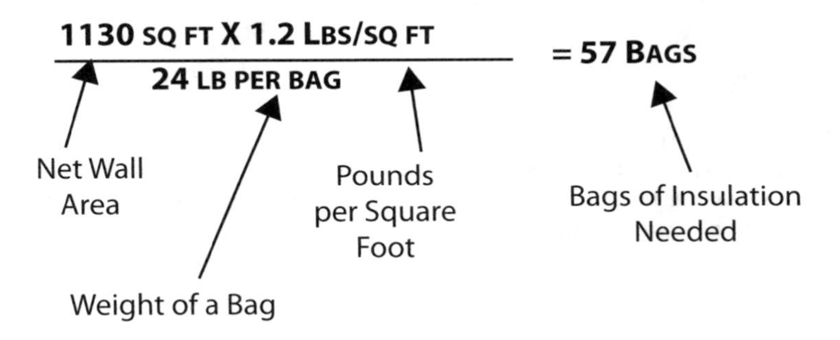


*STEP 4: Calculate bag count*
To achieve 4.0 lbs. per cubic foot, multiply net wall area by 1.2 pounds per square foot for a 2-by-4 wall (4.0 lbs. per cubic foot ÷ 12 x 3.5 = 1.2). Then divide by the number of pounds per bag to get the bag count.

## Example: Calculating Density of Wall Insulation

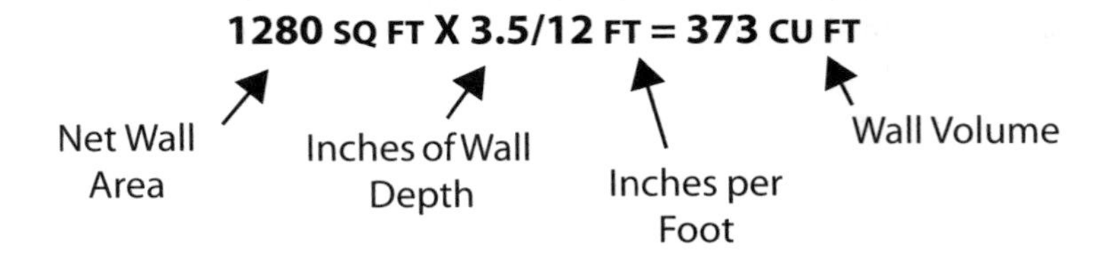


*STEP 1: Calculate wall volume*
Multiply the wall's surface area times the depth on the wall cavity converted to feet.

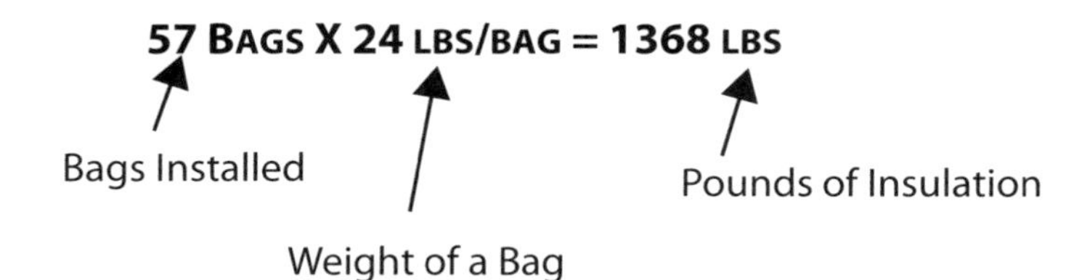


*STEP 2: Calculate weight of insulation*
Multiply number of bags you installed times the weight of a single bag to get the weight of the installed insulation.

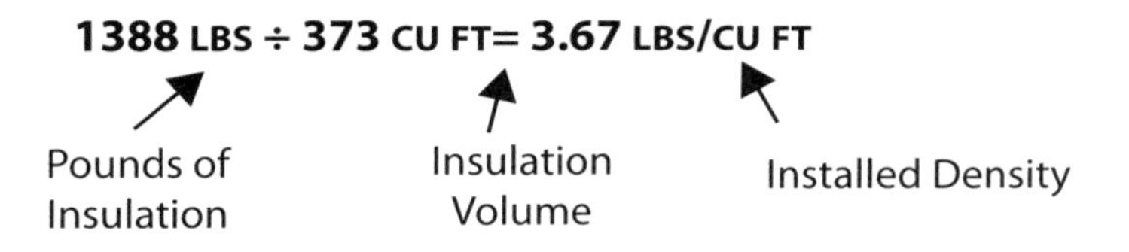


*STEP 3: Calculate density of installed insulation*
Divide pounds of insulation by cubic feet of insulation volume to calculate density.

# A–5 Calculating Mobile Home Insulation

Consider a 14′ x 66′ mobile home, totaling 924 square feet.

- ✔ Ceiling: 9″ cavity at the center and 2″ cavity at the edge with a 2″ batt
- ✔ Belly: $5^1/_2$″ cavity at the wings and $16^1/_2$″ cavity at the center with a 2″ batt fastened to floor bottom
- ✔ Walls: $3^1/_2$″ cavity with a $1^1/_2$″ batt at $7^1/_2$′ high

**General formulas**

CAVITY VOLUME X DESIRED DENSITY = WEIGHT OF INSULATION

WEIGHT OF INSULATION ÷ POUNDS PER BAG = BAGS OF INSULATION

### Ceiling Bag Count Estimates

1. Calculate the average ceiling cavity (9″ + 2″ = 11″) (11″ ÷ 2 = $5^1/_2$″ average cavity)
2. ($5^1/_2$″ cavity minus the 2″ batt = $3^1/_2$″ cavity). The existing insulation batt will compress when additional insulation is added, allow 1″ for compression ($3^1/_2$″ + 1″ = $4^1/_2$″ cavity)
3. Convert $4^1/_2$″ to feet (4.5″/12″ = 0.375′)
4. Multiply 0.375′ x 924 sq. ft. = 346.5 cubic feet
5. Multiply cubic feet by desired density: Fiberglass ceiling insulation density must be 1.0 to 1.5 lbs/cubic foot.

   a. 347 x 1.0 = 347 lbs. / 35(lbs/bag) = 9.9 bags

   b. 347 x 1.25 = 434 lbs. / 35(lbs/bag) = 12.4 bags

   c. 347 x 1.5 = 521 lbs. / 35(lbs/bag) = 14.9 bags

## Belly Bag Count Estimates

Calculate the average belly cavity (5-$^1/_2$″ + 16-$^1/_2$″ = 22″)

(22″ ÷ 2 = 11″ average cavity) (11″ cavity – 2″ batt = 9” cavity) The existing insulation batt will compress when additional insulation is added, allow 1″ for compression (9″ + 1″ = 10″ cavity)

1. Convert 10″ to feet (10″ / 12″ = 0.83′)
2. Multiply 0.83′ x 924 square feet = 767 cubic feet
3. Multiply cubic feet by desired density.
4. Belly insulation density at 1.0 to 1.5 lbs/cubic foot.
   a. 767 x 1.0 = 767 lbs. / 35(lbs/bag) = 22 bags
   b. 767 x 1.25 = 959 lbs. / 35(lbs/bag) = 27 bags
   c. 767 x 1.5 = 1151 lbs. / 35(lbs/bag) = 33 bags

# A–6 Refrigerator Dating Chart

Refrigerators are listed by brand name, followed by the coding system. If several manufacturers used the same system, they are listed together. Some rules of thumb for easy identification are: (1) Refrigerators that are any color of green, brown, yellow, pink, or blue (actually KitchenAid makes a new unit in cobalt blue); have mechanical handles; have doors held shut with magnetic strips; have rounded shoulders; have a chromed handle; or have exposed "house door" type hinges are at least 10 years old, and (2) the following brands have only been manufactured since around 1984 - Roper, Estate, KitchenAid, Caloric, Modern Maid, and Maytag.

| Brand(s) | What to look for | What to avoid | How to decode | Example |
|---|---|---|---|---|
| Montgomery Wards, Signature (2000) | Serial # - 1st two digits | n/a | Reverse the digits | 56xxxxx = 1965 |
| Sears, Kenmore, Coldspot | Model # - 1st & 3rd digits after (.) | n/a | Combine the digits | xx.6x2xxx = 1962 |
| Whirlpool | Model # - 1st 3 letters (pre 1982)<br>Serial # - 2nd digit (post 1982) | Serials with letters | No need<br>as 1st two digits Add "198_" to it | ABCxxx = pre 1982<br>x2xxx = 1982 |
| Amana | Serial # - 1st digit (pre 1986) | n/a | BLACKHORSE B=1, L=2 | Hxxxx = 1966 or 1976<br>61 is the oldest |
| Frigidaire | Serial # - 1st & 4th digit (pre 1989) | Serials with no letter in the 4th space | Add "196, 197, or 198" to the 1st digit. The letter in the 4th space is a month code used only on older models. | 3xxBxx = 1973 or 1983 |
| Gibson, Kelvinator | Serial # - 3rd digit (pre 1989) | n/a | Add "196, 197, or 198" to it | xx3xx = 1963 or 73 or 83 |
| White, Westinghouse | Serial # - 2nd letter (pre 1989) | Serials without letters | A,V,W=78, B=79, C=80 etc.<br>pre-1978, R=74, U=77 etc. | xLxxx = 1988<br>74 is the oldest year |
| Tappan, O'Keefe & Merritt | Serial # - 7th digit (pre 1989) | n/a | Add "196, 197, or 198" to it | xx xxx-x8xx = 1968 or 78 or 88 |
| Admiral, Crosley, Norge, Magic Chef, Jenn Air | Serial # - last letter | n/a | A=1950 or 1974 (+14 yrs)<br>B=1951 or 1975, etc. | xxxxxxD = 1953 or 1977 |
| General Electric (GE) | Serial # - 2nd letter | n/a | See chart below | xGxxx = 1950 or 1980 |
| Hotpoint | Same as GE with some exceptions. See GE and Hotpoint exceptions chart below | | | |

GE Decoder Chart:

| | | | | | | |
|---|---|---|---|---|---|---|
| A = 44, 65, 77, 89 | B = 45, 66 | C = 46, 67 | D = 47, 68, 78, 90 | E = 48, 69 | F = 49, 79, 91 | G = 50, 80, 92 |
| H = 51, 81, 93 | J = 52 | K = 53 | L = 54, 70, 82, 94 | M = 55, 71, 83 | N = 56, 72 | P = 57, 73 |
| R = 58, 84 | S = 59, 85 | T = 60, 74, 86 | V = 61, 75, 87 | W = 62 | X = 63 Y = 64 | Z = 76, 88 |

Hotpoint Exceptions: U = 61, V = 62, W = 63, X = 64, Y = 65, Z = 66, A = 67, B = 68

Revised 5/6/94

# *Tables and Illustrations*

## Energy Audits and Customer Relations


Energy Audits .......... 17
Auditor's Floor Plans .......... 19
Visualization .......... 19
Interior and Exterior Inspection .......... 20
Seasonal vs. Baseload Domination of Energy Use .......... 25
Top Six Energy Uses for U.S. Households .......... 27
Separating Baseload from Seasonal Energy Use .......... 28
Total Energy Use and the HERS Index .......... 29
The Summer Peak .......... 31
Range of Electric Baseload Consumption .......... 32
Carbon Emissions of Various Fuels .......... 33
Modern Dryer Dials .......... 43
Clothes Line .......... 43
Circulating Fans .......... 45
Ventilating Fans .......... 45


## Evaluating Insulation


Balloon Framing .......... 47
Platform Framing .......... 47
Infrared Scanner .......... 48
Low and High Attic Ventilation .......... 49
Finished Attic .......... 51
Finished Attic Best Practices .......... 52
Foam-Insulated Kneewall .......... 52
Insulating Closed Roof Cavities .......... 53
Insulating and Sealing Attic Stair Walls, Doors, and Stairs. 54
Insulating and Weatherstripping the Attic Hatch .......... 54
Stairway Hatch Dam .......... 55

Manufactured Retractable-Stair Cover.................. 55
Story-and-a-Half.............................. 57
Thermal Boundary Decisions........................ 58
Locating Foundation Air Barrier and Insulation .......... 60

## Diagnosing Shell and Duct Air Leakage

Air Leakage Concepts............................. 62
Questions to Ask and Answer Before Air Sealing ......... 64
Blower Door Components ........................... 66
Blower Door Test ................................. 67
Digital Manometer ............................... 67
Floor-Wall Junction............................... 73
Finished Attic.................................... 74
Recessed Light Fixtures ............................ 74
Balloon-Framed Gable Wall ......................... 75
Two-Level Attic................................... 75
Bypasses Under Bathtub ........................... 76
Exterior Walls & Stairs............................ 76
Cathedral Ceiling with Recessed Light.................. 77
Porch Air Leakage ................................ 77
Interior Door Test................................. 80
Bedroom Test .................................... 81
Building Components and Their Air Permeance ......... 82
Pressure-Testing Building Zones ...................... 83
House-to-Attic Pressure............................ 84
Attic-to-Outdoors Pressure ......................... 84
Zone Connectedness .............................. 85
Cantilevered Floor Test ............................ 85
Porch Roof Test................................... 85
Add-a-Hole Test 1 ................................ 87
Add-a-Hole Test 2 ................................ 87
Add-a-Hole Leakage Factors ......................... 88

Open-a-Door Test 1 .... 90
Open-a-Door Test 2 .... 90
Open-a-Door Leakage Factors .... 91
Pressure Measurements and Air-Barrier Location .... 93
House-to-Crawl-Space Pressure .... 94

## Evaluating Heating and Cooling Systems

Sealed Combustion Heaters .... 96
Static Pressure and Temperature rise .... 96
90+ Gas Furnace .... 97
80+ Gas Furnace .... 97
Radiator Temperature Control .... 98
Simple Reverse-Return Hot-Water System .... 99
Reset Controller .... 100
Oil Heating System .... 101
Sealed Combustion Space Heater .... 102
Space Heater Controls .... 102
Atmospheric, Open-Combustion Gas Burners .... 104
70+ Furnace .... 105
80+ Furnace .... 105
Gas-Furnace Output from Temperature Rise and Airflow (1000s Btuh) .... 108
Action Levels for Open-Combustion Gas Appliances .... 109
Combustion Standards for Gas Furnaces .... 110
Carbon Monoxide Causes and Solutions .... 111
Combustion Problems and Possible Solutions .... 111
Primary Air Adjustment .... 112
Input in Thousands of Btu/hr for 1000 Btu/cu. ft. Gas .... 114
Clocking the Meter .... 115
Measuring Draft .... 117

Barometric Draft Control . . . . . . . . . . 119
Minimum Oil-Burner Combustion Standards . . . . . . . . . . 120
Typical Safe Draft for Oil-Fired Appliances . . . . . . . . . . 121
Measuring Oil-Burner Performance . . . . . . . . . . 122
Wood-Stove Installation . . . . . . . . . . 126
Guide to Venting Standards . . . . . . . . . . 127
Testing Requirements for Combustion Appliances and Venting Systems . . . . . . . . . . 129
Flame Roll-Out . . . . . . . . . . 130
Worst-Case Depressurization . . . . . . . . . . 131
Negative Versus Positive Draft . . . . . . . . . . 132
Maximum CAZ or Mechanical Room Depressurization for Various Appliances . . . . . . . . . . 133
Draft Problems and Solutions . . . . . . . . . . 135
Areas of Round Vents . . . . . . . . . . 137
Two Vent Connectors Joining Chimney . . . . . . . . . . 138
Connector Diameter vs. Maximum Horizontal Length . . . 138
Clearances to Combustibles for Vent Connectors . . . . . . . 139
Masonry Chimneys . . . . . . . . . . 139
Clearances to Combustibles for Common Chimneys . . . . 140
All-Fuel Metal Chimney . . . . . . . . . . 141
Chimney Terminations . . . . . . . . . . 142
Roof Slope and B-Vent Chimney Height (ft) . . . . . . . . . . 142
Flexible Metal Chimney Liners . . . . . . . . . . 143
AGA Venting Categories . . . . . . . . . . 144
B-Vent Chimney Liner . . . . . . . . . . 145
Characteristics of Gas Furnaces and Boilers . . . . . . . . . . 146
Passive Combustion-Air Options . . . . . . . . . . 148
Combustion Air Openings: Location and Size . . . . . . . . . . 149
Recommended Cross-Sectional Area of Metal Supply and Return Ducts at Air Handler . . . . . . . . . . 152
Round-Duct Square-Inch Equivalency for Metal Ducts . . 152

Airflow and Climate. . . . . . . . . . . . . . . . . . . . . . . . . . . . . . . . . . 153
Fan Curves . . . . . . . . . . . . . . . . . . . . . . . . . . . . . . . . . . . . . . . . 154
Furnace Operating Parameters. . . . . . . . . . . . . . . . . . . . . . . . . . . 156
Adjustable Drive Pulley . . . . . . . . . . . . . . . . . . . . . . . . . . . . . . . 157
A Fan/Limit Control. . . . . . . . . . . . . . . . . . . . . . . . . . . . . . . . . . 157
Pressure in T wo Measurement Systems . . . . . . . . . . . . . . . . . 158
Duct Blower Mounted to Air Handler. . . . . . . . . . . . . . . . . . . . 159
Static Pressure Probe . . . . . . . . . . . . . . . . . . . . . . . . . . . . . . . . 159
Duct Blower Mounted to Main Return . . . . . . . . . . . . . . . . . . 160
True Flow® Meter . . . . . . . . . . . . . . . . . . . . . . . . . . . . . . . . . . . 163
Measuring Return Air with a Flow Hood . . . . . . . . . . . . . . . . 164
Visualizing TESP . . . . . . . . . . . . . . . . . . . . . . . . . . . . . . . . . . . 165
Total external static pressure (TESP) . . . . . . . . . . . . . . . . . . . . 167
Total External Static Pressure Versus System Airflow for a Particular System . . . . . . . . . . . . . . . . . . . . . . . . . . . . . . . . . . 167
Depressurized Central Zone. . . . . . . . . . . . . . . . . . . . . . . . . . . 168
Pressurized Bedrooms . . . . . . . . . . . . . . . . . . . . . . . . . . . . . . . 168
Furnace Filter Location . . . . . . . . . . . . . . . . . . . . . . . . . . . . . . 169
Restricted Return Air. . . . . . . . . . . . . . . . . . . . . . . . . . . . . . . . . 171
Finding Duct Air Leaks. . . . . . . . . . . . . . . . . . . . . . . . . . . . . . . 172
A Pressure Pan . . . . . . . . . . . . . . . . . . . . . . . . . . . . . . . . . . . . . 173
Pressure-Pan Test. . . . . . . . . . . . . . . . . . . . . . . . . . . . . . . . . . . 175
Problem Return Register. . . . . . . . . . . . . . . . . . . . . . . . . . . . . . 175
Dominant Return Leaks. . . . . . . . . . . . . . . . . . . . . . . . . . . . . . . 176
Dominant Supply Leaks. . . . . . . . . . . . . . . . . . . . . . . . . . . . . . . 176
Duct Leakage Standards . . . . . . . . . . . . . . . . . . . . . . . . . . . . . . 177
Total Duct Air Leakage Standards for Homes . . . . . . . . . . . . 178
Testing Ducts Before Air-Handler Installation . . . . . . . . . . . . 178
Total Duct Air Leakage Measured by the Duct Blower . . . 180
Measuring Duct Leakage to Outdoors . . . . . . . . . . . . . . . . . . 181
Panned Floor Joists. . . . . . . . . . . . . . . . . . . . . . . . . . . . . . . . . . 183
Flexduct Joints . . . . . . . . . . . . . . . . . . . . . . . . . . . . . . . . . . . . . 184

Plenums, Poorly Sealed to Air Handler.................. 184
Sectioned Elbows.................................. 184
Duct Insulation ................................... 185
Cast-Iron Sectional Boilers ......................... 186
Expansion Tank, Air Separator, and Vent................ 189
Zone Valves ...................................... 189
Purging Air ....................................... 190
One-Pipe and Two-Pipe Steam Systems ................ 191
Two-Pipe Steam Systems ............................ 191
Steam Traps ...................................... 193
Inside a Programmable Thermostat .................... 194
Electric Baseboard.................................. 196
Electric Furnace ................................... 196
Is Strip Heat Activated? ............................ 197
Heat Pump ....................................... 198
Compiled Research Results on HVAC Performance...... 201
Air-Conditioner Sizing .............................. 203
Charge-Checking................................... 204

## Baseload Measures

Insulation R-Values ................................ 206
Water Heater Insulation.............................. 207
Setting Hot-Water Temperature........................ 208
Water-Saving Shower Heads .......................... 209
Measuring Shower Flow Rate ......................... 210
Standard Gas Water Heater .......................... 211
Fan-Assisted Water Heater ........................... 212
Sealed-Combustion Water Heater....................... 212
Sealed-Combustion Tankless Water Heater.............. 214
Obsolete Tankless Water Heater........................ 214
Closed Loop Antifreeze System ....................... 216
Drainback System .................................. 216

Recording Watthour Meter. . . . . . . . . . . . . . . . . . . . . . . . . . . . . 218
Refrigerator Consumption Example . . . . . . . . . . . . . . . . . . . . . 219
Compact Fluorescent Lamps. . . . . . . . . . . . . . . . . . . . . . . . . . . 221

## Windows, Doors, and Exterior Insulation

Exterior Shading. . . . . . . . . . . . . . . . . . . . . . . . . . . . . . . . . . . . . 224
Trees for Shade. . . . . . . . . . . . . . . . . . . . . . . . . . . . . . . . . . . . . . 226
Exterior Sliding Storm Windows. . . . . . . . . . . . . . . . . . . . . . . . 226
Clip-on Storm Window . . . . . . . . . . . . . . . . . . . . . . . . . . . . . . . 226
Doubling Windows . . . . . . . . . . . . . . . . . . . . . . . . . . . . . . . . . . . 227
Weatherstripping Double-Hung Windows. . . . . . . . . . . . . . . 229
Weatherstripping Doors . . . . . . . . . . . . . . . . . . . . . . . . . . . . . . 230
Minor Door Repair. . . . . . . . . . . . . . . . . . . . . . . . . . . . . . . . . . . 230
Threshold and Door Bottom . . . . . . . . . . . . . . . . . . . . . . . . . . . 230
NFRC label . . . . . . . . . . . . . . . . . . . . . . . . . . . . . . . . . . . . . . . . . 232
Replacement Window and Sill Angle . . . . . . . . . . . . . . . . . . . 233
Flashing a Flanged Window. . . . . . . . . . . . . . . . . . . . . . . . . . . . 234
Safety Glass Around Doors. . . . . . . . . . . . . . . . . . . . . . . . . . . . 236
Windows Near Walking Surfaces . . . . . . . . . . . . . . . . . . . . . . . 236
Fire Egress Windows. . . . . . . . . . . . . . . . . . . . . . . . . . . . . . . . . 236
Exterior Foam Insulation . . . . . . . . . . . . . . . . . . . . . . . . . . . . . . 237

## Health and Safety

Effects of CO . . . . . . . . . . . . . . . . . . . . . . . . . . . . . . . . . . . . . . 240
CO from Range and Oven. . . . . . . . . . . . . . . . . . . . . . . . . . . . . . 241
Advanced 4-Speed Range Fan . . . . . . . . . . . . . . . . . . . . . . . . . 242
Moisture Sources . . . . . . . . . . . . . . . . . . . . . . . . . . . . . . . . . . . . 245
Moisture Sources and Their Potential Contributions . . . . 246
Dust Mites. . . . . . . . . . . . . . . . . . . . . . . . . . . . . . . . . . . . . . . . . . 247
Well Sealed Crawl Spaces . . . . . . . . . . . . . . . . . . . . . . . . . . . . . 248
Knob-and-Tube Wiring . . . . . . . . . . . . . . . . . . . . . . . . . . . . . . . . 250

Finding the N-Value ... 254
Fan Sizes for Homes with Average Air Leakage ... 255
Multi-Port Exhaust Ventilation ... 257
Specifying Exhaust Fans ... 258
Fan Capacity, Maximum Noise Rating, & Efficacy ... 259
Supply Ventilation ... 259
Centralized Balanced Ventilation ... 260
Heat-Recovery Ventilator ... 261

## Evaluating Mobile Homes

Typical Components of a Mobile Home ... 263
Bowstring Roof Details ... 266
Wall/Roof Details on Newer Homes ... 266
Bowstring Roof Cavity ... 266
Standard Mobile Home Construction ... 269
Older Mobile Home Construction ... 269
Checking Walls ... 270
Mobile Home Ducts ... 271
Floor Return Air ... 272
Air-Leak Locations and Typical $CFM_{50}$ Reductions ... 275
Glass Interior Storms ... 276
Plastic Storms ... 276
Mobile-Home Double Window ... 277
Mobile-Home Double Door ... 278
Mobile-Home Door ... 278

## Appendices

Typical Table from Insulation Bag ... 282
Insulation Coverage Table ... 282

# INDEX


## A

Add-a-hole test 85-86
Air barriers
  add-a-hole test 85-86
  air permeance of 82
  definition 79
  primary vs. secondary 79
  testing for leaks 77-86
  testing with manometers 82-86
Air conditioners
  inspections 201-203
  sizing 203
Air conditioning
  reducing costs of 43-44
  refrigerant charge 204
Air filters
  oil burner 123
Air handlers
  See also Blowers
  sealing holes in 96
Air leakage
  concepts 62
  effect 62
  goals of testing 63-64
  mobile homes 274-275
  of materials, rates 82
  sealing 73-77
  when to test 66
Air permeance
  of building materials 82
Air quality. See Indoor air quality
Air sealing 73-77
Air separator 189
Air shutters, oil 122
Airflow
  and climate 153
  blower speed 153
  dry & wet climates 153
  improving low 169
  measuring 151-164
  studies 151
  testing for unbalanced 167-168
  troubleshooting 164-168
Air-to-air heat exchangers 260-261
Alarms
  carbon monoxide 243
  smoke 242
American Gas Association
  venting categories 144
Annual Fuel Utilization Efficiency (AFUE) 144
Appliances
  energy measures 205-209
Asphalt felt 232
Attics
  hatches 77
  insulation 48-53
  ventilation 49-50
Automatic fill valve 190
Awnings 224

## B

Backdrafting 126-130
Barometric dampers 119
Baseload
  analysis example 28
  measures 205-210
Basements
  thermal boundary 59-60, 94
Blinds
  exterior 224
  Venetian 224
Blower doors
  airtightness limits 253-256
  components/description 66-68
  preparing for tests 68-69
  pressure diagnostics 77-86
  simple zone testing 80-81

test procedures 70
testing 66-79
testing air barriers 82-86
Blowers
controls 155
Boilers
corrosion 186
efficiency 189-190
low-limit control 189
maintaining 42
maintenance/efficiency 186-187
sizing 97
Building tightness limit. See Minimum ventilation level
Building tightness limits 252, 253, 253-256
Burners
gas, servicing 127-128
nozzle for oil 122
oil 118-123
Bypasses 73-77

## C

Cad cell 121
Carbon emissions
per unit of energy 33
Carbon monoxide 240
alarms 243
causes of 240
causes/solutions 111
exposure limits 241
standard for oil 110, 120
testing 129, 241
CAZ 148
CFL. See Compact fluorescent lamps
CFM50
defined 66
Charge
refrigerant 204
Chimney liners
insulating 143
sizing 143
Chimneys 139-142
all-fuel 141
clearances 140
house-pressure effect 63
masonry specifications 139
measures to improve draft 134
retrofit liners 142, 145
termination 141
types 139
when to reline 144
Client relations 264
Clothes dryers
efficient use 43
Clotheslines 43
CO. See Carbon monoxide
Coils
cleaning 201
Combustion
oil standards 109, 120
problems/solutions 111
testing/analysis 105-123
the chemical process 104
Combustion air 146-149
cfm requirements 130, 146
confined spaces 147-148
methods of providing 146
unconfined spaces 147
Combustion losses
excess air 189
Combustion testing
drilling holes 110
Combustion zone
definition 130, 146
Comfort
staying cool 43-44
Compact fluorescent lamps 220-221
Concrete vapor-proofing 249
Condenser coils
cleaning 201
Conditioned space
definition of 57
versus unconditioned 58

Consumption
of energy 24
Contracts 34
Convectors
fin-tube 190
Cooling
energy saving tips 43-44
with fans 43
Corrosion 186
Costs
measure selection 25
seasonal/baseload 26
Crawl spaces
thermal boundary 59-60, 94
Customer education 40-44
Customer relations 15-38

## D

Dampers
balancing 155
Diagnostics
airflow 164-168
building shell 77-84
equipment for 279
house pressure 176-177
pressure-pan testing 173-175
unbalanced airflow 167-168
Doors 228-229
bottoms and sweeps 229
mobile home 278
repair 228-229
repairing 228
replacement
mobile homes 278
weatherstrip 228-229
Draft
and duct improvements 134
measuring, illus. 117
over-fire 120
strength & types of 129-130
Duct blower
leak-testing 178-181
measuring airflow 158-161
Ductboard
deteriorating facing 183
Duct-induced house pressure
176-177
Ducts 150-155, 171-185
design airflow 151-153
duct-airtightness testing 178-181
evaluating leakage 171-175
finding leaks 172-175
hangers 182
house-pressure effect 62
improvements to solve draft
problems 134
leakage standards 178
measuring airflow 158-164
mobile homes 270-274
pressure-pan testing 173-175
sealing boots and registers 76
sealing chases 76
sealing leaks 181-183
sizing 151-152
static pressure 164-166
troubleshooting leakage 172-183
Dust
lead 249

## E-F

Education
customer 40-44
Efflorescence 247
Electric heat 194-200
baseboard 195-196
furnaces 196
Electrical safety 250
Energy
baseload measures 205-210
consumption 24
Energy audit
ethics, bias 37
health and safety 22
interior/exterior inspection 18-20
mechanical inspection 20-21

Energy auditor
responsibilities 15-38
Energy audits
ethics, bias 37
Energy factor
water heating 212
Energy recovery ventilators 260-261
Energy use
analysis 24-28
analysis, example 28
Ethics 15-38
Excess air
oil burners 120
Exfiltration
See also Air leakage
concepts 62
Expansion tanks 188, 189
Fan curves 154
Fans
for cooling 43
Filters 202
air, installation 97
changing 41
Flexduct
joints 182
Flow hood 163
Flue dampers. See vent dampers
Flue-gas analysis 119
Fluorescent lamps
compact 220
Furnaces 150-185
installation 96-97
mobile homes 270
operating parameters 156
replacement 96-97
sealing holes in 96
temperature rise 155

## G

Gas burners
clocking gas meter 113
operation of 104
Gores 182
Grilles
cleaning 41
Ground moisture barrier 60, 249

## H

Health and safety
inspection 22
mobile homes 264-265
Heat pumps
efficiency 197-198
room 199-200
testing 198
Heat recovery ventilators 260-261
Heating systems
electric 194-200
electric baseboard 195-196
electric furnaces 196
forced-air 150-185
heat pumps 197-198
hot-water 186
hydronic 97-100, 187-190
oil-fired 118-123
replacement 100
room heat pumps 199-200
steam 190-193
High limit
hot-water heating 188
steam 192
House pressures
limits 168
measuring 67
problems with 63
reducing 134
unbalanced airflow 167-168
HRVs.
See Heat recovery ventilators

Hydronic heating systems 187-190

## I

IAQ. See indoor air quality
Indoor air pollution
  controlling 239-241
Indoor air quality 240-241, 253-256
Infiltration
  concepts 62
Inspections
  air conditioners 201-203
  final 35
  health and safety 22
  in-progress 35
  interior/exterior 18-20
  mechanical systems 20-21
  wall insulation 55
Insulation
  accessing walls 55
  attic 48-53
  coverage, mobile home 266-269
  exterior 237
  floor, mobile home 267-268
  hydronic pipe 99
  hydronic piping 190, 193
  mobile home 266-269
  roof, mobile home 266-267
  steam piping 190, 193
  wall, mobile home 269
  water heaters 205-207
Intermediate zones
  definition 58

## J-M

Kneewalls 74
Landscaping
  for shade 225
Laundry
  energy savings in 43
Lead paint 249
Lead-safe weatherization 249
Leakage area 72
Lighting 220-221
  recessed 76
Line-voltage thermostats 195
Low-flow shower head 209
Low-limit 99
Manometer 160, 162, 163
  digital 67
Manometers
  digital 130
  hose connections 67
Mesh tape 182
Metering
  refrigerators 217-219
Mildew 247
Minimum ventilation level 65
Mobile homes 263-278
  air leakage 274-275
  auditing 264
  belly insulation 267-268
  construction/components 263
  door replacement 278
  ducts 270-274
  furnaces 270
  health and safety 264-265
  insulation 266-269
  insulation coverage 266-269
  repairs 265
  roof insulation 266-267
  storm windows 276
  wall insulation 269
  water heaters 275-276
  windows 276-277
  windows/doors 276-278
Moisture
  and health 246
  barriers, ground 60, 249
  sources 244-246

Mold 247

## N-O

National Fire Protection Association
standards 126
Natural gas
heat content 115
leak testing 113
Neutral pressure plane 62
NFPA. See National Fire Protection Association
Oil burners 118-123
air filter 123
excess air 120
ignition 119
maintenance/adjustment 122-123
nozzles 122
performance indicators 110, 120
Oil filters 123
Oil pressure 110, 120
Outdoor thermostat 199
Over-fire draft 120

## P-Q

Paint
failure 247
lead 249
Pipe insulation 190, 193
DHW 208-209
Plumbing penetrations
sealing around 75
Pollution
controlling sources 239-241
Porch roof
testing air leakage through 85
Power venters 145
Pressure
measuring differences in 67
pan testing 173-175
pascals/IWC conversion 158
See also House pressures
WRT notation 67
zone leak-testing 82-84
Pressure boundary
See also Air barrier, Insulation
Pressure pan testing 173-175
Pressure tank 98
and pump 98
Pressure-relief valve 98, 188
Primary air
adjustment 112
Programmable thermostats 195
Propane 144
finding leaks 128
Pumps
hydronic, installation 98
Quality assurance 36
Quality control 36

## R-S

Radiators 190
Recessed lights 74
Refrigerant
charge 204
Refrigerators
evaluation and replacement 216-219
metering 217-219
Registers
opening 41
Repair
doors 228-229
windows 228
Repairs
mobile homes 265
Reset controllers 190
Rough opening 234
R-values
determining 47-55
Safety
electrical 250

Shade trees 225
Siding
replacement 237
Sizing
air conditioners 203
Smoke alarms 242
Smoke number 120
Soffits
kitchen 74
Solar heat-gain coefficient 232
Stack effect 62
Static pressure 164-166
Steady-state efficiency 110, 120
testing for 119
Steam heating 190-193
Steam traps 191, 193
Stick pins 185
Storm windows 226
Subcooling 204
Sun screens 224
Superheat 204
Superheat test 200-201
Supply ventilation 259

## T-V

Tape
holding power 183
Temperature rise
furnace 110, 155
The Energy Conservatory 161
Thermal boundary
See also Air barrier
basements and crawl spaces 59-60, 94
definition 57
ideal location 93
Thermal bypasses
locations of 73-77
sealing 73-77
Thermal resistance
calculating 47-55
of insulation materials 280
Thermostats
cooling settings 44
heating settings 41
line voltage 195
outdoor 199
programmable 195
two-stage 199
Torchiere 220-221
TrueFlow® 161
Tyvek 232
U-factors
determining 47-55
window 232
Unconditioned spaces
definition of 57
Utility bills
analysis, example 28
Vapor-proofing
concrete 249
Venetian blinds 224
Vent connectors 136-138
clearances 139
materials 136
specifications 137
Vent dampers 190, 191
Ventilation
attic 49-50
balanced 259-260
determining need for 252
exhaust 257-258
supply 259
systems 257-261
whole house 257-261
Venting
See also Ventilation
AGA categories 144
atmospheric 126-143
fan-assisted 144

## W-Z

Water heaters
draining sediment 43
efficient use 43

energy efficiency 205-208
insulation 205-207
pipe insulation 208-209
replacement 210-212
mobile homes 275-276
sealed-combustion 212
setting temperature 207
Water temperature
setting 207
Weather-resistant barrier 231, 232
Weatherstrip
attic hatches 77
doors 228-229
windows 228
Wind 62
Windows 223-237
doubling 227
exterior treatments 224
measuring 234, 235
mobile home 276-277
repair 228
replacement 231-237
safety 235-236
shade trees 225
shading 223-225
storm 226
waterproofing 233
weatherstrip 228
Windows/doors
mobile homes 276-278
Wood decay 247
Wood heating 123-126
clearances 123
inspection checklist 125
Wood stoves
UL-listed 123
Work orders 33-34
Worst-case draft test 129-130
Zones
combustion-appliance 130
input vs. reference 67
intermediate 171
pressure testing 82-86
simple pressure test 81